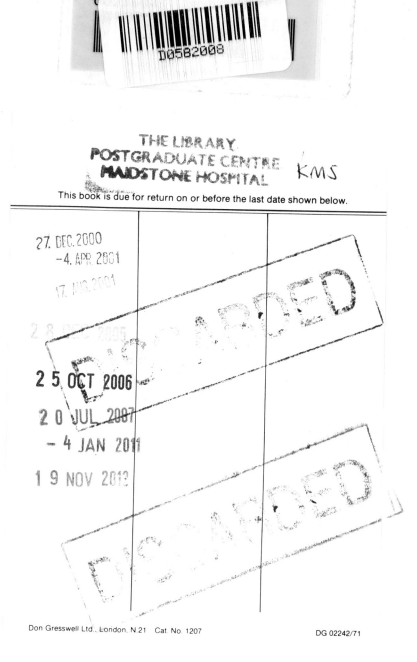

Managing knowledge in health services

Edited by

Andrew Booth

Director of Information Resources, School of Health and Related Research, University of Sheffield

Graham Walton

Faculty Librarian (Health, Social Work and Education), University of Northumbria at Newcastle and Assistant Director (Strategy), Information Management Research Institute, University of Northumbria at Newcastle

Library Association Publishing

London

Published by
Library Association Publishing
7 Ridgmount Street
London WC1E 7AE

Library Association Publishing is wholly owned by The Library Association.

First published 2000

British Library Cataloguing in Publication Data
A catalogue record for this book is available from the British Library.

ISBN 1-85604-321-5

Typeset in 11/14pt Elegant Garamond and Castle by Library Association Publishing
Printed and made in Great Britain by MPG Books Ltd, Bodmin, Cornwall.

Contents

The contributors

The editors

Andrew Booth BA MSc DipLib ALA is Director of Information Resources, School of Health and Related Research, University of Sheffield. He is an information professional, lecturer and researcher with 15 years' experience of management in a wide range of health information settings. After working in NHS libraries from 1983 to 1990 he was employed by the King's Fund Centre, where he managed three national information services. In November 1994 he moved to the School of Health and Related Research, University of Sheffield, where he directs an information resource to support evidence based health-care. Andrew coordinates a module on Systematic Reviews and Critical Appraisal for a Masters in Health Services Research and Technology Assessment, and is an Honorary Lecturer within the Department of Information Studies. Having researched and published extensively on literature searching and critically appraising the evidence, his research outputs include three published systematic reviews for the NHS Health Technology Assessment Programme and a further two in progress. The compiler of the ScHARR Guide to Evidence Based Practice and the world wide web resource, *Netting the Evidence* – used by the Cochrane Library as an authoritative starting-point for evidence based practice – he sits on the editorial boards of *Evidence Based Healthcare* (formerly Evidence Based Health Policy and Management) and *Journal of Clinical Excellence*. Andrew was recently elected Chair of the LINC Health Panel Research Working Party where he is developing methods of systematic review and critical appraisal for health librarianship.

Graham Walton BSc MA MBA FETC ALA is Faculty Librarian (Health, Social Work and Education) at the University of Northumbria at Newcastle and Assistant Director (Strategy), Information Management Research Institute, University of Northumbria at Newcastle. Graham has been working in health information and librarianship for over 20 years. He originally worked in the NHS Highland Health Sciences Library in Scotland. Most of his professional life has been spent in the higher education sector. His current post includes responsibility for three university libraries and supplying a library and information service to over 5000 health students. He has also been active in research, including managing projects on health professionals' information needs and the eLib IMPEL2 project. His current interests are the cultural and organizational implications of moving to electronic information delivery and the information needs of community practitioners.

The contributors

Linda Banwell BA MA PhD ALA is Senior Lecturer in the School of Information Studies at the University of Northumbria at Newcastle, and Research and Development Manager of the Information Management Research Institute at the University of Northumbria at Newcastle. A chartered librarian with experience in academic and special libraries, she has a PhD in computer science, specializing in human–computer interaction. She subsequently became a contract researcher and then a lecturer specializing in research methods. Her research interests focus on people-centered issues in information system design and implementation and evaluation in a range of application areas including health, education and public libraries.

Sharon Dobbins BA ALA is Trust Librarian, City Hospitals Sunderland NHS Trust. She previously worked for the British Council in the UK and Bangladesh, and for Dorset Institute of Higher Education (now Bournemouth University). Professional interests are the development of library and information services, particularly electronic facilities, user education and staff development.

Louise Falzon BA DipInf ALA is Information Officer at the School of Health and Related Research, University of Sheffield. She began her library career in the public sector, working for Berkshire County Council. She then moved to Sheffield Hallam University where she specialized in health and nursing. Her current post combines her other main area of interest, which is training.

John Hewlett MSc (InfSci) ALA MIInfSci **is** Director, Northern and Yorkshire Regional Library Advisory Service. He was Regional Librarian for North East Thames for the previous 16 years, and is particularly interested in the improvement of library information services by staff training and performance.

Alison Hicks BA MLib ALA MIInfSc is Trust Librarian, Gloucestershire Royal NHS Trust, where she currently manages the library and information service at

Gloucestershire Royal NHS Trust. She previously worked at ScHARR, University of Sheffield and the University of Wales College of Medicine. Alison is particularly interested in developing training resources to support evidence based practice and clinical governance.

Donald M Mackay MA MA, ALA became Enquiry Services Manager, Cairns Library, University of Oxford following three years as Librarian at the Health Education Board for Scotland. He recently completed a Masters dissertation on the training needs of CHI providers in Scotland. Current professional interests other than CHI include evidence based healthcare, quality in LIS and the needs of long distance users and community based healthcare workers.

Jane Mackenzie BA MA ALA is Business Development Manager at the Library and Information Development Unit, Thames Postgraduate Medical and Dental Education. After ten years' working in libraries in Colleges of Further and Higher Education in London and then Central Scotland, she moved to the health sector to manage, initially, the King's Fund College Library and then the merged College/Centre Libraries, including a move to the Cavendish Square Library. Prior to her current position she spent two years as R&D Information Manager in the Chief Scientist Office in the Scottish Health Department (including close involvement with the SLIC Review of Scottish Health Libraries). Professional interests include quality and performance management, CPD and career development of library staff, move to networked, electronic information delivery and use of evidence base by LIS practitioners.

Suzy Paisley MA ALA is Senior Information Officer at the School of Health and Related Research, University of Sheffield. Her interest in health information began at Sheffield Hallam University, where she specialized in health and social sciences. She joined ScHARR to set up the Trent Institute for Health Services Research Information Service, supporting the research activities of NHS staff in Trent. Her main area of interest is in literature searching to support systematic reviews and evidence based practice.

Christine J Urquhart BSc MSc PhD MIInfSci PGCE is a Senior Lecturer at the University of Wales, Aberystwyth. Her recent posts include librarian at a nursing college, and Principal Researcher on a value project. She has directed several research projects (EVINCE, GIVTS projects) and several systematic reviews.

Introduction

Reading the January 2000 headlines from the front pages of *The Times* newspaper provides a succinct overview of the agendas and issues facing those involved in healthcare delivery. Political parties are accused of using healthcare issues for their own purposes. Concern is expressed about where the funding will come from to pay for the new 'super drugs'. Health services have struggled to cope with a flu epidemic to which the older population is more susceptible. The first arm transplant has taken place.

Health library and information service (LIS) providers are not impervious to the effects of this external environment. They have a central role in ensuring that appropriate knowledge is available to health professionals to ensure that the right decisions and actions are taken to address such issues. Providers of health LIS cannot escape from the dramatic changes that are shaping healthcare. In 1995 Michael Carmel assembled the second edition of *Health care librarianship and information work*. In this snapshot of the then health LIS world the Internet existed, but only justified two pages of coverage. The concept of evidence based practice had emerged but had not had any discernible impact on LIS professionals. End user searching of online databases took place rarely, if at all. In 1995 the same book by Carmel described the high level of change in health services that had taken place across the world in the early 1990s. Since this book's appearance the rate of change has accelerated, affecting all aspects of healthcare. The radical nature of such change necessitated a new approach to, rather than simply a revisit of, the subject matter of Carmel's original work.

The purpose of this book is to define and investigate the context, principles and practical skills needed to effectively manage the knowledge base of healthcare. The book identifies and analyses the function and value of information in healthcare. It describes the rapidly evolving role of health information provision and provides a toolkit of practical knowledge for health information providers and users. To facilitate these aims and objectives the book is divided into three separate parts. Part 1 provides the contextual background to healthcare and health information services. The wider health environment is described along with an evaluation of the characteristics of health LIS users. The range of health LIS and the providers who work in these services is outlined in all its complexity and diversity. An overview of developments in consumer health information completes this first part.

The focus for Part 2 is on the principles underlying the way health information resources and services are organized and managed. The first chapter in this part examines how health LIS, and the staff who work in them, should be managed. The importance of user needs analysis is discussed, illustrated by different methodological approaches. Subsequent chapters look at how to make and present a case effectively, how to identify resources for the health LIS and how the LIS should be organized. Developments in the delivery of, and access to, resources are allocated a chapter within this part. The final three chapters in Part 2 consider marketing services, evaluating services and training the users.

In Part 3, the skills needed to make effective use of the knowledge base are described. Formulating the question along with establishing the appropriate sources where the answers might be located are examined. Database searching techniques as well as Internet searching skills are briefly outlined. The development of new approaches needed to filter and evaluate the knowledge base are described. Organizing a personal knowledge base and keeping up to date are the topics of the last two chapters. The book then concludes by examining important trends and themes that the contributors believe will occupy the LIS professional agenda in the early part of the 21st century.

Wherever possible Part 1 is written from a global perspective, but many examples are based on practice in the UK. Parts 2 and 3 are relevant to health LIS across the world and draw extensively on the published knowledge base. This book is intended to be of use to all library and information service providers and students in the field. It should also be of great value to the increasing number of healthcare professionals, such as research and development coordinators and clinical effectiveness/governance facilitators, required to access health information as part of their working roles.

The editors would like to thank all contributors for the quality of their writing and their adherence to deadlines! Special thanks are extended to two further individuals: Michael Carmel for inspiring the writing of this book and Dr Anne Wales for her early contributions to the book's structure. Finally the editors would like to acknowledge the considerable advice, assistance and technical support provided by the commissioning editor for the Library Association, Beth Barber, and also the tolerance of our respective wives and families!

Andrew Booth and Graham Walton

Part 1

Contextual background to healthcare and health information services

1

Health services: a contemporary approach

Graham Walton

Introduction

Information services do not function within a vacuum. Indeed it is likely that the library and information service (LIS) which does not take into account the external environment will quickly cease to exist. The providers of services must look to the outside world and create regular 'snapshots' of what is happening in the external environment. A key skill is differentiating between those issues that will significantly impact on LIS, those that will have limited relevance and those with minimal relevance. For those providers of healthcare LIS the dangers in ignoring the health environment are two-fold. Services can be developed that are not required which will result in the LIS becoming atrophied. The other risk is that necessary services will not be developed and prospective users will go elsewhere.

The purpose of this chapter is to identify the major drivers that are shaping the health external environment at the beginning of the 21st century. This chapter is structured around a Sociological, Technological, Economic and Political (STEP) analysis of the health external environment. Johnson and Scholes (1999) have outlined the value of this approach where the STEP analysis identifies key environmental influences that are likely to drive change. This analysis should help LIS staff consider the differential impact of key drivers on the strategic options available.

Providers of LIS could use the STEP analysis to consider strategic options but that is not its primary purpose. It provides a structure to the many diverse and influential drivers that are shaping healthcare. The intention is to provide an informed insight into the challenges facing health service providers.

This STEP analysis has been developed through the contributions of various experts. Between June 1999 and October 1999 a draft STEP analysis was produced. This was circulated to a range of professionals involved in healthcare delivery including a consultant surgeon, a research physiotherapist, an organizational performance development officer and a commissioning support manager. They refined the analysis which resulted in the final establishment of the drivers that provide the structure for this chapter. In *Sociological factors* the emphasis on self, health inequalities and demography (especially the increase in the numbers of elderly) were identified. Information and Communications Technology (ICT), biological and pharmaceutical developments and the development of medical equipment made up the *Technology* drivers. In terms of *Economic* factors, cost containment, evidence based practice and rationing were included. Finally ideology, collaboration versus cooperation and globalization were established as key *Political* issues.

The literature used to provide detail on the STEP factors has been identified using three important criteria: currency, expertise of authors and the authors' abilities to present comprehensive overviews. Interested readers will be able to follow up specific source material to expand on the level of detail given below.

Sociological

Emphasis on self

In society, people are being expected to take more responsibility for their own lives in many areas eg education, pensions. This is mirrored in healthcare with the move to patient or client empowerment where the patient is seen as part of the healthcare team and works in partnership with clinicians (see Chapter 5). They are involved with decision-making about their treatment. Empowerment is concerned with enabling people to take control of their own lives, and the systems and processes that enable them to do so. This trend was first evident in the area of special needs but is spreading into other aspects of healthcare. Barlow and Harrison (1996) describe the trends where consumers are given more power and are placed at the centre around which services must revolve.

The emerging literature relating to patient education indicates that the emphasis should be on increasing patient influence and involvement in the therapeutic regime and encouraging the patients' potential for self-care (Skelton, 1997; Van Eijsk and Haan, 1998). This move to patients being empowered and taking control is demonstrated in the increasing use of complementary medicine. Barnes (1998) points to the UK homeopathy market alone being worth £20 million. In the United States 34% of Americans have used at least one unconventional therapy and annual expenditure on these therapies was $13.7 billion (Vincent and Furnham, 1999).

Inequalities

In 1978 the World Health Organization issued the Declaration of Alma Ata which acknowledged the global inequalities in health (World Health Organization, 1978). Health inequalities are present at many levels. There are marked differences in health service provision in the developed compared with the developing world. Many diseases, which are seen as minor and easily treated in the developed world, are life-threatening in the developing world. At the continental level, inequalities in healthcare have been found across 11 European countries (Mackenbach et al, 1997). In all these countries the risk of morbidity/mortality is higher in lower socio-economic groups. Whitehead, Scott-Samuel and Dahlgren (1998) highlight that concerns are being expressed across Europe about health inequalities and that the gaps may be widening. Inequalities are also present within different regions in the same country. Shaw, Dorling and Brimblecome (1998) provide evidence supporting a widening gap between regions. Research from Bristol University is reported by Laurence (1999) to illustrate this disparity. The death rate in people under 65 is now more than two and a half times higher in the worst parts of Glasgow compared with the prosperous parts of southern England.

Demography

Many authors have identified that a significant factor for healthcare is the increasing life span. As people live longer they will form a greater percentage of the total population.

- Life expectancy has increased 2.5 years in Britain between 1971 and 1991 (Ebrahim, 1997)
- The number of old people aged over 75 will increase by 80% over the next 68 years (Appleby, 1998)
- In this century alone expectancy has increased by more than 25 years (Butler, 1997).

The implications for healthcare include increased health costs (Appleby, 1998), the crucial role of family/friends as unpaid carers (Ebrahim, 1997) and the increased need for medical research (Butler, 1997). The most significant impact of an ageing population on healthcare is that the older person has increased susceptibility to acute diseases (eg falls, infections) as well as chronic ones (eg cirrhosis, emphysema). Health professionals will have to treat increasing numbers of chronic and acute illnesses as the elderly population increases. They will have to establish how life can be added to years not years to life.

There are other demographic and epidemiological factors that will impact on health services. These include the dramatic impact on the structures of families (Cox, 1997) where there will be fewer young people around. Increased divorce rates, more women as family heads, more working women, high levels of teenage pregnancy and increased rates of unemployment are also significant.

Technological

The technology drivers validated by the health professionals were reassuringly similar to those in the literature (Wasunna and Wyper, 1998). The cautionary overview provided by Wasunna and Wyper highlights the problems and pitfalls at a global level attached to integrating technology into healthcare. The issues attached to the introduction of technology vary considerably depending upon whether it is in the developed or the developing world. It is impossible to do justice to all the technological developments impacting upon health. Replacement and assistive devices, nanotechnologies (molecular manufacturing) and environmental and food technologies are all relevant in the wider health environment but are merely noted here.

Information and communication technology

The dramatic developments in information and communication technologies (ICT) have significantly impacted on health services. Telemedicine is a discipline that aims to give equal access to care whether a patient is 'in the Scottish Highlands . . . in the Australian bush . . . frail or elderly' (Doughty, 1998, 36). Telecommunications allow data to be transferred efficiently from one place to another. More powerful computers organize the processing, storing and retrieving of information more efficiently than otherwise possible. Electronic developments ensure that data can be inputted automatically from sensors. Wallace

(1998) has provided a balanced perspective. He outlines the two opposing arguments about telemedicine. Some see that it 'will do for healthcare what personal computers have done for the office'. The opposing perspective is that the clinician/patient relationship is threatened and telemedicine is an intrinsically unsafe way of practising. There are also significant barriers to implementation. These include the gap between health needs and the technology, patients' resistance, clinicians' resistance, confidentiality, data security and health service management systems. The implications of ICT are that geographical location will no longer be important. Paradoxically Wasunna and Wyper (1998) emphasize that these developments are a feature of the developed world. A technology that is supposed to remove distance barriers may in fact be reinforcing the difference between the developed and the developing nations.

Towards the end of the 1990s the installation of the NHSnet began to impact upon health professionals. The likelihood is that easy access to a networked computer will be essential for many facets of healthcare delivery. Spitzer (1998, 165) has observed that 'control of databases, accessibility to knowledge and management of information is likely to become critical to professionals and lay people alike'. There is evidence in the UK that problems such as limited access to computers, low specification machines, absence of NHSnet connections and limited information technology skills need to be addressed before ICT is integrated into health services (Capel, Banwell and Walton, 1998).

Biological and pharmaceutical developments

The impressive developments in biology and pharmacology witnessed in the 20th century have continued at an unrelenting pace. Advances have occurred in molecular and cell biology. There is a more detailed understanding of the immune complex and genetic disorders. Progress in genetic science is leading to applications in many areas of clinical care (Bell, 1998). These include early diagnosis and the discovery and development of drugs. The human genome project is having a major influence on healthcare (Brooker, 1999). It is acknowledged as the largest internationally coordinated undertaking in the history of biological research. The project is providing extensive new knowledge on the genes involved in inherited diseases, birth defects and even susceptibility to infection. It is becoming much easier through the project to understand, detect, prevent and treat many disorders. Biomaterials for medical use have also progressed. This allows natural tissue structures to be mimicked by the biomaterials used in surgery to provide biological functions (Suh, 1998).

Drugs are being developed which can exert more precise control over body physiology. This has been achieved by increasing knowledge in three main areas: molecular structure of tissue sites, the organs where diseases present and the drugs themselves (Wasunna and Wyper, 1998).

Medical equipment

Medical equipment is seeing an increased emphasis on safety and user-friendly operations (Wasunna and Wyper, 1998). The development of minimally invasive surgical techniques represents a major breakthrough as it provides the double benefits of reducing patient discomfort as well as reducing bed occupancy. In a detailed review of developments in coronary artery surgery, Loop (1998) highlights the potential for robotic control in minimally invasive surgery to add greater precision, ease of use and safety. Notes of caution have been expressed by Heald and Morgan (1997), who feel the superiority of laparascopic surgery over open surgery is unproven, even for gall-bladders and appendixes. Writers on healthcare technology voice concerns that their impact will be limited unless resources are available to cover the costs when introducing new technologies. The centrality of ensuring clinicians have both the knowledge and the skills to maximize the impact of the technology is also underlined.

Economic

Cost containment

It has been estimated that in the USA health costs will rise by 3.1% each year until 2007 (Blumenthal, 1999). In France there was a 4–5% increase in expenditure on healthcare between 1991 and 1996 (Durand-Zaleski, Colin, Blum-Boisgard, 1997). Most developed countries are wrestling with the need to keep control of expenditure on healthcare. Current and future contributors to the increasing costs include the implementation of information and communication technology, the high costs of tests and treatments, equipment costs and an older population which makes more demands on health services. In the USA healthcare providers have the strength in the market-place to resist demands for reduced healthcare prices.

The dilemma facing deliverers of healthcare is starkly illustrated when looking at the care for persons with HIV/AIDS (Gallagher, 1999). Such patients will continue to command high-cost care and frequent interventions until treatment is available. There is a need to deliver quality care and, at the same time, contain costs. Achieving both these aims is a major challenge facing health services and various strategies have been developed and tested. For example in France (Durand-Zaleski, Colin, Blum-Boisgard, 1997) there has been a reduction in what have been identified as unnecessary tests and treatments. Mandatory guidelines on procedures and prescribing have been introduced. Doctors not complying with these strategies are open to fines. Other approaches have been to reduce the length of hospital stay for patients. Care programmes could be amended by unpicking the whole healthcare process and re-assembling with cost and quality as the focuses (Theis, 1998).

Evidence based practice

It could be argued that including evidence based practice (EBP) under the 'economics' heading is inappropriate. The need to improve the effectiveness and efficiency of interventions is more important than reducing expensive treatments that have limited outcomes. EBP can influence healthcare economics as much as clinical care. The concept of EBP is investigated in more depth elsewhere in this book (Chapters 15–19) but it is of sufficient importance to be identified as a major driver.

When the concept of EBP emerged in the last few years it was known as 'evidence based medicine' as it was originally developed by the medical profession. As other health professions have applied the concept 'evidence based practice' has been seen as more appropriate. When looking at literature on the concept of EBP, several authors (Colyer and Kamath, 1999; Gilbert and Logan, 1996; Sandall, 1998) go back to a definition proposed by Sackett in 1996. He says that EBP is the 'conscientious, explicit and judicious use of current best evidence in making decisions about the care of individual patients . . . evidence based medicine means integrating individual expertise with the best available external evidence from systematic research'.

Some early commentators (Gilbert and Logan, 1996) questioned whether EBP would be a passing fad or be at the centre of future clinical decision-making. Views are now being expressed that the long-term significance of EBP is at last being recognized and acknowledged (Colyer and Kamath, 1999). A pragmatic approach is taken by Green (1998) who sees it as a formal combination of rigorous data and common sense. In recent years a more sophisticated viewpoint has developed whereby merit is not seen in randomized control trials (RCTs), megatrials and meta-analysis per se but in the selection of the appropriate study design for the question (Wennberg & Sackett, 1997).

Some reservations have been expressed about the move to EBP (Goodman, 1999) including criticisms that EBP is the development of a 'cookbook' of clinical guidelines which dictate slavish adherence to particular regimes. It could also be seen as an attempt to erode practitioners' autonomy. The difficulty of applying evidence to practice is apparent in the identification of 'grey zones' of clinical practice (Naylor, 1995). A further criticism is that the continuity of caring and supportive clinical staff is devalued. Whilst general acceptance is emerging that EBP is a significant trend, much work has been done to identify barriers to its integration into practice (Newman et al, 1998; Nolan, 1998; Sandall, 1998). It is significant that nurses and midwives have been foremost in conducting 'barrier' studies. In 30 years of nursing literature it has been acknowledged that research has not been utilized in practice; if EBP is to become widespread the resistances must be overcome. The following barriers have been identified: perceived lack of authority by staff (other than medical staff) to introduce change in patient care, poor quality of published material, circulation of clinical guidelines without an implementation strategy and an unsupportive health service professional and employment structure.

Rationing

Various commentators have observed that rationing has always been present in the UK National Health Service and in other countries (Goodman, 1998; Maxwell, 1995). With the UK NHS 1946 Act it was acknowledged that available resources were finite. Rather than use the pejorative term 'rationing' many countries have preferred to apply 'prioritization' to describe those healthcare demands which are not met when there are insufficient funds (Honigsbaum et al, 1994).

Two different approaches to rationing have developed. Rationing can take place *implicitly* where the strategy is hidden. Waiting lists are extended and fewer treatments and cheaper drugs are made available. Patients are given information about treatment outcomes that may make them decide against that intervention. The dangers in implicit rationing are that individual clinicians drive the rationing, which will lead to unfairness. The opposite strategy for rationing is where it is *explicit* to both clinician and patient which treatments are available for which illnesses. Goodman (1998) has described how different countries have approached the issue of having implicit or explicit healthcare rationing. She identifies the most widely publicized priority-setting process as happening in the State of Oregon in the USA where services being included in Medicaid (US health insurance scheme) programmes were prioritized.

Rationing healthcare is a very difficult, emotive process. At a political level governments do not wish to be seen to be introducing rationing which will be unpopular and influence voting behaviour. Hunter (1995) has pointed out that health service staff wish to have clear and explicit rationing policies to be laid down from central government which will relieve them from shouldering the blame. The development of a National Institute for Clinical Excellence (NICE) in the UK is a response to this demand with high-cost interventions being closely scrutinized for cost–benefit. All healthcare systems ration care. The issue is not whether but how.

Political

An editorial in the *Medical Journal of Australia* (Swerissen, 1998, 205) outlines concisely and clearly why health is always contested at the centre of politics: 'Scarce resources must be allocated, in circumstances of imperfect information, for competing and irreconcilable claims made by different groups, and some of these groups may face catastrophic consequences if no action is taken . . . Health programs and services represent only some of many claims for scarce government resources.' The increasing awareness of the centrality of politics in health is developed and illustrated by Masterson and Maslin-Protheroe (1999) who have produced a book which focuses solely on nursing and politics.

Ideology

Political ideologies are sets of beliefs and ideas that provide the basis for some kind of political action. Simplistically, national healthcare systems are somewhere on a spectrum with, at one end, the tax-financed, integrated state provision 'Beveridge' model. At the other end is the 'Bismarck' social insurance model in which the insurance funds may be, to a considerable extent, independent from the government (Taylor-Gooby, 1996). The way the British National Health Service has changed over the past 50 years to reflect the ideologies of the different political parties in power is well documented by Denny (1999). The mix between private and public financed healthcare is always contentious. This is nowhere better illustrated than in the largest and most significant country adopting the 'Bismarck' model: the USA. It has been estimated that there are currently 43 million Americans not insured for healthcare (Blumenthal, 1999). In 1994 President Clinton attempted unsuccessfully to introduce health reform based around universal health insurance care. Various commentators (Blumenthal, 1999; Ginzberg, 1998) have seen the defeat of this bill as a critical moment for political ideologies of healthcare. Providers of healthcare have to be prepared to alter their services fundamentally depending upon the ideology of the political party in power.

Collaboration versus competition

In the 'Bismarck' model a driving force can be the introduction of private sector skills and strategies into health where principles of competition underpin funding allocation. Market forces are expected to address such issues as top-heavy bureaucracy and lack of accountability. A feature of the past decade has been the strength of the views advocating either that principles of competition or that principles of collaboration should drive healthcare (East, 1999). In more recent years the voices calling for collaboration appear to be being heard more strongly. In the USA hospital networks are being set up, mergers are taking place between hospitals and academic health institutions are amalgamating (Ginzberg, 1998). Recent evidence for this trend in the UK is provided with the government's proposals that the health and social services should develop joint working (Department of Health, 1998d). Commentators question whether the long-standing organizational, cultural and professional differences between health and social care professionals will make these plans for joint working impossible to achieve (Hiscock and Pearson, 1999; McCurry and White, 1999).

Globalization

Globalization can be understood as the 'process by which human societies are moving from global to international relations' (Lee, 1998, 900). Faster transport systems and information and communication technologies have contributed to health politics functioning at the global level. There is heightened awareness that events in one country can impact on health issues in countries far away (eg the 1986 Chernobyl nuclear accident). With rapid travel, a tourist or business person can be infected abroad with a contagious disease and return before symptoms appear. Prospects of global warming have given further impetus to global health politics. In 1948 the World Health Organization (WHO) was set up to take responsibility for international public health and other health matters. WHO will have to change to meet the challenge of increased globalization. The need for change is acknowledged by Lee (1998), as is the need for careful, informed management of this change.

Conclusion

This chapter has aimed to bring together in a structured way developments in the many areas of life that influence how healthcare is provided. Criticisms of the STEP analysis are that it introduces artificiality and a sense that everything can be compartmentalized. In the real world there is a high level of interconnectivity where different trends influence and dictate to each other. This is illustrated using the demographic trend of an increased elderly population.

Case study

With more elderly people there will be pressure to develop more sophisticated pharmaceutical treatments to meet their needs. The emphasis on empowerment will support vocal and powerful older consumers of healthcare. The increased health costs resulting from caring for an older population will have to be addressed. With the 'greying' of politics, political parties will have to develop health policies to ensure they have the support of the large number of older voters. Providers of healthcare will be forced to look at rationing even more as the costs increase.

Some of these developments may appear peripheral to the suppliers of health LIS, but they will all impact in varying degrees. The health information worker has to monitor continually this external environment and assess what effect it will have on the service they deliver. There will always be some unpredicted trend or development just over the horizon. The health information workers who survive and thrive will be the ones who can discriminate between significant trends that need urgent action and those that will have minimal impact.

Key points

Healthcare is influenced by many factors. Library and information services have to be informed by the health external environment. Major drivers identified in the STEP analysis are:

- *Sociological*: the emphasis on self, health inequalities and demography (especially the increase in the numbers of elderly)
- *Technological*: Information and Communications Technology (ICT), biological and pharmaceutical developments and the development of medical equipment
- *Economic*: cost containment, evidence based practice, rationing
- *Political*: ideology, collaboration versus competition, globalization.

2
Health service users of information

Christine Urquhart

Introduction

It is easy to forget in debates about the costs of high technology treatments or developments in biotechnology that staff account for the majority of health service costs. Human resource management policies have to ensure that staff are being deployed effectively, and that staff are educated and trained to deliver appropriate care. Clinical governance requires healthcare organizations to demonstrate that care is of the appropriate quality, and this, in turn, requires that the right people have the right information at the right time. A quick fix to training or organizational development is not going to work in an era that emphasizes lifelong learning and organizational development. Solutions to continuing professional development and organizational change need to be structured carefully and with commitment. As health library and information services (LIS) have traditionally been closely associated with clinical education, the greater commitment to education and training presents many opportunities. There are also challenges, as resource constraints have not disappeared. It is more important than ever that information services are targeted carefully, and that librarians ensure that services are based on evidence concerning patterns of need and use.

This chapter considers changes in the health workforce, and the social trends which may affect LIS strategic planning for them. The greater consumer interest in healthcare, and the trend towards more self-care affect not only the type of information required by health professionals and consumers, but also the power relationships implicated in communicating and sharing health information. For information service providers such changes affect the way networking – hard and soft – should be supported. Organizational changes, such as an increasing emphasis on the primary care team and multidisciplinary working also have an effect on the way information will be used in practice. An Audit Commission report (1995) on information management in acute hospitals observed that 'the main obstacle to getting better value out of information is that staff seldom understand its value or potential'. To change this lack of awareness, LIS services should understand current users – and potential ones.

This chapter discusses:

- trends in human resource management policies and changing patterns of employment
- trends in education and training of the health workforce
- the roles of health professionals and changes in those roles
- evidence concerning the patterns of information need and use
- implications for user support, including education and training in information skills.

Human resources in healthcare

The UK NHS employs over one million people in total. Of these, around two-thirds are involved in direct care and one-third form the management and support staff (Department of Health, 1999d). Nursing, midwifery and health visiting form by far the largest proportion of health professional staff (330,600 whole-time equivalent staff in 1997, 332,200 wte staff in 1998). Despite the media rhetoric, there has, apparently, been a recent decline in management and support staff (260,900 wte staff in 1995, 248,600 wte staff in 1998). On the other hand, the number of hospital, public health medicine and community health service medical and dental staff in England has risen since 1995 by 24% to 68,460 in 1998, and the number of hospital medical staff has grown by 36% over the same period (Department of Health, 1999c).

Notable trends and figures include:

- a steady increase in the percentage of female hospital medical staff (a rise of 72% since 1988 to 20,210 in 1988 (statistics for England))
- an increase since 1988 in the number of overseas qualified medical staff (statistics for England)
- in 1997, 88% of nursing, midwifery and health visiting staff were female, compared with 33% of hospital medical and dental staff (Central Statistics Office, 1999)

- a large rise in the number of multi-partner GP practices and practice staff. In 1970, 20% of GPs worked single-handed; in 1997 (England and Wales) 1,156 practices employing six or more GP principals covered around 25% of the population (Office of Health Economics, 1997)
- over half of all GP registrars are women (*Wellard's NHS handbook, 1999–2000*, 1999).

Such trends reflect changes in the workforce generally. There are more women participating in the workforce in most OECD countries (see OECD, 1999 for participation rate rise between 1987 and 1997). Reasons, though complex, may include improved arrangements for childcare, more part-time employment and changes in patterns of male employment.

The national human resources framework developed for the NHS (eg Department of Health, 1998e) puts greater emphasis on the organizational structures required. Recent employment legislation, to comply with the European Social Chapter, will impact on patterns of employment in the NHS. An emphasis on partnership between employer and employee is reflected in parental leave, paternity and maternity leave, and restricted use of short-term contracts. The working time directive does not yet apply to doctors in training but does cover all other staff. Improvements in working conditions, combined with more family-friendly policies, may help to recruit and retain staff in geographic areas and clinical specialties where there are shortages at present.

Effects of clinical governance and human resource management policies

Clinical governance and human management policy changes have implications for LIS.

First, there is the obvious emphasis on clinical effectiveness. Administration and clerical staff to serve patient care – and health LIS – will be judged in terms related to the quality of patient care and clinical governance.

Secondly, the number of part-time staff is unlikely to decrease – and one wte staff may mean two individuals with distinct information needs. An increasing number of female medical staff, who are likely to combine a career with family responsibilities, means that service planning will be more difficult.

Thirdly, managers are under pressure to deliver clinical governance. As Mintzberg pointed out 21 years ago, 'the two most effective means to control an organization from the outside are (1) to hold its most powerful decision maker

– its chief executive – responsible for its actions, and (2) to impose clearly defined standards on it, transformed into rules and regulations' (Mintzberg, 1979, 289). The number of sources of standards, rules and regulations increases rapidly: guidelines, service frameworks, evaluation programmes and performance assessment frameworks, as detailed in Taylor (1999). Patient expectations increase, but resources are finite and the demand for healthcare apparently limitless. Healthcare managers have many options to balance and their enthusiasm for evidence based medicine may be tempered by the need to provide evidence of other service quality measures, while keeping a tight financial control. Managers' information needs are more diverse and likely to remain so.

Fourthly, the medical staff population is moving away from the white male hierarchy, but the opportunities are not equal – yet. The full-time professional career is still viewed as the norm even though demography has long ago forced the conventional career as a means of delivering care to be abandoned (Davies, 1990). More junior medical staff will likely prefer to study at home, rather than retreat to the hospital library. For the flexible workforce information services have to be delivered 'without walls'. For many professionals the home personal computer has blurred the boundaries of home, work and professional education. Students entering higher education will increasingly expect to have access to the university network available from their study bedrooms. Health LIS need to deliver services to meet the demands of graduates with those expectations.

Trends in education of health professionals

The undergraduate health professional curriculum in the UK is moving away from a heavily 'fact' oriented content to a teaching and learning strategy which a) is more problem-based, b) recognizes the importance of practice in the community and c) emphasizes lifelong learning.

Nursing education in the UK has seen major changes with the move of pre-registration nursing education into higher education (Project 2000). The survey of Demonstration Districts found that practice staff were largely positive about this change with several commenting that new students made staff reflect more on their practice and look up research (Jowett, Walton and Payne, 1994, 89). The nursing curriculum, both in pre-registration and post-registration programmes of study, often emphasizes reflective practice, as envisioned by Schon (1987), allied with the need to promote nursing research and evidence based nursing practice.

The hopes and assumptions driving these changes in the curriculum and educational philosophy are that:

- health professionals will acquire lifelong learning skills and thus actively seek to update their practice
- learning is more relevant to actual practice, but grounded in evidence and 'knowledge based'
- practice will better reflect the needs of society (eg more emphasis on the maintenance of health than curing of disease).

For the information service provider the implications are:

- a wider range of resources required (broader curriculum)
- more intensive use of resources (evidence based practice)
- more sustained need for support (lifelong learning).

Problem based learning

For health LIS, problem based learning (PBL) appears to present greater opportunities to integrate information services into the undergraduate curriculum. Eldredge et al (1998) describe how subject librarians (library liaisons) at the University of New Mexico collaborate with staff and students to support learning on simulated cases for Phase One of the medical school curriculum. Fitzgerald (1996) discusses how the role of the librarian has developed at McMaster University. Schilling et al (1995) evaluated the librarian's component of PBL sessions and found services useful or very useful.

More basically, perhaps, the introduction of problem-based learning increases student use of the library (Marshall et al, 1993; Rankin, 1996). While this is to be welcomed, the experience of Project 2000, with its move from ward based training into higher education, warns that librarians may suddenly have to cope with rapidly increasing demand with limited resources which do not match that demand.

Many librarians welcome the introduction of problem based learning and reflective practice in the curriculum on the grounds that it should:

- produce graduates with a more informed attitude toward literature searching and critical appraisal

- increase library usage statistics, both at undergraduate level and at post-graduate level.

Some studies suggest that PBL is not the panacea it may seem. Christakis (1995) points out that, despite many proposals to reform medical education, the themes (burgeoning medical knowledge, need for more 'generalist' skills) remain surprisingly constant. McGowan (1995) compared perceptions of life-long learning among graduates from traditional curricula and those from problem based learning curricula. The only statistically significant difference was a preference for continuing medical education as a method for gaining new knowledge. This was attributed to the possibility that PBL students enjoy their medical school experience more than students following the traditional curriculum and are more receptive to the notion of formal continuing medical education. Graduates of both curricula relied on colleagues as their first information source, and PBL graduates did not make greater use of health libraries. The evidence is equivocal, and may reflect the difficulty of evaluating the effectiveness of any educational programme. There are few evaluation studies of PBL that can be synthesized usefully (Woodward, 1997).

The idea that general problem-solving skills will be retained and that these will include an attitude towards seeking the evidence is not easy to reconcile with studies of clinical reasoning that suggest that problem-solving skills are somehow enmeshed with biomedical knowledge. There are several theories about the development of clinical reasoning (Boshuizen and Schmidt, 1992; Patel, Evans and Groen, 1989), but most suggest that experts do not conventionally 'problem solve' (Schmidt, Norman and Boshuizen, 1990).

A cautious conclusion might be that continuing professional development requires continuing support to consolidate information skills. This requires a receptive audience, and a means of reaching that audience. There are still problems in ensuring that the educationalists and the librarians cooperate and collaborate to ensure that information skills are integrated into the curriculum effectively. It is not simply the planning stage that is important: librarians should have the opportunity to evaluate, via summative or formative student assessment, the success of their teaching and support (Urquhart et al 1999, Chapter 7), particularly at the postgraduate level.

Roles of the health professional and the changing professional/patient relationship

The health professional is primarily involved in providing or supporting patient care, but there are other roles that health professionals undertake as well as that of 'technically expert care provider'. Most roles support the 'technician' care provider, in some way. It is useful, however, to make distinctions between the patterns of information need and use of the 'practitioner', 'educational', 'research' and 'management' roles. The professionals themselves may not recognize these distinctions, a fact that has to be acknowledged. Brember and Leggate (1985) identified the 'researcher/practitioner' role – those clinicians who fulfilled different roles at different times in different places. Clinical directors are clinicians – but also managers. The balance is problematical, and often professional values, inculcated over many years, affect perspectives on the importance of particular role variations.

Changing roles of professionals and patients

The rise of consumerism has affected the relationship between health professional and patient or client. The traditional relationship is of the patient as the passive recipient of healthcare: the new relationship supposes that patients, their carers and community groups should have more involvement in clinical decision-making (NHS Executive, 1996). Despite the rhetoric, some commentators point out that clinical decision-making at the point of service delivery has remained the prerogative of the healthcare professions: 'the secret garden of professional practice: the way in which higher level decisions about funding are transmuted into clinical decision and how resource constraints affect medical judgements about treatment' (Klein, Day and Redmayne, 1996, 83). Plans to devise a successor to the *Patient's Charter* have not been wholly successful. The concept of the *Patient's Charter*, promoted by the previous Conservative government in the UK, did raise awareness of the patient viewpoint. However, health professionals resented the imposition of conditions and target setting which might detract from clinical objectives. The new charter sought a better partnership, but responses suggest that more consultation will be required.

Professional educators and opinion leaders

Many health professionals are educators, both formally (as mentors, clinical teachers, clinical tutors) and informally (as 'opinion leaders' or 'information gatekeepers' or 'change agents'). LIS tend to see health professionals more in their formal education role. Both the Value and EVINCE projects demonstrated that the actual patterns as reflected in the types of information requests presented to the library did not reflect the actual patterns of information need and use in practice (Urquhart and Hepworth, 1995a, b; Davies, et al, 1997). Libraries tend to be used to satisfy formal education needs – whether for teaching (other professionals) or for learning (at pre-registration, post-registration or postgraduate levels). Such needs may be specific (eg what is the research evidence for the effectiveness of a particular drug treatment?) but informal education may be less easy to define and its questions more vague and ambiguous. Much informal education may in practice be as much to do with reinforcing professional values as with transmission of information and knowledge. Studies of information needs and communication in medical practice (eg Forsythe et al, 1992) suggest that 'information needs' are varied, and are not always expressed fully or formally. They may involve local knowledge rather than global knowledge, and require knowledge of the situation for interpretation. Opinion leaders are not always aware of this role when clinicians consult them for advice (Weinberg et al, 1981) but their importance in verifying and affirming knowledge is attested in many studies (Smith, 1996). For nurses, a common information-seeking strategy might be to search the literature, but also seek advice from a local expert (Davies et al, 1997; Urquhart and Davies, 1997).

The health professional as researcher

The role of researcher is a familiar one to LIS staff. Researchers depend on access to the latest information and they value information services highly. Clinical effectiveness requires all health professionals to demonstrate awareness of research, but for most this may only require access to digests rather than primary research papers. Thus there are a small number of 'active' researchers but an increasing number of 'passive' researchers.

The health professional as manager

Many health professionals are also managers, and their expectations differ from those in the practitioner, educator and researcher roles. The focus in the latter three roles is largely on one-to-one relationships or the 'individual' role. Managing is more about the orchestration of performance, and working with other professionals, both within and beyond the group to which that individual belongs. One of the incidental observations in the Value and EVINCE studies was that the term 'colleague' to a doctor almost invariably meant another doctor, to a nurse another nurse. Terms such as 'colleague' or ' healthcare team' should be used with caution – the so-called primary care team often does not meet accepted criteria for team functioning (West and Poulton, 1997). Information-sharing within different groups of professionals may be very different to that within the same group of professionals. The emphasis on inter-professional education may change this, but professional attitudes are often deeply rooted. Head (1996) noted that hybrid managers (health professionals who had moved into management) had a different pattern of information needs from career managers, those who had entered the health service directly as managers.

Orchestrating the professional roles

There are various implicit expectations of clinical governance. First there is the recognition that practitioners need to be up-to-date in their knowledge; they need to be competent in their practice. Collecting together a group of up-to-date and competent health professionals does not necessarily guarantee high-quality service delivery. A 'good performance' depends on more than that. Nowlen (1988) distinguishes three models of continuing education for the professions – the update model, the competence model and the performance model. In the first two models the emphasis is on the individual. The performance model is different as it stresses the importance of the individual within the culture, and the package of previous experiences, the cultural 'baggage' the individual carries with them. Performance is complex – and rarely changed by a single variable.

Patterns of information need and use: the research evidence

This section reviews factors that may affect the patterns of information need and use. Understanding these may help to predict future needs and plan appropriate provision. Most information needs here are 'expressed needs', where action was taken to acquire information. Often, information needs are ignored or not expressed, and the LIS must act creatively to anticipate such needs.

Synthesizing the evidence

Synthesizing the evidence is difficult for several reasons. Studies may evaluate the effectiveness of a particular service, or information resource (such as MEDLINE on CD-ROM) which makes interpolation or forecasting of future needs difficult. Quantitative studies tend to be limited geographically or by scope or by subject group, making generalization difficult. Qualitative studies provide valuable insights, but to questions rather than answers. This synthesis sets out evidence for and against some 'statements' or assumptions about health professionals' information behaviour.

Why do health professionals need information – primarily for patient care purposes?

The evidence is difficult to synthesize as:

- Research designs have assumed that there is only one 'purpose', or one main purpose.
- Studies from the information provider perspective tend to consider, quite justifiably, reasons for using particular sources in the library (whether printed or electronic). Examples of this type of study include the <ISBN> project (Wakeham, Houghton and Beard, 1992) which studied the reasons why nursing professionals and nursing students used particular sources of information (library, private journals, colleagues, ward based information).

Other studies suggest that the pattern of purposes is much more complex and that a search for information, particularly information that is found in the literature or in sources such as the Cochrane Library or MEDLINE databases, may only be undertaken if there is more than one reason for seeking information. Both the Value project (Urquhart and Hepworth, 1995a, b) and the EVINCE project (Davies et al, 1997) found that the patterns of information need were complex, and often there was more than one reason for seeking information, particularly when some effort was required to find it. Patient care accounted for 37% of the critical incidents (general information-seeking incidents), but only 13% of the library search requests examined in the Value project (Urquhart and Hepworth, 1995a, b). For nursing professionals in the EVINCE study, 71% of critical incidents involved patient care, but only in 17% was patient care the sole reason. Similarly patient care was involved in 34% of information service requests, but was the sole reason in only 2% of the requests (Davies et al, 1997, 50). As indicated earlier, a health professional may have various roles – patient care provider, researcher and educator, and this spectrum must be remembered when examining patterns of purposes.

The pattern of purposes observed by the library service is likely to be different from clinical practice. Library services are more concerned with providing answers to queries concerned at least partly with education or research (Urquhart and Hepworth, 1995a, b; Davies et al, 1997; Childs, 1994). Researchers use library services such as journals, databases and the Internet intensively, for research purposes, but their information behaviour also includes consultation with colleagues (Grefsheim, Franklin and Cunningham, 1991; Murray, Carey and Walker, 1999).

Sources of published information, whether the research literature or hospital activity statistics, provide the hard data, but many health professionals and managers require the 'soft' data that can be obtained only from people. They often need to use both hard and soft data to answer problems. A study of managers in the NHS (Dawson et al, 1995, Chapter 7) notes the problems of finding suitable indicators for the quality of healthcare services. Managers do, however, increasingly need the 'hard' clinical evidence to help in decision-making, and a study by Beatty (1996) of health managers in Ireland found that 98% cited 'keeping up to date' as a reason for using text information, and 77% cited 'evidence for decision-making' as another reason.

Does making information resources more accessible increase their uptake and use?

Information-seeking involves effort, and while it seems plausible that making resources more accessible will decrease the effort and increase the likelihood that resources will be used, other factors must be considered. Time spent seeking and appraising information is time spent not doing something else. The personal and professional values of the health professional are likely to affect the decision to spend time, however short, on an information quest. Much biomedical literature is written by researchers for researchers (Haynes, 1990), only some of the questions that arise in the course of patient care may be easily answered from the literature (Gorman, Ash and Wykoff, 1994) and even databases such as the Cochrane Library are unlikely to be instantly useful, particularly for primary care practitioners (Urquhart et al, 1999, Chapter 5). It may be useful to think of a two-stage information-seeking model (Gorman and Helfand, 1995), with benefits considered first and choice among resources considered second, and ease of access governing the second stage only. The evidence concerning how benefits, or values, are ascribed to particular sources for particular tasks is uncertain. Whether health professionals are demotivated by the costs of information acquisition or motivated by the benefits may depend on personal factors, the urgency of the task, severity of the patient problem, and the likelihood that an answer will be found (Urquhart, 1999, Chapter 5). For example, Klein et al (1994), in an examination of the effectiveness of online searching on length of stay and patient costs found that test cases were generally more expensive than control cases, as the cases for which searches were conducted were generally more severe. Family doctors in an observational study spent less than two minutes pursuing an answer to a question, and most questions were not pursued (Ely et al, 1999).

Are the needs of community healthcare practitioners different from those of hospital staff?

Much health LIS provision has traditionally been based in hospitals, and sited in or near postgraduate medical centres. Such libraries are now multidisciplinary and serve all staff, but librarians have concerns about the needs of staff who are working in the community, in general practice at some distance from the main hospital site. Organizational structures for healthcare delivery outside the acute hospital sector are quite different from the clinical directorates, wards and departments found in hospitals. Information needs assessment is necessary, and various local studies have been done (Capel, Banwell and Walton, 1998). To some extent the question might be better posed as: to what extent do the location of care and the job role of the practitioner affect the pattern of information needs and use?

It would be useful to be able to profile groups of users by job title or location of care and plan accordingly, but only if the information needs and information skills of the individuals within those groups are similar. The evidence is mixed. During the period of postgraduate training it is possible to say that most junior doctors show certain characteristics concerning information behaviour, and one expects to see, as they progress, some differences, related to clinical experience and knowledge (Urquhart, 1998; Urquhart, 1999, Chapter 4; Urquhart et al, 1999, Chapter 6). Once beyond the postgraduate training stage their individuality seems to assert itself in information-seeking styles. Various methods of grouping nursing staff were attempted in the EVINCE project but, somewhat surprisingly, there seemed little difference in the patterns of information sources used. Although sample sizes may be too small to detect differences there were few significant differences in profiles of purposes of information need (Davies et al, 1997, 38–40). Acute hospital staff were significantly more likely to use ward resources (or resources at base) and drug information services than community staff (Davies et al, 1997, 59–61), but otherwise the patterns were similar in their reliance on colleagues and personal collections. Attempts to categorize the nursing staff in other ways proved difficult. It is plausible, as a small-scale survey indicated (Urquhart and Crane, 1995), that extent of participation in postgraduate or post-registration education will influence the patterns of information behaviour adopted by an individual. This may well be a better predictor of information behaviour patterns than the job title or work location.

Do health professionals use information provided by LIS to help improve clinical decision-making?

While this might seem self-evident, the problem remains of demonstrating that information supplied does have a useful impact. There may be a time-lag between information uptake and use and studies show that LIS (and sources such as MEDLINE) tend to be used more for education and research than for direct patient care. Many health libraries have been concerned to demonstrate their effectiveness in terms of patient care, and methodologies have been developed to demonstrate whether information supplied by the libraries in response to requests is used in clinical decisions. Many studies have used a version of the methodology used in the Rochester study (Marshall, 1992). The different results obtained in several 'value of information' studies, (Urquhart and Hepworth, 1996) suggest that care is needed in the study design, and the user perspective should be paramount (Urquhart, 1999, Chapter 3). A version of the Rochester methodology was used for a small-scale study of physiotherapists (Grieves, 1998), and the methodology used for the Value project (Urquhart and Hepworth, 1995) was adapted for a study of nursing (and midwifery) professionals in the UK (Davies et al, 1997).

Enhancing information skills of health professionals

Ensuring that evidence based resources are used in practice, awareness, education and training is necessary. Librarians have long been aware of the pitfalls of the apparently simple clinical request, and the appeal of the easy interface for novice end-users. A study of 4000 end-users by the NLM found that clinicians preferred to do their own searching, citing familiarity with the subject, speedier results, and enjoyment of searching as the main reasons (Wallingford et al, 1990). Better interfaces, improved help and error messages, the availability of digests of research, reviews and guidelines will all help to make searching easier for the average health professional.

Part of the task for the librarian is persuading health professionals that training and support are necessary. Part of the difficulty is the recognition that information might be applied to a clinical problem, and that information might be formal (eg published research) or informal (eg expert advice). (The EVINCE project suggested that 25% of nursing professionals might be confident (expert) information seekers, but 20% have limited knowledge of sources and information skills (dependent). Those in between may be narrowly focused (using a few sources, 15%), aware, but less sure about strategies (15%) and with some (novice) knowledge of sources and strategies (25%) (Davies et al, 1997).

Education in information skills is accepted as part of the undergraduate curriculum for health professionals and it is possible to provide user education which is integrated into the curriculum at the undergraduate level in a team teaching approach (eg Martin, 1998). Evaluation tends to be limited to immediate feedback and there are few studies which discuss longitudinal feedback of the type described by Fox, Richter and White, (1996). Librarians themselves have training needs concerned with the planning and organization of teaching programmes or user education strategies (Cumbers and Donald, 1998). (See Chapter 14.) The expertise of librarians could be deployed better in supporting health professionals in information retrieval, but that requires support for the librarians in training needs analysis, and better integration of information skills education into postgraduate programmes or continuing professional development such as clinical effectiveness programmes. Example projects include NICE (Barker, 1999), Surf Doctors (Craven, Griffin and Sinclair, 1998) and GIVTS (Urquhart et al, 1999). Evaluation of the effectiveness of training in terms of impact on clinical practice is possible (though difficult) (Urquhart et al, 1999, Chapter 7) and, similarly, evaluation of training through summative assessment on postgraduate education programmes should be possible, though this requires collaboration and trust between the library and the educational establishment (Urquhart et al, 1999, Chapter 8).

Conclusion

This chapter has considered some of the changes in the organization of the human resources in healthcare, noting the rise of multi-disciplinary arrangements for care provision in primary care, the increasing number of women doctors, and government regulations which are more in tune with supporting family carers. To meet the needs of the 'portfolio' career professional, libraries need to be flexible in the way services can be packaged to meet user needs.

Changes in the education of health professionals towards a more reflective and evidence based practice require a long-term viewpoint. Initiatives such as problem based learning present opportunities, but the initiatives need to be evaluated carefully.

Health professionals perform many roles – as managers, educators and researchers as well as practitioners. Their patterns of information need and use seem to differ according to the role. Clinical governance and evidence based practice require many health professionals to undertake unfamiliar roles. Libraries can support health professionals with their new roles, but to do so librarians need to be aware of the way information is generated and used in practice, in informal communication as well as through formal education processes and the research literature. Patterns of information need and use are often complex, changing with developments in technology, but evidence exists to help make predictions about future needs.

Evaluation of user education and support, particularly in the postgraduate, post-registration and continuing education career stages, has been limited. This problem is allied with the difficulty of evaluating the impact of health library and information services. Methodologies are evolving and the future is hopeful. The conventional hospital libraries will have to form alliances with education providers and trainers, with those charged with the responsibility of getting research into practice and with the new providers of consumer health information to ensure that services provided are integrated and evaluated in a manner that makes sense to the health professionals and the healthcare consumers.

Key points

- A greater emphasis on portfolio careers demands a flexible response from libraries in the services offered.
- Problem based learning provides librarians with opportunities, but such initiatives also require careful evaluation.
- Patterns of information need and use are complex, and require consideration of formal and informal needs and use, as well as the different roles undertaken by health professionals.
- Librarians must work with educationalists and those involved with continuing professional development to evaluate information skills training.

3
Health service libraries

Jane Mackenzie

Introduction

The network of health library and information services (LIS) makes a major contribution to management of the knowledge base of healthcare. Healthcare knowledge and literature continue to grow exponentially and practitioners are inundated by information sources and products in their pursuit of evidence based practice. Health LIS collect, organize, collate, interrogate, synthesize, disseminate, promote and enable access to health-related information for all involved in the delivery of patient care, undergoing training or undertaking research. The pressures of government policy, technological development and an increasingly demanding and sophisticated user-base require that libraries constantly evolve and seek new ways to deliver services and support users. As a recent strategy highlights, 'Libraries in the health service are no longer [only] physical entities, confined within four walls' (Cornwall and South Devon, 1999).

This chapter provides a snapshot of the present situation in the UK and highlights developments that impact on the health information professional:

- by identifying political and strategic influences and describing recent library reviews
- by discussing current patterns of provision for health service staff in the UK
- by highlighting the functions and services of health LIS
- by noting briefly the role of independent libraries and specialist services.

The focus is on libraries within the UK health services (specifically England), but developments of note in other countries are also covered. The underlying aim is to highlight developments that are shaping many of the structures described and leading to very different models of provision and ways of working.

Policy context and strategic direction for health service libraries

Fifteen years of major reforms (1979–94) have had a major influence on health service library and information provision in the UK (Haines, 1995). The 'revolution' has not stopped; the first change in government in the UK for 18 years and the increasing realization of 'the information society' have, if anything, increased the speed and level of change. In the move along a continuum from traditional to digital provision, libraries must be dynamic, flexible and proactive in their response to change in order to ensure sustainability. The enthusiasm with which new roles have been developed to meet the needs of the increasingly demanding user-base have been widely chronicled (Haines, 1996; Sawers, 1997; Merry, 1997a; Fuller et al, 1999).

Even adopting the narrow definition, 'libraries serving health professionals working, training and undertaking research in the United Kingdom National Health Service (NHS)', is to encompass a wide range of libraries and services.

There are the conventional services:

- NHS trust and health authority-managed services
- a significant number of higher education-managed services
- the royal college and professional body libraries of the different clinicians and specialisms

and also new types of service:

- not described as libraries but providing specialist support and packaging of information, eg the Aggressive Research Intelligence Facility (ARIF) and the Information Service of the NHS Centre for Reviews and Dissemination (CRD)
- electronic libraries or web gateways such as Organiziing Biomedical Networked Information (OMNI).

As Fowler (1998) states, 'All health libraries are individual and are the product of current and historical funding and sponsorship, varying considerably in size, shape, service provision, ethos and client group.' The majority of 'workplace' libraries, those in receipt of funding to provide health information-focused services to staff working and training in the NHS, are managed within NHS trusts and health authorities. University-managed libraries also play a major role, many within a hospital setting. More than 500 individual services are involved across the UK and patterns of provision and funding are complex and challenging. Their history is well covered by Connor (1989), Carmel (1995) and Merry (1997a). The literature influencing and recording the activity of health service libraries, even in recent years, is vast. Sixteen years of change are chronicled by *Health Libraries Review*.

Early developments

In 1985 King Edward's Hospital Fund for London (1985) published proposals concerning 'the contribution library services can make to the provision and use of information in the NHS'. Library professionals and many external organizations took great interest in the provision and quality of health service libraries, but within the NHS itself libraries were not very high on the agenda. Until 1997 the only specific health service guidance concerning library provision for healthcare workers was *Library Services in Hospitals* (HM(70)23) published by the Department of Health and Social Security in 1970. Invariably, library services in hospitals meant services for doctors. Libraries in medical schools and nursing colleges, whilst primarily serving students, frequently provided services to doctors or nurses. Arrangements for use of higher education libraries were mainly historical, based on custom and practice or goodwill; formal agreements were rare and changes in provision were reactive rather than being systematically developed. During the late 1980s, and particularly during the 1990s, use of information by health professionals began to climb the agenda. Recently a number of activities and strategic documents have required proactive responses from information professionals working in health service libraries.

The Cumberlege seminars

The Cumberlege seminars of 1992 and 1993 (British Library, 1992 and 1993) highlighted that 'more than half of all NHS staff have no access to a library service geared to their professional requirements'. They recommended that 'responsibility for library and information matters should be given a clear locus at the highest level in the Management Executive of the NHS'. The Cumberlege seminars identified a number of strategic objectives:

- to improve the quality of the knowledge base and its coordination
- to improve local organization and transmission of the knowledge base
- to ensure wide dissemination of the knowledge base through use of 'new' technology
- to identify, promote and disseminate good practice.

The messages of the Cumberlege seminars fell on responsive ears. A cross-sectoral LINC Health Panel was established in 1996 with the broad remit to improve availability of health information, increasing the effectiveness of healthcare library and information services through collaborative effort and integrated representation.

LIS policy in the 1990s

The appointment of the first NHS Library Adviser for England and Wales eventually enabled the publication in 1997 of HSG(97)47 (Department of Health, 1997a), the first specific health service guidance on LIS for over 20 years. As the NHS Library Adviser wrote in December 1998: 'The main achievement of the guideline itself has been to put libraries back on the NHS agenda and to give a sharper focus for what still needs to be done to ensure that library services can operate effectively in support of patient care.' (Fraser, 1998).

The role of HSG(97)47 was to:

- highlight the contribution of libraries to the delivery of high-quality healthcare through support for evidence based decision-making, continuous learning and research
- acknowledge issues around inequity of access for all groups, complex funding patterns and lack of strategic direction
- identify a number of key principles as the basis for future development:
  - NHS libraries should be multidisciplinary and meet the needs of all staff groups, supporting effective clinical practice, education and training and research
  - Resources will vary but should be appropriate to local need and include increased use of electronic networks

 – Coordination of funding required
 – Region-wide coordination crucial to effective development.

HSG(97)47 required trusts and health authorities to develop strategies for LIS provision for all staff thereby providing an opportunity for library managers to ensure library developments were on the agenda of key decision-makers.

In a broader context, government policy such as *A service with ambitions* (Department of Health, 1996), and its equivalents in other parts of the UK, increasingly stressed the importance of the information to the NHS. Emphasis was placed on improving information to support clinical effectiveness, research, audit, service delivery and lifelong learning. Policy issued since the election of the Labour Government in 1997, starting with *The New NHS* (Department of Health, 1997b) and UK equivalents contains themes and commitments, outlined in Table 3.1, which continue to affect health service libraries.

Table 3.1   *NHS policy and health service libraries*

NHS policy	Why influential for health service libraries
1997: *The new NHS: modern, dependable*	Setting general context for all subsequent policy; statutory duty of partnership rather than competition to maximize the effective and efficient use of resources; requirement for an informed workforce; key role of information technology in helping to achieve the objectives of the health service.
1997: EL(97)58, *Education and training planning guidance*	Emphasis that 'library and information services are critical to the development of evidence based practice and clinical effectiveness'.
1998: *A first class service*	Focus on quality of service and clinical governance. 'A quality organization will ensure that . . . evidence based practice with the infrastructure to support it is in day-to-day use.'

Table 3.1	*continued*
1999: *Continuing professional development: quality in the new NHS*	New emphasis on lifelong learning and the need for Continuing Professional Development (CPD). 'Local library and IT strategies should provide a framework for ensuring equal access for all staff groups to the learning resources which support work based CPD.'
1998: HSC(98)168, *Information for health* 1999: HSC(99)200, *Information for health – full local implementation strategies*	Library issues initially raised in HSG(97)47 are integrated into these major policy documents setting out the new information strategy for the health service; library involvement in the development of local implementation strategies for information for health; commitment to develop a National electronic Library for Health (NeLH)

Developments in education of health professionals

Policy developments were accompanied by changes in other areas. Major educational reforms have also impacted on health service libraries (Haines, 1995). These include changes in educational provider and funding mechanisms as well as in curriculum content and mode of delivery. New educational processes and methodologies have introduced self-directed and problem based learning which require greater use of information resources and related skills. This has had a major impact on higher education libraries providing services to medical, nursing and other healthcare students. In turn, as these students undertake clinical placements and move fully into clinical practice, workplace health libraries encounter demands for training support, more flexible access and wider varieties of resources. There has been a move from the 'garbage can model of medical decision-making' to a 'problem solving approach' (Braude, 1989).

The move of nurse education into higher education highlighted issues on the organization and funding of LIS for the nursing profession. A report commissioned by the LINC Health Panel (LINC Health Panel, 1997) summarizes these issues. The report made several key recommendations:

- improved cooperation and communication between trusts (hospitals) and universities
- the need for adequate funding to support access to LIS for all nursing groups
- good practice models in contracting and management arrangements
- the development of electronic solutions to the problems of distance users
- the provision of services at the point of need
- adequate user education support systems
- the development of joint working programmes for the networking of information systems.

Reviews of health LIS provision

Many questions have thus been raised about the capacity and role of health LIS. In the late 1990s a number of reviews attempted to respond to these by examining health LIS. They resulted from increasing pressure on existing services and a growing awareness of the library's role in contributing to the delivery of effective patient care. In addition, concern had been clearly identified by the Cumberlege seminars regarding the ability of libraries to fulfil this role. These reviews focused on provision for health professionals in different regions of the UK – North West, Trent, South West, Northern and Yorkshire and Scotland (Scottish Library and Information Council, 1998). The reports of these reviews, and the North West report in particular, expand on issues covered in this chapter.

In general the reviews highlight similar issues:

- An increasing emphasis on quality, audit and research and the need for healthcare delivery to be based on knowledge of best practice.
- Lack of strategic planning and complex funding patterns resulting in inequitable access and lack of clarity about funding levels.
- Compared to the number of health service staff and their diverse needs for information support for effective clinical practice, research and education library provision was invariably inadequate and its quality variable.
- Services which did exist were not well publicized or integrated with wider research, education and staff development networks.
- Relevant LIS were not readily accessible for many healthcare profession-

als due to geographic or time limitations or uncertainty with regard to funding, particularly for those in community and primary care settings.

- Outside the higher education providers 24-hour access to valuable electronic and networked resources was limited and even within HE licence restrictions raised barriers for NHS staff.
- Evidence showed widespread need for extensive training in information searching and handling skills amongst health professionals.

Many of the proposed recommendations and solutions highlight similar themes:

- The need for proactive coordination of health libraries to ensure equality of access to, and effective use of, available resources through cooperative purchasing and management.
- The need to secure and integrate financial resources to deliver the recommendations identified by the reviews.
- The promotion of LIS as a key element in the delivery of high-quality healthcare through support for clinical governance and evidence based care.
- The need to integrate the library with other knowledge management resources and processes and for it to work more closely with IM&T teams.
- Increased support for librarian development.
- Plans to move to increased use of electronic networks for 24-hour delivery of information.
- Incorporation of information-seeking and handling as core skills required by effective healthcare professionals.

Implementation of recommendations from these reviews continues to provide a major challenge for many library managers, working with local stakeholders. Health LIS are now subject to scrutiny by funders, users and other stakeholders and effective responses require flexibility and innovation.

Pattern of provision of health service libraries in the NHS
Regional library units and networks

In most health regions of the UK (eight English regions plus Scotland, Wales and Northern Ireland) a small team has responsibility for strategic development and coordination of library and information provision for NHS staff. These teams, generically known as 'regional library and information units' (RLIUs), hold differing places within the management structure of the NHS and have different structures, strategies and activities. As the director of one of these units has said (Swaffield, 1999), 'We are all doing the same thing, but working in different structures and different cultures.' RLIUs sit within the local health library network with whom they have diverse 'relationships' but shared goals. Cooperative arrangements typically include interlending schemes, union lists and databases, study days, joint purchasing of resources and participation in discussion lists and web developments. RLIUs have frequently developed as a result of increasing cooperation within very active local networks. As Edward and Prior (1998) observe with regard to the West Midlands, 'There was concern amongst network librarians that, although the network was functioning through interlending activity, much more coordination and planning was needed at a regional level to enable the network to operate effectively in other more strategic areas.' Carmel (1998) provides a very useful overview of RLIU activities. In general they focus on:

- strategic and operational planning and development to support national, regional and local strategies
- professional advice and partnerships with all stakeholders, particularly users
- ensuring effective and appropriate allocation and use of levy funds
- coordination of services and resources to ensure effective and efficient service delivery
- development and implementation of quality improvement processes
- support for professional and personal development of library staff.

Typically RLIUs have a key role in coordinating responses to, and implementing, the strategies and reviews outlined above. The RLIU websites, the Regional Librarians Group and NHS Library Adviser web pages attest to these activities.

Organization and management of libraries

The 1997/8 edition (Murphy, 1999) of Regional Librarian Group (RLG) data includes responses from 430 libraries across England, Scotland, Wales and Northern Ireland. The analytical report makes clear that this does not include all potential respondees. The focus is on trust based NHS-managed LIS. Service provision provided by university-managed libraries is neither reflected by RLG returns nor identifiable from other national data collections. Details on specific health service libraries are included in directories published by the British Library (1997) and The Library Association (1997) and may be available on regionally focused websites. Recent editions of the directories include over 800 UK health library services, the majority being hospital, higher education institution (HEI) or health authority-managed. RLG highlights the following profile for health service libraries in 1997/8:

* 1000 staff, approximately half with professional qualifications
* 2,569,585 loans and 668,220 photocopies supplied
* 135,591 mediated searches undertaken
* an average of 33 staffed opening hours per week
* bookstock of 2,606,150 with 210,542 items added in 1997/8
* an average of 117 journal titles held.

Major issues identified by Haines (1995) persist although many are being addressed by the strategies and reviews mentioned earlier. It is now widely accepted that health service libraries should be multidisciplinary and provide access and services for all NHS staff. However extending the limited resources to all client groups is still an issue, particularly with regard to users in primary and community care settings. There is evidence of increased investment in library provision within health authorities – a likely response to the development of purchasing intelligence functions in the 1990s, wider functions for public health departments, the need to meet information needs for delivering health improvement plans and increasing demand from the new primary care groups.

Medical and health libraries in higher education institutions not only serve more than 200,000 medical, nursing and other healthcare students, but also fulfil a key role in information provision for other local NHS users. Medical school libraries have a long tradition of supporting training grade doctors and increasing numbers provide support for other NHS staff. With colleges of nursing merging into HEIs the number of specific 'nursing libraries' on trust sites has gradually decreased. Library provision for nurses and other non-medical staff was included in general education contracts and focused on main HE libraries. Increasingly there are models of close working between NHS-managed and

HE-managed networks as users move frequently between the services both in a geographic sense and at various stages of their careers. The increasingly demanding user-base requires that libraries work in partnership, being unlikely to meet all potential demand working in isolation. New models for commissioning library services for the nursing and allied health professions have developed from projects undertaken by NHS Education and Training Consortia working with the RLIUs. In South West Region the education consortia, strengthened by membership from postgraduate deans, are taking a major role in commissioning LIS. The Follett review in 1993 (Higher Education Funding Council for England, 1983) highlighted challenges facing HE libraries: growth in student numbers; increase in cost of print resources; decline in library spending and a need to exploit new information technologies. The review led to initiatives that address serious shortfalls in library and information resources. These initiatives in turn resulted in innovative projects to ensure that uptake of new technologies was cost-effective, comprehensive and well focused. Examples include the e-Lib projects with their emphasis on exploiting the role of LIS manager as facilitator and capitalizing on the increasing availability and accessibility of electronic information resources.

Variations in provision are confusing to users and a major stimulus for all providers, whether NHS or HE, to seek partnerships to ensure equal and transparent service provision for all users (Bryant, 1997; 1999). A key challenge is the complexity of funding mechanisms.

Funding and contractual arrangements

In 1997/8 more than £28 million was spent on health service libraries (Murphy, 1999). This is a conservative figure that neither includes all relevant expenditure nor all relevant services. This is particularly with regard to resources allocated to networked electronic information resources, funded at consortium or regional levels, and not reported in individual LIS returns. The Trent Review (1998) observed 'The present funding regime impedes multi-disciplinary provision, does not encourage strategic planning and has no explicit provision for capital developments. Funding is complex and difficult to unravel.' Most library services are not commissioned directly, but are included in contracts primarily concerned with the education and training of medical and non-medical staff. There is no consistency in arrangements nationally and funding usually relates to historical supply patterns. The major sources of funding for LIS for NHS staff in England are identified in Table 3.2 but allocation principles and mechanisms vary between, and sometimes within, regions. The North West Region review (1998) describes this as a consequence of 'not previously recognizing the provision of library and information services as a separate corporate requirement within the NHS, supporting the core business of patient care'. This complexity and lack of clarity is receiving attention in many areas with a view to improving management of funding and equity of access.

Table 3.2   *Possible sources of NHS LIS funding*

Funding source	Staff group and purpose
Medical and Dental Education Levy (MADEL)	Postgraduate medical and dental education (increasingly with element of support for multi-disciplinary LIS)
Non-Medical Education and Training Levy (NMET)	Non-medical education and training (main use is to commission programmes of education and support for these from HEIs)
Service Increment for Teaching (SIFT)	Medical/dental undergraduates – service costs incurred as a result of teaching
Research and Development Levy – support funding (R&D)	Support for all undertaking R&D-related activity. Costs of research-related LIS support should be included in bids for funding
Trust/health authority funding	All staff for support for evidence based practice and CPD

Every health service library will receive funds from one or more of the streams in Table 3.2. Most services have a principal funder: NHS trust libraries are primarily funded through MADEL (or UK equivalents); health authority (HA) libraries are funded by the HA; HE libraries serving the NHS, whose primary source will be HEFCE (Higher Education Funding Council for England), may also receive funding from NHS funding streams, particularly MADEL or NMET. Effective coordination of funding streams has a major potential impact on ensuring access for all NHS staff.

Increasingly these complex funding arrangements, particularly where the NHS invests in university libraries, are managed through service level agreements (SLAs) or other contract mechanisms. In many areas the university library is a key provider and lack of clarity around access and services restricts use of their valuable resources by health service staff. Explicit funding mechanisms, such as SLAs, define the investment, the services and the users for whom services will be provided along with mechanisms for monitoring and revising the agreement. SLAs range from one-to-one arrangements to complex agreements covering a number of NHS organizations and a wide variety of users. The SLA mechanism provides an opportunity to integrate the funding streams. In developing an SLA all partners gain an understanding of the needs, priorities and issues of all stakeholders – users, funders and providers. Where a service is being negotiated for users, 'access' is not the only factor. Arrangements must enable services and resources to be targeted at the needs of users.

Services and functions of health service libraries

LIS networks have been quick to respond to the challenges raised by policy and environmental changes and the reviews. There is evidence (Merry, 1997a) of new services being developed in response to new groups of users and increasing user demands. Examples include:

- the development of specialist outreach services to provide information or training support to users in their workplace
- enhanced mediated information retrieval at the point of need (eg the clinical librarian role)
- the undertaking by many libraries of critical appraisal, filtering or synthesis of information as a response to the increasing amount of information available
- the development of content for focused, locally relevant websites and mechanisms for managing dynamic resources and addressing issues of information quality
- the increasing exploitation of electronic networks to deliver information to the workplace (wards, surgeries, offices), for example the 'virtual library' or the Local Multidisciplinary Evidence Centre (LMEC) currently being piloted in North West Region

- the development of novel advice and information skills training to enable users to access and use information resources more effectively.

Libraries deliver a wide range of services (identified, for example in the Draft Specification for LIS 1999–2000 in Cornwall and South Devon, 1999) including:

- access to the healthcare literature through purchase of databases such as MEDLINE, CINAHL, EMBASE, Psychlit, Healthcare Management Information Consortium, British Nursing Index, and AMED
- local selection and purchasing and joint purchasing across sectors and organizations
- collection development and management of print, electronic and multimedia resources
- development and maintenance of catalogues and directories
- document delivery
- evaluation and monitoring of the service to ensure user-led development
- promotion of information use for clinical effectiveness and training on information use and knowledge management
- responding to specific information needs by searching the literature, identifying appropriate material and synthesizing information.

A recent key issue has been the development of electronic provision, forcing libraries to reconsider their roles and take on new, more flexible ways of delivering services. These pressures are not unique to health LIS and are well covered in the professional literature (Hanson and Day, 1998; Carpenter, 1999; Clark, 1999). As Toth and Fraser (1999) highlight, 'So it is not a question of *if* health libraries become more digital, but of *how* the NHS handles that inevitable (and on the whole desirable) process.' The process of developing a National electronic Library for Health (NeLH), a target of *Information for health* (NHS Executive, 1998a and 1999b), will only be successful if it is integrated with local digital library initiatives. Many services are initiating electronic delivery at the place of work through extensive use of networks and intranets. As Blansit and Connor (1999) emphasize, 'Changes in the practice of medicine and technological developments offer librarians unprecedented opportunities to select and organize electronic resources, use the Web to deliver content throughout the organization, and improve knowledge at the point of need.' They also point out that 'The current electronic marketplace requires much vigilance, considerable patience, and continuous evaluation'. Carpenter (1999) emphasizes that it is not just about adding new services to existing services, it is also important to tackle 'the difficult issues of the interaction between people and electronic library resources, systems and services'.

As Crawford (1999) states, 'In the 1990s, the Internet, especially the World Wide Web, introduced online technologies to a vast number of people, changing the role of libraries and librarians and possibly challenging the existence of the library as an institution.' Extensive use of the web is evidenced by regional and local websites that enable access to a range of information resources. In addition specialist Internet sites have been developed with the HE sector-funded eLib project Organising Medical Networked Information (OMNI) being one example. As with other library services the challenge is to combine optimum service through appropriate use of traditional skills and resources with exploitation of new and developing technologies.

Quality and impact of health service libraries

Operating in an environment that is increasingly quality driven and evidence focused has lent momentum to the drive towards quality in health service libraries and the need to assess their impact. In the UK the pressure, described by Fowler (1998), to ensure that health service libraries deliver according to best practice has culminated in a checklist and accompanying toolkit being developed by the LINC Health Panel Accreditation Working Group (LINC Health Panel, 1998a, b). Earlier mechanisms for assessment generally focused on processes used by royal colleges or local schemes and the absence of a national accreditation framework became a matter of concern. The LINC checklist, though intended to be applicable to every type of health service library, is not yet in widespread use. NHS libraries have major concerns around their capacity to undertake accreditation and the lack of support from stakeholders. The quality of LIS for health students within higher education is monitored by the Quality Assurance Agency for Higher Education. At a national level, academic subjects are reviewed according to discipline on a periodic basis. Six broad areas are reviewed at each higher education provider with LIS being examined under a 'Learning Resources' umbrella. Such quality assessment requires considerable work and thought. However, the view expressed by a LIS manager whose service went through the LINC Health Panel accreditation process (Sharp, 1999) was that, despite the difficulties, the benefits were that it:

- was a positive force for change
- was a catalyst for closer interaction with users
- motivated library staff and contributed to team building
- raised the profile of the library
- introduced a mechanism to ensure on-going proactive improvement.

Standards setting, quality assessment and benchmarking of health service libraries have also received much attention in the USA and Canada, evidenced from the websites of their respective medical library associations. In a quality-driven environment it is vital that all services, including libraries, ensure their quality and the LINC Health Panel tool may be one such mechanism. 'Quality ensurance' also requires clarity around the outcomes of a service, in the case of libraries the assessment of 'impact'. This has received much attention in the professional literature in general, and specifically within the healthcare field (Marshall, 1992; Klein et al, 1994; Urquhart and Hepworth, 1995a; Davies et al, 1997; Urquhart and Davies, 1997).

Specialist services

A result of the increased need for, and amount of, healthcare information has been a focus on services concerned solely with the delivery of a specific library-type service. Two such services demonstrate the imperative to consider new responses to the needs of all users.

The NHS Centre for Reviews and Dissemination (CRD) has a national remit to provide information relevant to the NHS on effective healthcare (Sheldon, 1996) It develops its own systematic reviews and deals with enquiries from health researchers, NHS managers and consumer groups. It also disseminates information through databases and publications such as _Effectiveness Matters_ and _Effective Health Care_. The CRD Information Service provides a free enquiry service to healthcare professionals, researchers, managers and information workers, on the results of systematic reviews of research and economic evaluations, in subjects related to healthcare interventions and the organization and delivery of health services. Their external role also includes production of the NHS CRD website and development and maintenance of free NHS CRD databases. Information Service staff also contribute to information-related training and research.

The Aggressive Research Intelligence Facility (ARIF) emphasizes its remit as 'advancing the use of evidence on the effects of healthcare in the West Midlands'. A specialist unit of four people based at the University of Birmingham, its role is to improve the incorporation of research findings into population level healthcare decisions in the NHS in the West Midlands region (Hyde, 1996). Staff help healthcare workers access and interpret research evidence, particularly systematic reviews of research, in response to particular problems. ARIF is a collaboration between the Department of Public Health and Epidemiology, the Department of General Practice and the Health Services Management Centre at the University. Funded by the Research and Development Department of the NHS Executive, West Midlands, ARIF opened in 1996 and, following an external review, was extended to 2003. The nationally available ARIF website summarizes research information and makes available resources useful in making healthcare decisions more evidence based.

Health service libraries – professional and independent

With no equivalent to the US National Library of Medicine in the UK, the government and independent LIS provide a rich collective national resource. The British Library directly delivers services and products and acts as a major support through the Document Supply Centre (BLDSC) and the Health Care Information Service. Haines (1995) refers to 'over 20 professional association and over 40 other medical research libraries in the UK situated in the Royal Societies, the Royal Colleges, the Postgraduate Medical Institutes etc'. These usually represent the professional or membership body of a particular healthcare profession and provide services mainly, though not always exclusively, to their own members. Not every body has its own library, and resource provision and service delivery are uneven. Funding may derive from organizational income, membership or charitable income or direct library membership fees. Services such as those provided by the British Medical Association, the Royal Society of Medicine and the Royal College of Nursing are of immense value, not simply to their own members, but also as a major back-up for document delivery to the network of health libraries. Some offer a portfolio of membership schemes with corporate membership for other organizations or library services. Major services are outlined below with more information being available on websites or in health library directories.

The Royal College of Nursing (RCN) Library, founded in 1921, has a stock of over 65,000 volumes and receives over 400 current journals on nursing and related subjects. It provides lending, photocopy and literature searching services to RCN members, contributes to the British Nursing Index (available in print, CD-ROM and Internet versions) and provides document delivery services to other health libraries.

The Royal Society of Medicine (RSM) has one of the largest postgraduate bio-medical libraries in Europe. It has a collection of 2000 current periodical titles, 10,000 periodical titles in all and a total collection of half a million volumes. The Library and Information Service provides a cost-effective range of high quality services to members and non-members including literature searches and document delivery. It provides support and advice on search strategies, undertakes searches, provides regular current awareness services and can receive queries via e-mail, letter, telephone or fax or in person. Services are primarily for members of the RSM but there are a variety of membership schemes.

On its very detailed website the *British Medical Association (BMA)* Library highlights its role: 'The BMA Library . . . exists to deliver to BMA members the fastest and most comprehensive medical information service that current technology allows. Collections are focused on helping working doctors and surgeons provide the best possible care for their patients; and the links with the BMJ are as close as ever – with the collections underpinned by exchange arrangements and review copies.' It supports many more healthcare professionals through the document delivery service it provides to less well-stocked health libraries.

The Library of the *King's Fund* focuses on the management aspects of health-care rather than clinical information. The collection's subject strengths include NHS management, community care, commissioning, quality management, user involvement, primary care, health inequalities, healthcare financing, health economics, ethnic health issues, London healthcare, management and organizational development. The collection has a unique emphasis on informally published literature within UK healthcare and covers government documents, books and journals.

Health service libraries – international

Developments across the world during the 1990s amplify the themes identified from the experience of the UK. A few of these are signalled below with others covered on the websites of the extremely active, national health librarian associations. These include the US Medical Library Association (MLA), the European Association of Health Information and Libraries (EAHIL) (as well as associations in individual European countries) and the Canadian Health Libraries Association/Association des bibliothèques de la santé du Canada (CHLA/ABSC). These associations support the continuing development of the profession and provide guidance and standards-setting support for service development. For example US and Canadian associations provide standards and benchmarking guidance for health libraries, widely used nationally and internationally. Many improvements are driven and enabled by the valuable networking, cooperative working and sharing of good practice supported by the associations and the enthusiasm of their members.

The US *National Library of Medicine (NLM)* is the world's largest medical library. The library collects materials in all areas of biomedicine and healthcare, as well as works on biomedical aspects of technology, the humanities, and the physical, life, and social sciences. The collections house 5.3 million items – books, journals, technical reports, manuscripts, microfilms, photographs and images. NLM produces MEDLINE and other databases which underpin health service libraries internationally.

The US *National Network of Libraries of Medicine (NN/LM),* with a current membership of 4545 services, was the first comprehensive national library network (1967). Under the leadership of the National Library of Medicine and through the participation of medical libraries and other information resources, it has developed into a well organized and effective network for meeting the information needs of health professionals in the USA. Activities include document delivery, Internet connectivity, technology awareness, and outreach and reference services to health professionals.

In Canada the *CHLA/ABSC* has established a steering group to develop a strategic plan for the implementation of a national network of libraries for health (Marshall, 1998).

Elsewhere, as in the UK, change has been influenced by technological and societal changes and specific policy developments. For example, research was commissioned 'to review levels of access to information and library services for healthcare staff, patients and the public in Ireland' following the publication of *Shaping a healthier future: strategy for effective healthcare in the 1990s* by the Department of Health (MacDougall, 1995).

Conclusion

This overview highlights recent developments within health LIS, primarily within the UK. Since the 1990s changes and innovations within healthcare and society have had a major impact on the spectrum of health service libraries. Health LIS continue to play a major part in managing and enabling access to the knowledge resources of healthcare. Health LIS will continue to adapt to, respond to and initiate change in delivery, in the light, for example, of

> a MORI survey for Which? Online in August 1999 which estimated that more than one fifth of the UK adult population were using the Internet and many reports which estimate at least doubling of this over the next few years.

> We are only at the dawn of the world of e-information and its so-called knowledge age. Threats and opportunities abound for the information professional . . . History clearly shows that the consequence of an inability to evolve adequately fast to a changing environment is extinction. (Clark, 1999)

> NHS libraries will continue to act as the bedrock of many of the services we provide by delivering timely and accurate information to clinicians and managers. (Sir Alan Langlands, Chief Executive, NHS Executive 1998))

> Today's technological advances coupled with health care reform, health policy and economic issues raise new challenges for functioning successfully in the future. It is critical that medical librarians become key players in this scene. (Naomi Broering, MLA past president)

Key points

- Technological developments, changes in policy and practice of delivery of healthcare, and changes in education of health professionals have had a major impact on health service libraries during the 1990s.
- In terms of the UK based services, developments such as the appointment of an NHS Library Adviser, service reviews and regional librarian appointments in most regions have provided an opportunity for influencing at a strategic level and improved coordination at an operational level.
- Increased Internet use and the roll-out of NHSnet are influencing decisions on service delivery, eg increase in provision of 24-hour access to information resources via electronic networks. Access to the knowledge

base will need the same degree of technical consideration and support as management and patient information systems.

☞ The National electronic Library for Health (NeLH) will complement existing library services, rather than replace them.

☞ New models of outreach information support to users in offices, on the wards and in primary care and community settings are being developed.

☞ New roles for library professionals will influence patterns of health library provision – for example moving to a knowledge management focus will require extensive use of personal and electronic networking outside the physical library.

Relevant websites

Aggressive Research Intelligence Facility
http://www.hsrc.org.uk/links/arif/arifhome.htm
British Medical Association Library
http://www.library.bma.org.uk/
eLib: The Electronic Libraries Programme
http://www.ukoln.ac.uk/services/elib/
Joint Information Systems Committee
http://www.jisc.ac.uk/
The King's Fund
http://www.kingsfund.org.uk/
Local Multidisciplinary Evidence Centre (LMEC) South Cheshire
www-lmec.chester.ac.uk
National electronic Library for Health (NeLH) Prototype
http://194.129.181.161/
National Library of Medicine (US)
http://www.nlm.nih.gov/nlmhome.html
National Network of Libraries of Medicine (US)
http://www.nnlm.nlm.nih.gov/#map
http://www.nnlm.nlm.nih.gov/mr/recnetmem.html
NHS Centre for Reviews and Dissemination – Information Service
http://www.york.ac.uk/inst/crd/infoserv.htm
OMNI: Organizing Medical Networked Information
http://omni.nott.ac.uk/

Project Connect (North Thames)
http://www.nthames-health.tpmde.ac.uk/ntrl/welcome.htm
Royal Society of Medicine Library
http://www.roysocmed.ac.uk/librar/page6.htm

4
Health service information providers

John Hewlett

Introduction

Health service information providers work within the National Health Service, higher and further education (HE and FE), other areas of the public sector such as social services and public libraries, the voluntary sector and charities, and the private sector. In the NHS they include clinical audit staff, clinicians, clinical informaticians, consumer health information providers, epidemiologists, health promotion staff, information managers, information officers, librarians, medical records staff, public health experts, statisticians, and all their clerical, paraprofessional and other support staff; and they may provide this information face-to-face, through telephone helplines or through electronic networks and web pages.

With such a spectrum of health service information providers, this chapter will concentrate on healthcare library and information services (LIS) staff.

Context

Within the NHS, LIS staff are often linked with education since their funding has historically been with postgraduate medical, dental and nursing education. Management responsible for LIS staff have been traditionally (medical) clinical tutors, but the line management of librarians is tending to move to information or corporate management departments.

Education for nurses and the professions allied to medicine has recently moved into HE or FE, and this has resulted in major changes for LIS staff, and closer links with the local education institution for many NHS staff. Cultures in the NHS and in education are very different, and have affected staff in both sectors.

A further change is the development of 'local health informatics services', as recommended by *Information for health* (NHS Executive, 1998). 'IM&T specialists will work alongside clinicians, clinical informaticians, public health experts, epidemiologists, clinical audit staff, librarians and others who contribute towards meeting local health information needs' (NHS Executive, 1998, para. 6.85). This is particularly noticeable in geographical areas where librarians are working in 'patch' groups to provide support and input in the Full Local Implementation Strategies (FLIS) for *Information for health*. This sort of development was foreseen and recommended by Brittain and MacDougall (1993).

Convergence of library services and IT departments is proceeding in some HE institutions, and is likely to develop in the NHS, as local health informatics groups evolve; library staff will develop their IT skills, and IT staff will develop additional information skills. Lynch (1999) writes convincingly of the breaking down of boundaries between 'published' literature and research data, between research databases and clinical patient data, and between consumer health information and professional literature; and about the roles that librarians will need to play in the early 21st century.

Numbers

The NHS Regional Librarians' Group (RLG) carried out censuses of staff providing library services to NHS personnel in 1978 (NHS Regional Librarians Group, 1979) and 1985 (NHS Regional Librarians Group, 1987), and have recently published collections of annual statistics which include staffing figures (Murphy, 1999). The censuses showed an increase in staff of 72%, from 755 staff in 1978 to 1302 in 1985; and a possible decrease to 966 (full-time equivalents) in 1997/98. The number of service points also rose and then fell, from 1045 in 1978 to 1114 in 1985, and in 1997/98 down to 538.

Exact comparisons are difficult. Education for nurses and professions allied to medicine has moved from the NHS into HE and this has resulted in staff moves: staff are still serving nursing students though now university-employed rather than NHS-employed. RLG statistics do not now clarify whether university healthcare and medical school library staff are included in every region. Collection of figures is inevitably incomplete, and differently incomplete from year to year.

A significant increase has been in LIS staff employed in health authorities. In 1985 the Northern and Yorkshire Regions employed two staff in the two regional health authority libraries: in 2000 there are three staff at the Northern and Yorkshire (single) Regional Office Library, and 11 (of 13) health authorities employ qualified librarians. These staff perform an information role, delivering reformatted, processed or packaged information to managers on demand, and often before demand, and they are often perceived as valuable members of the management team.

Numbers of healthcare LIS staff working in universities are not known, as there is no single assessment of HE or FE LIS staff working directly or indirectly with healthcare. 105 universities in the United Kingdom employ 7865 staff (SCONUL, 1999) and many of these will be staff working with health-related areas: medicine, nursing, physiotherapy, pharmacy, and so on. Some universities have restructured their staff so that there are no longer subject specialists, and all staff deal with all users of a service point; others have broadened subject groupings so that, for example, a 'health, education and social work' campus library serves a range of adjacent subject areas, and the 'health' element cannot be separated out.

Similarly, there are no figures on staff employed in LIS in the industrial, commercial or voluntary sectors. These may be pharmaceutical or commercial companies, medical charities, or voluntary support groups for consumers with specific disorders: and may have LIS ranging from very advanced networked resources to small collections of printed materials (Creaser and Spiller, 1997).

Figures for NHS IM&T staff are not collected nationally, and it is impossible to estimate how many staff work in the NHS supplying information. The groups of NHS staff mentioned earlier come from a wide variety of professions, and may be counted within these professions, but they are rarely seen as related to each other as information providers.

Changing roles

NHS libraries are changing from a 'just in case' mode, where information is found and stored against possible future need to a 'just in time' mode where only specifically requested information is gathered and provided to the user. This is even more the case where libraries serve managers in NHS trusts and health authorities who need quick answers to questions – at the time it is required; the librarian provides information pro-actively, instead of answering questions reactively, or stores and maintains a collection of printed materials.

Case study 1

Keith Black, Librarian at Borchester Health Authority, is responsible for supplying published information to the managers. He sees the main challenge as keeping himself well enough informed about health authority business to supply information before the managers know that they want it. He acts as the 'eyes and ears' for senior managers to send them things they might not otherwise see. He is directly involved in the preparation of bids for research monies, and his expert literature-searching skills help a consultant to prepare a successful bid for £80,000. His Chief Executive says, 'A professional source of information, including evidence based searches, has become increasingly invaluable to me personally; it will form a critical component of the more rigorous analytical framework of the health authority as we get to grips with a new and more challenging role.'

Librarians' traditional roles are being replaced by wider roles, and as LIS staff develop their services there is a greater need for skills in teaching and training, in information technology, and in promotion and marketing. MacDougall and Brittain pointed this out after conducting research into information use and information needs in the NHS (MacDougall and Brittain, 1992).

Some posts have strategic and management roles – Health Service Guideline (97)47 requires all NHS trusts and health authorities to have an LIS strategy (Department of Health, 1997a) – and the post-holders need appropriate skills and experience; and some have high-level project management roles. 'Their [NHS libraries'] most valuable resource, the librarians, will play a central part in the development and delivery of the National electronic Library for Health's aims and objectives' (Muir Gray and de Lusignan, 1999).

An antecedent of the first pro-active roles for librarians was the clinical medical librarian (CML) project, which began in 1971 as a way of giving clinical teams information related directly to patient care. CML librarians attended ward rounds to identify information needs, ran literature searches, and presented the information back to the team; their role was 'to provide information quickly . . . to influence the information-seeking behaviour of clinicians, and improve their library skills; and to establish the medical librarian's role as a valid member of the health team' (Cimpl, 1985). Objections to CMLs include: that librarians' knowledge of medical terminology is inadequate; that they do not clearly understand many of the questions asked during rounds; and that the cost is prohibitive. But the cost of case-related information is less than the cost of one chest X-ray or one set of electrolyte studies. Two useful reviews of the subject have been published (Cimpl, 1985; Makowski, 1994). CML roles have seen a renaissance in recent years.

Developing services to primary care across a wide geographical area is also giving librarians new roles, some distanced from those they have traditionally occupied. Rose (1998) gives a range of these: campaigner, strategic planner, outreach worker, educator and trainer, organizer and disseminator of secondary sources of information, researcher, and marketer. The role of the librarian in the local health informatics group will often be as a trainer in information skills, where the other members of the group do not have such expertise (see Chapter 14).

Library assistants have also graduated to a higher level as more assist in the teaching and training of users. A subject librarian said to Walton and Edwards (1999), 'In fact what our senior library assistants are doing, with one or two exceptions, is what I was doing as an Assistant Librarian, ten years ago, possibly six years ago.' Library assistants often now have National Vocational Qualifications or City and Guilds qualifications, and some have IT qualifications and a role in maintaining library IT equipment.

Skills and competencies

The skills needed by information professionals are constantly changing, and at present 'the [library] profession is currently in an interim phase, where skills in handling both printed and electronic information are required' (Garrod, 1997). They have expanded from the list of knowledge and skills for pre-registration trainees which suggested three levels of knowledge: understanding of the concept, its application, critical examination and evaluation of it (Hewlett, 1988).

This evolution is examined by Barry (1997), who looks particularly at the information skills needed in academic research by doctoral students and, by extension, by the librarians who deal with these students. She deals exhaustively with the process, from question analysis to evaluation of results, but does not discuss the wider range of skills needed by librarians.

Stenson, Raddon and Abell (1999) have looked at skills and competencies needed for first- and second-level posts in three different branches of the corporate sector, including the pharmaceutical industry. They have broken down competencies into seven areas of ability:

- ability to gather and analyse data in context (analysis)
- ability to make decisions based on reasoned argument that maximize value and minimize cost (cost control)
- knowledge of critical path solutions to information problems (subject knowledge)
- ability to interact in ways that maximize business outcomes (communication)
- ability to translate user needs into retrieval strategies (retrieval)
- awareness of the context of information management and its application to the organization (organization)
- ability to use computer equipment to a high standard to achieve business outcomes (computer literacy).

The Electronic Libraries (eLib) programme is looking at the exploitation of IT in order to create the effective library service of the future. One of the projects (SKills for new Information Professionals, the SKIP project) looked at the groups particularly affected by change: senior managers, who need management skills rather than professional skills; subject or information librarians (as most NHS library information staff are); and library assistants, a group increasingly doing work previously undertaken by professional staff. The project considered the 'skills and personal qualities most required by employers', grouped as personal qualities and transferable skills; IT skills and areas of expertise; electronic and networked information resources; and traditional information skills. Garrod (1997) gives a detailed checklist.

Palmer (1996) also gives a checklist of skills for librarians working in healthcare:

- organizational politics
- how to operate in a market-place
- how to negotiate
- how to use and teach critical appraisal as a means to filter the literature
- why research-based decision-making is important in healthcare and in the librarians' own profession
- how to teach in all contexts, from individuals to large groups
- how to facilitate learning
- knowledge of new information sources and products
- knowledge of new technologies

- familiarity with the Internet (and now the NHSnet)
- how to create personal storage and retrieval systems.

Case study 2

Keith Black is working with the librarians from the local NHS trusts – the acute trust, the community trust and the learning disabilities trust – and with the regional librarian (IM&T) to develop a strategy for LIS for the full local implementation strategy (FLIS), due to be finalized by March 2000. His role is to help stakeholders realize the potential of LIS, to help them with a vision of how these services might look in five years' time, and own the process of putting together this vision which is agreed by all. For this he needs skills in marketing, negotiating and facilitating learning, all underpinned by knowledge of the organization and its politics.

He has arranged a meeting for NHS staff in IM *and* IT, education, training and development, clinical audit, health promotion and other interested groups. Together they have heard speakers from the different stakeholder groups, brainstormed their ideas and produced a strategy (building on the library strategy developed after the publication of HSG (97)47) which will fit into the FLIS. For this meeting he needed good organizational skills, communication skills and good knowledge of the electronic environments, both now and future.

Keith has then taken this to the FLIS Board (of which he is a member) where he has negotiated for the inclusion of the major part of the library strategy into the FLIS, ensuring that LIS will be seen as part of the local health informatics service.

It is clear that new competencies needed by information providers will be additional to the traditional library skills: and these skills, particularly question analysis (see Chapter 15) and information retrieval (Chapters 17–19) will remain paramount for front-line staff.

Training needs

Health Service Circular HSC 1999/200 recommended that 'staffing levels, skills and experience should form an integral component of Health Informatics Services Reviews' (NHS Executive, 1999b). It recognized the importance of appropriate skills for library staff in order to support users in the efficient use of technology to access and appraise relevant evidence sources, which would be needed in local specialist education and training plans. In some regions these general education and training plans are being drawn up to reflect information skills training needs of librarians and of their users. NHS regional library and information units have from their beginnings provided training for the health-care librarians on their patch, and have often included other healthcare information professionals from within and outwith the NHS. Many of these are in response to training needs analyses (Stewart, 1995) and some are undergoing regular change and development (NHS Executive Northern and Yorkshire, 2000). A national training needs analysis is planned for the early months of 2000 to assist with the planning of a national framework for healthcare librarian development (Fraser, 1999a).

Brittain and Maggs (1993) pointed out the growing demands and expect-ations from NHS staff to have sophisticated information resources and retrieval skills. They found evidence of an information skills shortage, with information departments which had too few staff with appropriate skills and knowledge. They proposed improved partnerships with universities for education and train-ing in health informatics at higher levels. This was followed up by Dyer and Rolinson (1995) who looked at the adequacy of university education for health-care management and library services in a changing health service; and by Farmer and Richardson (1997) who studied academic–practitioner liaison for education, and attitudes towards it.

Implications for continuing professional development (CPD)

'Lifelong learning is an investment in quality' (Department of Health, 1999b). The current government emphasis on lifelong learning is developed by the DoH Circular HSC 1999/154 on continuing professional development, which describes the need to keep pace in a changing world, where technology changes rapidly, and the NHS changes even more rapidly. There is an emphasis on prac-tical issues, including:

- the role of monitoring, peer review and appraisal in determining CPD activities
- the role of new technology and distance learning in maximizing learning opportunities and customizing the process
- how the expertise of professional and statutory bodies can best support local CPD, within the context of clinical governance

- the educational infrastructure within every health organization to identify and meet CPD needs.

The document (Department of Health, 1999b) also discusses the range of different learning styles, as well as 'going on courses'; adult learners prefer a variety of ways of learning, and may be able to learn in two or three different ways simultaneously. It recommends that all health professional staff should have a personal development plan (PDP); that this might be linked with personal or professional appraisal and organizational objectives; and that it should be reviewed annually. 'Active learning among staff has to be encouraged. They will need to become skilled learners, continually looking for opportunities to upgrade skills and knowledge' (Walton, Day and Edwards, 1995).

The Library Association offers a wide range of CPD possibilities, including its own qualifications, formal CPD provision and a framework document for CPD, through its branches and groups (Wood, 1999).

An early project, part of the IMPEL project (Walton, Day and Edwards, 1995), looked at the training needs for staff competencies for the effective management of networked information services. Based on case studies at six UK universities which had reached 'a significant level of electronic library development', it found eight groups of staff training needs which related to style as much as to content of training:

- a basic level of computer literacy
- long-term IT skills training
- a structured programme for training linked in to the information strategy
- training together with computer services staff
- training geared to individual needs
- more interaction and exchange of experience outside the home institution
- training on a formalized basis
- time to practise new skills.

The content of the training, resulting from role changes, included managerial skills, advice on team working and communication, training for the trainers, and multiskilling for converged services staff (Walton and Edwards, 1999).

Preferred learning styles are considered by Lacey Bryant (1995) who writes primarily for the solo librarian, but whose suggestions are useful for all staff working in small units. She writes about the needs for a wide range of skills, particularly flexibility, as solo librarians who want to move onward (usually into larger services) have to develop a portfolio of skills transferable to other roles or other sectors. Motivation can be either personal (to develop a career) or professional (to develop skills). External influences can also affect learning. Accreditation of LIS by external assessors has been seen as a means of developing personal and professional improvement by Weist (1995) and Sharp (1999).

Farmer and Campbell (1998) write about the relationships between CPD and career success, without giving hard-and-fast definitions for either. Successful professionals recommend to other younger professionals that they should take part in CPD in order to keep up to date, considered to be absolutely vital in dealing with change and retaining professional status: 'CPD is the fashionable name for what committed professionals have always been doing.' Similarly, career success is achieved by a whole package of factors that mean that the professional is skilled, motivated, well networked and ready to take on new challenges.

In summary, continuous professional development comprises a range of tools and outcomes, appropriate to the individual, to improve skills and underpin knowledge, in order to keep pace with a fast-moving environment, and to assist towards required career development.

Professional associations

This section lists the major associations and groups for health information providers, particularly librarians, with websites for most of them listed at the end of the chapter.

A wide range of (UK) groups serve healthcare information providers, pointed out by Palmer (1994) after a Library Association Medical Health and Welfare Libraries Group conference. She urged the formation of 'an umbrella body . . . which can represent the interests of all groups' and that a unified voice is essential if healthcare information professionals are to establish national credibility. The LINC Health Panel has been formed to perform a coordinating role for most of the library groups related to healthcare.

Aslib (formerly the Association of Libraries and Information Bureaux) is a corporate membership group, based in London, primarily for 'special librarians' working in the industrial or commercial sectors. Aslib publishes a number of information-related serials and books: and there is a Biosciences Group which promotes the exchange of information in the fields of biology, agriculture, medicine and the environment; the group provides a useful programme of meetings.

ASSIST, the Association for Information Management and Technology Staff in Health, was formed in 1993 for staff involved with planning, implementing and running information systems. Because the professional background and training of this group is varied, ASSIST is developing accreditation for training courses for 'information managers'. The group has a branch structure based on (pre-1996) NHS regions, and over 700 members.

Information Focus for Allied Health (INFAH) is an independent group of librarians working with the professions related to medicine (chiropody, dietetics, occupational therapy, physiotherapy, etc). These professions are numerically small, and their information needs can be easily overlooked; INFAH acts as a forum for discussion on how this can be overcome.

Information for Managers in Healthcare (IfMH) is a subgroup of The Library Association Health Libraries Group, aimed particularly at librarians working with, and providing information services for, healthcare managers.

The Institute of Information Scientists is 'the professional association for people involved in all parts of the information chain', and many healthcare librarians are members of the Institute and The Library Association. The Institute emphasizes the provision of information (rather than library services) and has a smaller membership. The Institute and the Association have agreement in principle on a merger, and negotiations are continuing, notably about a name for the joint association.

Libraries for Nursing (LfN) was established in 1980 as the Nursing Interest SubGroup (NISG) of The Library Association Health Libraries Group, but changed its name in 1993. It provides a communication and education network for all library staff interested in services for nurses, midwives and their allied professions.

The Library Association Health Libraries Group (formerly the Medical Health and Welfare Libraries Group) is a subgroup of The Library Association, formed in 1978 by merging two previously separate groups in order to unite members of The Library Association in the field of health libraries, to provide a forum for discussion, and to promote the interests of the profession. The Group publishes a quarterly newsletter aimed at keeping healthcare librarians updated, which includes a current literature column. The newsletter is republished three months later in the quarterly *Health Libraries Review*, published by Blackwell Science.

The Library Association is the professional association for librarians in the

UK, with over 26,000 members, based in London. Library Association Publishing produces a range of library-related books.

The NHS Regional Librarians Group arose from informal meetings between regional librarians in the 1970s, and became formally ratified in 1979; the Group now has membership from all the NHS regions and from Northern Ireland, Scotland and Wales. It is an ex officio group, in that membership is by appointment to a substantive post with regional responsibility for library services across a region, which might be advisory, commissioning or managing library services.

University Health Sciences Librarians (UHSL) was established in 1996, to act as a 'forum for the interchange of ideas and to contribute towards the discussion of issues relating to health sciences in HE'.

The University Medical School Librarians Group (UMSLG) is the representative group for the librarians of undergraduate and postgraduate medical schools in the United Kingdom and the Republic of Ireland. The web pages provide a useful calendar and list of members.

In addition there is the *European Association for Health Information and Libraries* (EAHIL) which was constituted in 1987, and seeks 'to improve library services to the health professions by co-operation and shared experience across national boundaries'. EAHIL produces a newsletter and directory, and convenes a biennial conference of medical and health libraries in Europe.

Conclusion

Health service information providers, whether serving healthcare professionals, educators and students, industry or commerce or the general public, work in a world which is rapidly changing. Technology is advancing, user expectations are expanding, and the structure and infrastructure of the work environment changes almost daily.

In this context it is necessary to keep our skills updated and, if possible, move our skills forward in advance of the market. Professionally we need to keep our information services modern and dependable so as to provide the best information, the fastest service, the right evidence for our users; and personally we need to be ready to make the most of career changes.

There are many opportunities to improve our skills and knowledge, many different methods of learning to choose from, and many groups through which we can learn and develop. The 'free-floating goodwill' which exists between librarians (Lacey Bryant, 1995) can be used to find appropriate skills teaching, to ensure that our lifelong learning is adequate for the provision of quality services.

Key points

Health service information providers have to cope with continual major change:

- NHS culture is changing, often moving library information services away from education.
- The development of 'local health informatics services' will move librarians towards other healthcare information providers.
- The convergence of library services and IT departments is likely to develop further.

Librarians' roles are changing rapidly. They may develop into:

- strategic planners, managers, promoters and marketers of their services
- teachers and trainers
- pro-active providers of reformatted information, disseminators of secondary sources, outreach workers, clinical medical librarians
- researchers.

The skills and knowledge needed by health service information providers are constantly changing; they are transferable; and have differing levels of competence for different work.

Continuous professional development (CPD) is the way to keep skills and knowledge regularly updated. Appropriate CPD needs to:

- derive from a range of learning styles and results
- be appropriate to the individual
- keep pace with a fast-moving environment and assist towards required career development.

Relevant websites

Professional associations

Aslib
  http://www.aslib.co.uk/
Aslib Biosciences Group
  http://www.aslib.co.uk/sigs/biosciences/index.html
ASSIST
  http://www.assist.org.uk/assist
Biomedical Information (BMI) of the Netherlands Society of Librarians, Documentalists and Information Specialists
  http://www.konbib.nl/nvb/bmi/bmieng.html
Canadian Health Libraries Association/Association des bibliothèques de la santé du Canada
  http://www.med.mun.ca/chla/
Community Care Network
  http://www.hand666.freeserve.co.uk/ccn/ccn.htm
European Association for Health Information and Libraries (EAHIL)
  http://www.eahil.org/
Information Focus for Allied Health (INFAH)
  http://www.mailbase.ac.uk/lists/info-allied-health/
Information for the Management of Healthcare (IfMH)
  http://www.york.ac.uk/inst/crd/ifmh/
Institute of Information Scientists
  http://www.iis.org.uk/
Libraries for Nursing (LfN)
  http://www.la-hq.org.uk/groups/hlg/lfn.html
The Library Association
  http://www.la-hq.org.uk/index.html
The Library Association Health Libraries Group
  http://www.la-hq.org.uk/groups/hlg/hlg.html
Library and Information Cooperative Council (LINC) Health Panel
  http://www.lib.jr2.ox.ac.uk/linchealth/
Medical Library Association (USA)
  http://www.mlanet.org/about/
National Network of Libraries of Medicine (USA)
  http://www.nnlm.nlm.nih.gov

NHS Regional Librarians Group
   http://www.nthames-health.tpmde.ac.uk/rlg/
University Health Sciences Librarians (UHSL)
   http://www.sbu.ac.uk/lis/uhsl/
University Medical School Librarians Group (UMSLG)
   http://www.his.path.cam.ac.uk/umslg/umslg.html

Journals

Bibliotheca Medica Canadiana, published by the Canadian Medical Libraries Association
   http://www.med.mun.ca/chla/english/bmc.html
Bulletin of the Medical Library Association, published by the Medical Library Association
   http://www.mlanet.org/publications/bmla/index.html
Health Libraries Review, published by Blackwell Science for the Library Association Health Libraries Group
   http://wwwblacksci.co.uk/~cgilib/jnlpage.bin?Journal=
   HLR&File=HLR&Page=aims
Medical Reference Services Quarterly, published by Haworth Press
   http://bubl.ac.uk/journals/lis/kn/medrsq/index.html

Electronic discussion lists

BIBLIST (Scandinavia)
   http://www.lib.chalmers.se/extern/BIBLIST/index.html
Canmedlib (Canada)
   http://www.med.mun.ca/chla/english/canmedlibe.html
EAHIL-L (Europe)
   http://www.eahil.org/discussion_list.htm
evidence based-libraries (International)
   http://www.mailbase.ac.uk/lists/evidence based-libraries
lis-medical (UK and Ireland)
   http://www.mailbase.ac.uk/lists/lis-medical/
lis-nursing (UK and Ireland)
   www.mailbase.ac.uk/lists/lis-nursing

MEDIBIB-L (Austria, Germany and Switzerland)
http://medweb.uni-muenster.de/zbm/medibib.html
MEDLIB-L (USA)
http://listserv.acsu.buffalo.edu/archives/medlib-l.html

5
Consumer health information

Donald Mackay

Introduction

Consumer health information (CHI) has seen tremendous growth in the last 20 years. From small beginnings, in one or two libraries, hospitals and GP practices, the organized supply of health information to the public has grown into a large and important field very much at the forefront of government health policy.

Consumer health information is more than just information to help people cope with being ill. Everyone is a consumer of health information. It includes information on specific illnesses and conditions, on good health and the prevention of ill health in general, and information to enable us to make informed choices about medical treatment.

Historically, many studies have shown that giving information is an important factor in reducing anxiety and in enhancing compliance with medical treatment (Barnes, 1961; Ley, 1988; Webber, 1990; Hayward and Boore, 1994). The adequate provision of health information to the public is increasingly recognized as an important factor in the empowerment of individuals to make decisions about their own medical treatment and the maintenance of good health.

This chapter provides a brief overview of recent and current developments in CHI and identifies some of the many sources of health information available to the general public. Implications for health information professionals will also be discussed. It is intended to provide a useful overview of the topic.

The growth of consumer health information

Gann (1987) has adroitly highlighted the prominence of CHI: 'There is no doubt that Consumer Health Information has been one of the last decade's information "megatrends". The lay public have been interested in their own health since the earliest times and, as Gann points out, it was only the great medical and technological advances between 1930 and 1960 that 'served to enhance the power and mystique of doctors'.

Modern interest in consumer health information began in the USA with the development of CHI services in hospital libraries and other locations in the late 1960s and early 1970s. The best known of these, the Planetree Health Resource Centre, was established in the 1980s. In the UK, pioneers such as Sally Knight and Bob Gann set up or developed the first health information centres such as Health Information at Stevenage and Help for Health in Southampton in the 1970s. By the end of the 1980s similar centres had been set up in many areas of the country funded and typically backed by local library and health authorities. Services included health information shops based in the high street and centres based in hospitals, health promotion centres and public libraries. In 1991 the Consumer Health and Information Consortium (CHIC) was founded.

Many of the original health information services are still in existence, providing a wide range of services. These services include libraries of books, magazines, leaflets, cuttings, etc on health-related topics; information on self-help groups and charities; and access to databases and helplines. Examples include the Healthshop at Ninewells Hospital in Dundee, the Forth Valley Health Information Service and the shop-front at Health Promotions in Aberdeen.

There are numerous reasons for the growth of consumer health information provision and its wholehearted adoption by the UK government. Three of the most important contributory factors have been:

- increasing consumerism in society as a whole
- a growth in awareness that individuals can do much to improve their own health
- increasing costs of healthcare provision.

Consumerism

Society in general has seen tremendous advances in consumer power and consumer choice reflected in changing attitudes towards healthcare provision: 'People are no longer content to be told what's good for them' (Gann, 1995).

The very use of the term 'consumer' instead of 'patient' reflects this changing attitude.

Healthcare has become more focused on the recipient of care rather than the provider and the old 'Doctor knows best' paternalism has been challenged. However, as some of the limitations of applying a purely consumerist model to healthcare have become apparent (Charles et al, 1999; Coulter, 1999), the emphasis today seems to be evolving further – from this model to one of partnership between health professionals and their clients. Related trends include moves towards increasing patient involvement in research, lay involvement in decisions about service provision, evidence based patient choice, and the growing recognition of patients as experts in the management of their own chronic diseases.

In the late 1800s Wendell-Holmes (Holmes, 1911) announced to a class of medical students, 'Your patient has no more right to all the truth you know than he has to all the medicine in your saddle bags . . . he should only get so much as is good for him.' A century later *Saving lives: our healthier nation* declared that 'The Government recognizes the importance of individuals making their own decisions about their own and their families' health' (Department of Health, 1999f).

Self-care and individual behaviour

There is growing recognition among the public as well as governments that, partly because of the limitations of medical technology, 'our health depends on change in behaviour as individuals and communities, change which can only be achieved if ordinary people have access to information' (Gann, 1991).

In 1978 the *Declaration of Alma Ata*, one of the most important documents in modern health promotion, specifically stated that 'The people have the right and duty to participate individually and collectively in the planning and implementation of their health care' (World Health Organization, 1978). In 1986 *The Ottawa Charter* noted that access to information is one of the factors that 'enable all people to achieve their fullest health potential' (World Health Organization, 1986).

Developments in the UK

As a result of these and other factors CHI has seen tremendous development all over the world (Rees, 1991). In the UK, drawing on the WHO strategy, *The health of the nation* (Department of Health, 1992a), (England) and *Scotland's health: a challenge to us all* (Scottish Office, 1992) were released by the government. Both documents noted the importance of providing information to enable people to make informed decisions about their own health. The earlier documents *Working for patients* (Department of Health, 1989) and *Patient's Charter* (Scottish Office, 1991) had already outlined the public's rights to information on a range of topics including maximum waiting times, how to choose a GP and the right to 'accurate, relevant and understandable explanations of what is wrong; what the implications are; what can be done; what the treatment is likely to involve'.

Regional Health Information Services were set up to cater for these information needs and in January 1993 a nation-wide freephone health helpline was launched to provide access to the nearest one. Provided by different agencies in different parts of the country the service supplies a core set of information covering areas such as health conditions and treatment; local and national self-help and support groups; waiting times – based on the guidance provided by HSG (92)21 and HSG (95)44 (Department of Health, 1992b; Department of Health, 1995). The service is accessible anywhere in England, Wales and Scotland. It has been predicted that this service will be replaced or absorbed by a new service, NHS Direct, by the end of 2000.

Economics

In the light of ever-expanding healthcare costs, successive UK governments in the 1980s and 1990s have taken to heart the notion of the patient as consumer/partner with responsibility for their own health. Shackley and Ryan (1993) describe the government's ideal consumer as 'someone who can adequately assimilate information on the costs and quality of health care, and on the basis of such information, has an ability and a desire to make health care choices and is then prepared to search for the best "package" of health care in terms of cost and quality'.

The UK government document *Information for health* underlines the economic arguments for the importance of a more aware healthcare consumer. It notes that 'A well informed public on health and services means: people have more autonomy and control over their own lives and more choice; more appropriate and effective use of services; a reduction in the burden of appropriate calls on the NHS' (Burns, 1998).

Sources of consumer health information

Undoubtedly for most people the primary sources of consumer health information are health professionals. In a study of rheumatology patients researchers found that 'the majority of patients saw doctors as the prime, and often the only, source of information' (Farmer and Peffer, 1996). A survey carried out by the National Consumer Council (1998), *Consumer concerns 1998,* found that almost three-quarters of those interviewed said that they went to their GP for personal or family health advice.

However for various reasons – time constraints, the pressures of the consultation, the environment in which the communication takes place (eg a lack of privacy in a clinical environment is not conducive to good communication), poor communication skills and other factors – people do not always get the information they need from health professionals (Farmer and Peffer, 1996; Buckland, 1994).

What follows is a breakdown of just some of the other major sources of health information used by the general public. Inevitably, given the growth of this field, new resources and services will have appeared by the time of publication, but it is hoped that this will provide a useful taster.

Family and friends

A common source of CHI is family and friends. Kempson (1984) found that 'over half of the participants [in her discussion groups] had gleaned information from friends or other patients'. More recently a survey carried out by the Help for Health Trust noted that 'the three main sources of information, prior to consulting health professionals, were family, friends and books' (Olszewski and Jones, 1998).

Mass media

The media is also an important source of health information. Television has seen a surfeit of series such as *Watchdog Healthcheck* and *Trust Me, I'm a Doctor* and newspapers and magazines abound with health features and regular health advice columns. Many self-help groups and voluntary organizations (see below) also publish their own newsletters and magazines and Which?, the consumer organization, now produces a regular health magazine, *Health Which?* Unfortunately the quality of advice from the media varies tremendously, one recent study finding that 28% of columns surveyed contained advice that was 'dangerous and potentially life-threatening' (Broadway, 1995).

Popular medical books are very heavily used sources of health information, as are the many thousands of leaflets and booklets produced by organizations such as charities and self-help groups, royal colleges and other professional organizations, pharmaceutical companies and NHS organizations.

Community/local health councils

Community health councils in England and Wales, local health councils in Scotland, and health and social services councils in Northern Ireland are independent statutory bodies set up to represent users of the NHS in the provision of healthcare. They provide a valuable link between healthcare organizations and the people who use them. Their functions include the provision of information about the setup of the NHS and on how to access patient records; guidance on how to complain and other patient rights; monitoring of local NHS services; and the representation of users of health services on groups and committees. National umbrella organizations for health councils can be contacted at the addresses at the end of this chapter. Other organizations who deal with information about the NHS and who try to represent patients include the Patients' Association and the College of Health (who operate the National Waiting List Helpline).

Health education/promotion agencies

On a national level, the Health Education Board for Scotland, Health Promotion Northern Ireland, Health Promotion Division (Wales) and the Health Education Authority (soon to become the Health Development Agency) are the lead bodies for health education. Alongside their other activities, each of the mainland agencies has their own library or information service.

These services provide access to collections of books and journals on health promotion as well as a number of databases on the health and social sciences. They also provide a range of current awareness services and two of them produce their own bibliographic databases on health promotion and health education, *HealthPromis* at the HEA and the journals database at HEBS. Only the library at HEBS is open to the general public without restrictions; the others cater mainly for health professionals and students. All four organizations produce regular newsletters and updates, the most substantial being the HEA's *Healthlines* and HPANI's *Promoting health*. Local health promotion agencies are also active in every health authority and health board area and provide a range of services, often including a library or resource centre.

Telephone helplines

In addition to the national Health Information Service and NHS Direct (see below) consumers can access information on health from a range of other telephone helplines. These include government and charity helplines such as ChildLine, Sexwise and AIDSline as well as others provided by self-help groups, charities and commercial organizations. Despite worries about the quality of advice from some commercial services, large numbers of individuals contact helplines for information and advice. In Scotland the highly successful Smokeline has dealt with over 380,000 genuine calls since its inception in October 1992 (Health Education Board for Scotland, 1997).

Charities, self-help groups and support groups

Thousands of local and national charities, support groups and self-help groups throughout the UK provide information support to people on a huge range of health and social problems. These organizations can vary from one- or two-person bands to large national organizations such as the Samaritans, the Terrence Higgins Trust or The Imperial Cancer Research Fund. Among their many other activities, these organizations provide telephone helplines, leaflets, counselling, funding for research and information via the Internet.

Information about these organizations can be found in a range of local and national directories and databases in local public or medical libraries, health information services or local health councils. It is also worth consulting organizations such as local health promotion departments, Citizens' Advice Bureaux, Councils for Voluntary Service (CVS) or the voluntary service umbrella organizations (contact details at the end of this chapter).

Recent developments

Since taking power in 1997, the UK Labour government has encouraged the development of partnership rather than competition in healthcare and has taken a new look at the role of primary care and the development of information management and technology within the NHS. It has also introduced a number of new measures and initiatives in health promotion and public health.

Partnership

The emphasis is now on a partnership between the individual, government and communities to improve health. To quote *Patient and public involvement in the new NHS*, 'the key to delivering this ambitious programme is partnership: partnership between the NHS, patients and the public' (Department of Health, 1999e).

There is a recognition that people can improve their own health if they have the opportunity to make informed decisions, but also that there are areas beyond their control, such as poor housing, social exclusion and crime, where government must take a role. The White Papers *The new NHS: modern and dependable* (Department of Health, 1997b), *Saving lives: our healthier nation* (Department of Health, 1999f) and *Designed to care* (Scottish Office, 1997), and other documents such as the 1998 IM&T strategy document *Information for health* (Burns, 1998), have flagged up a number of initiatives with direct implications for consumer health information.

These include NHS Direct, the National electronic Library for Health (NeLH), health action zones, healthy living centres, health skills programmes and expert patients programmes. Developments elsewhere in the government's programme, for example the proposed bill on freedom of information, will also have an impact on health information.

Evidence based patient choice

It has been highlighted that 'patients want more than simply information; they need involvement too' (Richards, 1988). Even before the election of the new Labour government this theme of partnership had begun to emerge in CHI. Consumer health information began to cover more than what could be now described as coping information, that is, information about specific illnesses and conditions for patients and their families or contact details of self-help groups. In the light of the developments outlined above and the growth of evidence based healthcare, consumer health information started to include information on treatment outcomes and effectiveness.

The terms 'evidence based patient choice' and 'evidence informed patient choice' have been coined to define this 'use of evidence-based information as a way of enhancing people's choices when those people are patients' (Hope, 1996).

It has been argued that informed consumers may select more effective forms of healthcare which are appropriate to their needs and priorities, thus securing greater health gain and cutting down on demands for inappropriate treatments which will in turn reduce wastage. Patient involvement in decision-making may lead to increased compliance or enhance the placebo effect. It may also increase patient satisfaction with care and reduce the number of complaints or even litigation (Entwistle et al, 1996a; Entwistle et al, 1996b).

Evidence based patient choice is now a major component of evidence based healthcare (witnessed by the development of a consumers and communication group within the Cochrane Collaboration), and the role of the consumer in the NHS remains high on the agenda of the UK government. The 1996 *Patient partnership* produced by the NHS Executive emphasized four overall aims: 'To promote user involvement in their own care, as active partners with professionals; to enable patients to become informed about their treatment and care and to make informed decisions; to contribute to the quality of health services by making them more responsive to the needs and preference of users; to ensure that users have the knowledge, skills and support to enable them to influence NHS service policy and planning' (NHS Executive, 1996).

If people are to participate fully in decisions about their treatment it is essential that they have access to the evidence to inform their choices. A number of organizations and projects have been working in the area of providing understandable evidence based information to the public. These include the King's Fund, the Materials for Informed Choice-Evaluation (MICE) and The Informed Choice Initiative – a collaboration between the Midwives Information and Resource Service (MIDRS) and the NHS Centre for Reviews and Dissemination. Topics covered have included pregnancy, childbirth and postnatal care, anxiety, ulcerative colitis and HRT, and the use of a consumer health information service in the provision of outcomes information.

NHS Direct

NHS Direct is a national telephone helpline that provides 24-hour access to a wide range of information and advice from nurses and information workers.

Following on from a number of pilot studies (and despite a mixed reception) all of Great Britain will be covered by the end of 2000.

Although the first three pilot services were run by ambulance services, the second wave of services has brought in organizations such as community health trusts, GP cooperatives, existing health information services and social services – embracing the government's vision of 'seamless care' (Department of Health, 1999b). Developments announced by the Prime Minister in April 1999 include NHS Direct outreach (where nurses may contact callers after their original call to offer further advice or to remind them about appointments); the publication of an NHS Direct Healthcare guide; public information points providing access to NHS Direct; and the launch of NHS Direct Online as part of the NeLH.

Consumer health informatics

A common position in which doctors find themselves now is when they are 'confronted with a patient who has done a literature search, scanned the Internet, made a provisional diagnosis, and knows what he or she wants from the health service' (Richards, 1998).

An increasingly important aspect of the growth of CHI has been the development of consumer health informatics, defined by MacDougall et al (1996) as 'the application of computer and telecommunication systems for use directly by lay people'. This definition includes a large number of different projects and uses of technology.

Databases

In the UK there are three main national electronic databases of leaflets and support groups – *HEBS on CD*, HelpBox and the self-help groups database produced by the College of Health.

HEBS on CD, produced by the Health Education Board for Scotland, is a CD-ROM available in over 2500 locations throughout Scotland. It provides access to information on help groups, leaflets, health promotion projects, full-text publications and health statistics. Help for Health's HelpBox and the College of Health's database provide a similar (although more restricted) range of information and have been a staple of consumer health information services in England and Wales for some years now. Help for Health also produces the database *The NHS A to Z,* which is an invaluable guide to over 200 topics relating to health care and the NHS.

Other CD-ROMs on the market include a host of 'Home Doctor' types of product, other CDs providing information for patients such as *PatientWise* and Oxford *PILS*, and topic based CD-ROMs such as the HEA's *D-Code* CD.

Information points

Several organizations have produced touch-screen health information kiosks or community health information terminals (including the Healthpoint system developed at Glasgow University, and the InTouch system developed by Brann Ltd). These and other kiosks are now present in many locations including libraries, GP surgeries, and other public places. Various public access local authority based systems which contain at least an element of health information, such as CapInfo in Edinburgh, Signpost in Bromley and Grampian CareData, are also in place. Other applications of consumer health informatics include interactive TV and video, laser discs and, of course, the Internet.

The Internet

The spectacular growth of the Internet has seen the development of numerous applications for consumer health information. As well as being able to communicate with fellow sufferers through bulletin boards or newsgroups, members of the public can now access hundreds of thousands of sites on the world wide web that deal with health information. One study in 1999 claimed that a quarter of all material on the Internet is health related (Brown and Dickinson, 1999).

Many healthcare organizations and self-help groups have taken the opportunity to provide consumer health information online and there are a wide range of databases and directories which can be accessed free over the Internet. In the UK this includes the databases of CancerBACUP, the Terrence Higgins Trust, ASH, Alcohol Concern and many thousands of help groups, charities and medical organizations. The public can access MEDLINE free from its producer at the NLM as well as from a host of commercial healthcare sites, and can browse online journals such as the *British Medical Journal* and the full text of many other resources and databases traditionally the preserve of health professionals.

The Health Education Authority and the Health Education Board for Scotland have developed substantial websites, providing access to full-text resources as well as databases of statistics and support groups. HEBS' sites include a

CyberSchool, the HEBS Healthcentre and a virtual drugs warehouse. The HEA has launched a range of different sites covering topics such as healthy eating, smoking and alcohol abuse.

A major initiative flagged up in *Saving lives: our healthier nation* was the planned launch of NHS Direct Online. Originally planned as part of the National electronic Library for Health, this site provides access to a range of services including an 'interactive self-care guide and accredited information about hundreds of diseases and self-care groups' (Department of Health, 1999f). Organizations involved in the development of this service include the HEA, Help for Health and the Dr–Patient Partnership. Similar initiatives outside of the UK include MedlinePlus from the National Library of Medicine, the US Government's healthfinder and Australia's Healthinsite.

The sheer number of health resources on the Internet (and especially on the world wide web) and the frequency with which new resources are produced makes it impossible to provide an exhaustive list of resources in any specific area of health, far less in the whole field of CHI. However, some of the more general gateway sites are listed at the end of this chapter.

Quality in consumer health information

The explosion of consumer health information over the last two decades and especially the growth of CHI on the Internet and evidence based patient choice have led to increasing concern over quality. It has become apparent that quality extends beyond issues of layout and ease of reading (which nevertheless remain important). It is also important that the information is relevant and based on good-quality research.

As virtually anyone can publish information on the web many sites provide information that is at best mistaken or misleading, at worst dangerous. Fortunately a number of initiatives provide guidance and gateways to information of good quality. These include OMNI, healthfinder, Medical Matrix and Health on the Net.

A number of quality criteria and assessment tools for CHI materials have been drawn up over the last few years or are currently under development. These include Discern, the Materials for Informed Choice-Evaluation (MICE) project and QUICK, set up by the Centre for Health Information Quality and the HEA.

The Centre for Health Information Quality has the remit to 'act as a source of expertise and knowledge for the NHS and patient representative groups on all aspects of patient information in the aim of improving the NHS's capability, competence and capacity to provide good, evidence-based patient information' (Department of Health, 1996), and has since produced a number of publications in this area including newsletters and topic bulletins.

Implications for health information professionals

The growth and development of consumer health information has provided, and will provide, information professions with a range of challenges and opportunities. Partnership has been an ongoing theme in CHI in recent years and seems likely to become more important as time goes on. As MacDougall (1998) notes, 'These partnerships will be facilitated by information professionals who provide the access to information necessary for partnership to function effectively.'

The new NHS Direct may be staffed in many cases by nurses at the end of the telephone line, but information professionals are already playing a role, and many of the pilot services have included the existing health information services to a greater or lesser degree. In one pilot, for example, health information assistants were the first point of contact (Chapman, 1999).

Even when they do not actually act as front-line staff, the skills of well-trained health information professionals and an up-to-date collection – physical or virtual – of databases and other resources are essential components of an adequate health information service. Health information professionals will also have roles to play in developing information services and resources in projects such as health action zones and healthy living centres.

There is a growing role for health information professionals in the provision of health information over the Internet and on CD-ROM. To give just one example, the majority of the staff involved in the production and development of *HEBS on CD* have a library and/or information management qualification. Information professionals are well placed to contribute to the development of websites and other electronic health resources aimed at the general public.

The development of evidence based patient choice has created a need for resources based on sound evidence to aid patient decision-making. Information professionals can contribute to the identification and critical appraisal of primary research, systematic reviews and other sources of evidence that form the basis of evidence based health information leaflets and other resources.

To ensure that individuals have the best possible access to information about their health, health information workers in national and local CHI services will need to develop and maintain their existing expertise and develop a range of new skills. The expertise and skills required include a knowledge of local and national health service developments, a thorough awareness of what CHI resources and organizations are available, critical appraisal skills, information management skills, website development and other IT skills and good customer care and communication skills.

Conclusion

Consumer health information has developed from small beginnings into one of the major growth areas of information provision. Spurred on a by a number of factors, people are demanding to play a greater role in their own healthcare. In order to participate to their fullest potential as more equal partners in their own care, individuals, now more than ever, need adequate access to good-quality evidence based information. By maintaining their traditional skills, developing new expertise and taking advantage of the opportunities now offered, consumer health information professionals are well placed to meet this need.

Key points

- CHI includes information on specific illnesses and conditions, on good health and the prevention of ill health in general, and information to enable informed choices to be made about medical treatment.
- Individuals obtain information on health from a wide range of sources other than health professionals.
- The growth of CHI has been encouraged by increasing consumerism in society as a whole, a world-wide growth in awareness that individuals can do much to improve their own health, and by the increasing costs of healthcare provision.
- Themes to emerge in recent years include the patient and physician as partners in healthcare, evidence based patient choice, quality of information and services and consumer health informatics.
- Consumer health information is now at the forefront of UK government policy on health. Recent developments include the launch of NHS Direct, NHS Direct Online, and the Centre for Health Information Quality.

☞ Challenges and opportunities abound for health information professionals who are in an ideal position to facilitate access to information and
enable partnerships to develop.

Relevant websites

Charities/self-help groups

Alcohol Concern
    http://www.alcoholconcern.org.uk
ASH
    http://www.ash.org.uk
BUBL UK
    http://bubl.ac.uk/uk/charities/
CancerBACUP
    http://www.cancerbacup.org.uk
Charities Direct
    http://www.caritasdata.co.uk/
Charity Choice
    http://www.charitychoice.co.uk
Charity Commission
    http://www.charity-commission.gov.uk
Contact a Family
    http://www.cafamily.org.uk
National Association of Councils for Voluntary Service (NACVS)
    http://www.nacvs.org.uk
National Council for Voluntary Organizations (NCVO)
    http://www.ncvo-vol.org.uk/
Northern Ireland Council for Voluntary Action
    http://www.nicva.org/index.htm
Scottish Council for Voluntary Organizations
    http://www.scvo.org.uk/
Terrence Higgins Trust
    http://www.tht.org.uk
Wales Council for Voluntary Action
    http://www.wcva.org.uk

Consumer representatives

Citizens' Advice Scotland
   http://www.cas.org.uk
The College of Health
   http://homepages.which.net/~collegeofhealth
National Association of Citizens' Advice Bureaux
   http://www.nacab.org.uk/

Gateway websites

healthfinder
   http://www.healthfinder.org
Medical Matrix
   http://www.medmatrix.org
MedlinePlus
   http://www.nlm.nih.gov
National Institutes of Health's link pages
   http://www.nih.gov/health/
OMNI
   http://www.omni.ac.uk
Patient UK
   http://www.patient.co.uk

Government CHI websites

NHS Direct Online
   http://www.nhsdirect.nhs.uk
Healthinsite (Australia)
   http://www.healthinsite.gov.au
healthfinder
   http://www.healthfinder.org

Health promotion/education

Health Promotion Agency Northern Ireland
   http://www.healthpromotionagency.org.uk

Health Promotion Division, Library and Information Services, National Assembly for Wales
> http://www.hpw.org.uk

The Health Promotion Information Centre, The Health Education Authority
> http://www.hea.org.uk

Health Promotion Library Scotland
> http://www.hebs.scot.nhs.uk/

Quality

The Centre for Health Information
> http://www.chiq.org.uk

Discern
> http://www.discern.org.uk

Health on the Net
> http://www.hon.ch

OMNI Advisory Group on Evaluation Criteria
> http://www.omni.ac.uk/agec/

QUICK
> http://www.quick.org.uk

Telephone helplines

Telephone Helplines Association
> http://www.helplines.org.uk/

Government helplines in England and Wales
> http://www.open.gov.uk/doh/phone.htm

Government helplines in Scotland
> http://www.scotland.gov.uk/faq/hth-free.asp

Information about CHI

Bibliographic databases that are useful when trying to find out more about CHI include CINAHL, LISA, HealthPromis, the HEBS article database, CHID, MEDLINE and HMIC. Journals particularly worth consulting include *Patient i, Health Libraries Review, Health Expectations, Patient Education and Counselling,* the *British Medical Journal,* the *Health Libraries Group Newsletter, Journal of*

Advanced Nursing, He@lth Information on the Internet and *CHIC Update*. The Popular Medical Index, a useful index of health related articles in the popular press compiled by Sally Knight, is available from Mede Publishing.

Useful websites include Science Panel on Interactive Communication and Health (SciPICH) (**http://www.scipich.org**), CHiQ (**http://www.hfht.org/chiq/**) and CHIC (**http://www.omni.ac.uk/CHIC/**). In addition to the occasional coverage provided by the lis-medical mailing list there are a number of CHI mailing lists including consumer-health-informatics and quality-consumer-health-info on Mailbase (**http://www.mailbase.ac.uk**) and Health Education And Technology (HEAT) (**http://www.sph.unc.edu/heat/**). It's also worth getting on the mailing list for the regular current awareness e-mail from HPIC (**http://www.hea.org.uk**). The Help for Health Trust can be contacted at **http://www.hfht.org.uk**.

Part 2

Health information resources and their organization and management

6
Providing direction and management for health library and information services

Graham Walton

Introduction

The rapidly changing technology, coupled with clinical users with current needs that bear little resemblance to those of five years ago, means health LIS managers must develop new services and incorporate new technology. At the same time the health LIS are functioning within the turbulent health environment described in Chapter 1 where change is occurring in all areas. Two key areas on which the health LIS manager must focus to ensure that services 'fit' are strategic direction and managing staff. This chapter is therefore divided into two sections: strategic and human resource management. The intention is not to convey that one is more important than the other, but that they involve different approaches and skills. Strategic and people management are intertwined: an effective health LIS strategy will be damaged by ineffective staff management and vice versa.

The role of strategic management, informed by recent developments in the directions taken by health information services in UK NHS trusts, is discussed. The strategic process is outlined including strategic analysis, internal analysis, strategic options, evaluation of options and strategic implementation. This section is completed by discussions on the importance of different stakeholders to the strategy. Various business models, already applied within the library sector (Walton and Edwards, 1997), are used to develop the ideas within the health LIS context. The section looking at staff management discusses managing change, staff skills, teamwork and staff development.

Strategic direction in the health information service

Role of strategic direction in health information services

The actions of the health LIS staff determine whether the service survives, flourishes or withers. If a health LIS is to survive in the long term it needs to constantly adapt to the outside world. In the private sector, strategic management is primarily concerned with maximizing profits, but this driver has limited applicability to the health LIS where the driver is to maximize the effectiveness of the resources allocated for providing the service. Strategies have to match the needs of the external health environment and build on existing strengths already present in the health LIS.

Recent significant developments in the UK's National Health Service have increased the profile and importance attached to health information strategies. Health Service Guideline 97(47) (Department of Health, 1997a) was produced to rectify a situation where the lack of guidelines and complex funding had led to fragmentation of library and information provision within the NHS. The resulting guideline indicated that NHS trusts should draw up a library and information strategy covering all groups and this approach was strengthened in 1998 when the national health information strategy, *Information for health* was launched (Department of Health, 1998b). At a theoretical level, a centralized approach should ensure all NHS trust library and information services are strategically managed to support healthcare delivery. A review of how health LIS strategies have developed within a specific region (NHS Executive Northern and Yorkshire Regional Library Advisory Service, 1999) provides evidence that issuing central guidelines does not necessarily result in the appearance of LIS strategies or their implementation. Reasons for this are explored later in the chapter. Strategic management has an important role with Johnson and Scholes (1999) reporting on a study by Baden-Fuller and Stopford of rejuvenated businesses. It was found that the success of the business was the result of strategies, pursued on an individual basis, and the effective development of those strategies by management. Having an explicit approach to strategic management will increase the likelihood that a health LIS will supply the necessary services.

Strategic analysis of the environment

Burnes (1996, 12) has observed that it used to be assumed that 'organizations move from one stable state to another in a pre-planned manner. However . . . in the turbulent and chaotic world in which we live, such assumptions are increasingly tenuous and organizational change is more a continuous and open ended process than a set of discrete and self-contained events.' The inherent danger in the assumption of stability is that fixed responses will be developed for what are seen as fixed situations. Changes will not be implemented, new services not offered and new skills not acquired if there is no recognition that the world and health LIS have both moved on. Strategic analysis is concerned with identifying the future effect of the external environment on services.

A starting point can be to establish which environmental influences have been particularly important in the past and the extent to which changes may make them less or more significant in the future. This can be achieved by undertaking a STEP analysis where the key drivers in the external environment are grouped under the following categories: sociological, technological, economic and political. Johnson and Scholes (1999) provide more information on the STEP analysis. A STEP analysis was produced in Chapter 1 to provide a contextual structure of the health external environment. The STEP analysis does not stand by itself, but needs further study with the key influences and drivers of change being separated from those that will have minimal impact.

The health LIS, as part of the analysis, has to identify if there are factors in the environment that will influence its ability to position itself advantageously. By understanding the underlying sources of advantage much groundwork will have been accomplished in identifying strategic action. Further work is needed to examine the influences on the immediate environment of health LIS. Applying the five-force analysis developed by Porter (1980) can facilitate this. His approach supports the detailed examination of different sources of change and their respective implications. Within the health LIS context these five forces are:

- *Threat of new entry*. With the development of electronic services and globalization, commercial companies can set up competing information services which may prove attractive to funders. It is also possible within the same geographical area for there to be different providers of health LIS who may be approached to take over a service. Within the same organization different units can look to take over services previously operated by the health information service. Computer units are likely to see the networking of databases such as MEDLINE as part of their remit. Training sections may wish to deliver courses on appraising the evidence.
- *Power of supplier*. The level of power of suppliers to health information services is continually evolving. At one level, their power is limited

because the range of book suppliers, periodical subscription agents and software suppliers enables prices to be forced down and higher quality to be demanded. At another level they have significant power as suppliers of electronic databases can enforce legally binding contracts that dictate who can use the databases and the nature of their use.

- *Power of service users.* Along with other customer-driven services, users of health LIS are becoming more powerful. They can demand services that are available from desktops, that support evidence based practice and that equip them with the necessary information skills they need. If these are not forthcoming, they can look for other suppliers.
- *Substitute products and services.* This last decade has seen a proliferation in electronic health information sources: e-journals, the world wide web, end-user access to databases. This trend is unlikely to slow down and the health LIS provider has to establish how to deal strategically with this.
- *Jockeying for position.* Health LIS will cope with the above four forces in a variety of different ways with services being altered and developed. There is a need to establish how other health LIS are coping with the pressures/forces as well as developing services at the local level.

Internal analysis

Internal analysis is important because there is a need to know whether the health LIS has the capabilities to perform at the appropriate strategic level. Johnson and Scholes (1999) highlight the need to establish whether the internal competencies fit the external environment. One approach to this is to undertake a SWOT analysis (Strengths, Weaknesses, Opportunities, Threats) which has been used as a common-sense checklist for many years. The aim is to identify whether the health LIS's current strategy and its own strengths and weaknesses are still relevant and capable of dealing with the health environment.

Strategic options

Once decisions have been made concerning the broad strategy to be adopted by a health LIS, further decisions have to be made on the precise direction and methods needed to develop the strategy. Another business model that can be applied to health LIS is the product/market matrix (Ansoff, 1986). This model looks at the markets for services and the services themselves and establishes whether both are new or existing. By applying this model it is possible to establish four possible strategic options the health LIS can take:

- *Protect/build on current positions.* The chosen strategy here is to focus energies on protecting or building on the health LIS's current position. It may be occupied with maintaining existing library and information services to the current users. Protecting and building on current services could encompass seeking improved services through automating routine tasks like book issuing or periodical receipts. This protect/build option may prevent necessary new services required by users from being developed.
- *Service development.* This option is preferable for health LIS where there is a need to shift service patterns to meet the clinicians' changing needs. The key skill here is to establish and understand the changing need. There are risks to this approach in that developing new health LIS is expensive and may not meet the changing needs. The nature of the new health LIS needing to be developed means new competencies in such areas as information technology and teaching skills will have to be acquired.
- *Market development.* Health LIS are only used by a limited percentage of the health professionals who are entitled to them. It is possible to identify those individuals or groups who do not use the services and establish strategies to extend the services to them.
- *Diversification.* In this strategic option the health LIS considers directions that take it away from its current users and services. Diversification could involve teaching health professionals information technology skills alongside information skills. It may also include looking at offering health LIS to clinicians outside of the organization from which the health LIS operates.

Strategic evaluation

The recognized experts in strategic evaluation are Johnson and Scholes (1999) who have identified three types of evaluation criteria: suitability, acceptability and feasibility. Before a strategy is implemented the health LIS manager can apply these criteria to the different strategic options.

- *Suitability.* At a broad level the health LIS needs to unpick the strategy and establish whether it will be compatible with the changes identified in the environmental analysis.

- *Acceptability*. It is also important to identify whether the expected strategic outcomes will meet health LIS users' expectations. If a strategy has been to set up an electronic current awareness service on the hospital network, will it be a service clinicians will use? There is always some level of risk attached to strategies and it is important to assess whether this level of risk is acceptable. A health information service that decides as part of a strategy to move periodical subscriptions to electronic delivery has to establish how clinicians that have previously relied on the paper version will react.
- *Feasibility*. This evaluation is concerned with whether the health information service has the resources and skills to deliver the strategy and whether it will work in practice. Proposing to improve access by increasing opening hours to the health information service will depend on the resources being available. Developing a web based enquiry service as part of the strategy will succeed or fail on whether or not health LIS staff have web-authoring skills. The existence of an appropriate training budget is also crucial.

Strategic implementation

Implementing strategy is just as complex as identifying the way forward. Alexander (1989) has surveyed the public and private sectors to establish approaches that promote implementation. All staff members in the health LIS need to be involved and committed to the strategy. There should be effective two-way communication throughout the whole process. Sufficient resources should be available to support the strategy and the strategy itself should be based upon good concepts and ideas. An implementation plan should support the strategy and attempts be made to predict possible problems to prevent them occurring in the first place. A further approach to ensure effective implementation is to identify critical success factors (CSFs) which will dictate whether the strategy will stand or fall. The identification of the CSFs will allow attention and resources to be focused to ensure it does not fail.

In the implementation of strategy there has to be some level of control (Asch, 1989) but this is not a simplistic aspiration. The control process involves the social/person sense as much as the technical/financial sense. The coordinator of health LIS needs to set up information systems to provide data to monitor the progress of implementation of the strategy.

Stakeholders and strategy

The piecemeal implementation of the guidelines on library strategy was referred to earlier (NHS Executive Northern and Yorkshire Regional Library Advisory Service, 1999). One possible reason for this variable implementation is the extent to which all stakeholders were involved in the strategy. Health organizations have multiple stakeholders with different expectations and different levels of interest in, and power over, the health LIS or library strategy. If the manager of a health LIS analyses the extent to which the different stakeholders are likely to have an interest in the strategy they will be better informed as to how to deal with the various stakeholder groups/individuals. Not only does the level of interest need to be established, but also the power the individual stakeholders would have to influence the strategy adversely or otherwise. For example, if the Chief Executive of an NHS trust has high interest in the library strategy, it is likely that their power will ensure it has both a high profile and impact within the trust.

Managing people in the health information service

Managing change

A combination of the turbulent health external environment and the drive from the fast-developing technology ensures that health LIS do, and will continue to, experience change as a normal, regular activity. The manager of a health LIS will always encounter resistance to change from staff, as well as users. The way this resistance is managed will be pivotal to the future success of change management. Kotter and Schlesinger (1989) have identified why staff may resist change: parochial self-interest, misunderstanding/lack of trust, different assessments of the situation and low tolerance of change. Another commentator (Macadam, 1996, 38) has observed that barriers to change are through 'organizational inability to forge lasting trust and honesty between senior managers and workforce'. Further critical factors identified by several authors (Farley, Broady-Preston and Hayward, 1998; Farrow, 1997) are the importance of communication with staff, staff involvement and staff training to overcome resistance. Health LIS staff need to be involved early in the change process and fully aware of the changes proposed. They need to be given ownership of identifying the way forward to achieve changes.

Farrow (1997) and Corrall (1998) both highlight the disappearing traditional library hierarchies and the benefits of allowing front-line staff to act as change agents as well as to develop responsibility for managing change. The health LIS manager has to tread a fine line between maintaining control of the general direction the service is going whilst at the same time giving up control so staff can share responsibility for the change process. The involvement of staff in change management works well when there is a long lead in to incremental change with no imperative for rapid and major change. Burnes (1996) highlights the dilemma where the change has to be implemented quickly which will cause the manager to impose the change from the top in a directive manner. Staff resistance and concern will be present when change is progressed in this way, but certain situations (such as the urgent implementation of government policy and major changes in technology) make this unavoidable.

Staff skills

There are some generic traits that the health LIS manager needs to ensure are present in colleagues: creativity, innovation and flexibility. These skills are central to strategies developed in health information services that manage both the health external environment and the developments in information delivery.

Creativity

Numerous commentators have observed how creative skills are essential in the present era. McFadzean (1998, 309) highlights that creativity 'improves communication, promotes learning and the exploration of problems and helps develop new ideas, solutions and alternatives'. The centrality of developing new services and new ways of looking at problems has also been recognized within the library and information context (Corrall, 1998; Kesselman, 1994). There are arrays of techniques that can be used to encourage creativity including brainstorming, brainwriting, object stimulation, metaphors and thinking rich pictures (VanGundy, 1998). The manager has a crucial role to play in supporting and encouraging the creativity in health LIS staff. Majaro (1988) indicates that an organization needs a climate conducive to creative thinking, an effective way to communicate ideas and a procedure for managing the ideas. The manager can reduce the bureaucracy and hierarchies in health LIS to support creative thinking. They can make people feel safe to challenge assumptions and give them time to work on projects. Health LIS staff should be able to share their ideas with colleagues. Formal activities can help this, such as regular meetings, newsletters and suggestion schemes, but an informal ambience that encourages communication is more important. Once the creativity is in evidence through new ideas the health LIS needs to be able to manage them. The manager has to set up a sifting process to identify the ideas that are practical and procedures to develop the ideas into services, etc.

Innovation

Creativity and innovation are inter-related in that innovation is the process whereby creative ideas are turned into new products, services and procedures. Innovation should not be seen as a one-off response to a crisis but a continuous and constant process. Management gurus such as Drucker (1991) see innovation as a way to create purposeful/focused change. The health LIS manager has to exploit the creative ideas that emerge and use them to move forward in an innovative way. Health LIS have an advantage when it comes to being innovative in that they are very often small departments. Rosenfeld and Servo (1991) have pointed out that small units can be more creative and innovative because of their size. In encouraging innovation the health LIS manager's role becomes that of a facilitator and supporter of openness.

Flexibility

The need for a flexible workforce is a global trend that is also present in health information services. Goulding and Kerslake (1996) conducted a survey of 475 libraries in the UK to establish the extent to which flexible work patterns were in place. Factors identified in moving to a flexible workforce are the new technologies that need different working patterns, the demographic makeup of the library workforce with more working women and earlier retirements, and the government policies encouraging labour market flexibility. Having a more flexible workforce gives the health LIS increased capability to deal with changes that impact on services. In the survey Goulding and Kerslake (1996) found that flexible work patterns were present in support staff and professional staff. A flexible workforce enabled LIS to cope with variable workloads, cover services at weekends and retain valued staff. The challenge the health LIS manager faces with a flexible workforce is to ensure that all are included in activities and feel that they are valued.

Teamwork

Hall (1999) points out that the team based structure has been widespread in business and industry for over 15 years. Operating a health LIS on a team basis allows colleagues to share ideas, support each other and benefit from colleagues' expertise and skills. In a survey on teamwork in libraries, Hall (1999) established that characteristics of effective teams were mutual support, mutual compatibility, good communication and good leadership. The team leader focused more on the attitudinal/interpersonal aspects of teamwork rather than objective-setting or decision-making. The health LIS manager is therefore central to ensuring the team functions well. This extends to selecting the individuals that make up the team (Jago, 1996) where the right blend of people with professional expertise, different ideas and interpersonal skills are brought together. By bringing together in the health LIS people with different styles and backgrounds, issues can be approached from different angles. Belbin (1981) has attempted to identify the different mix of characters that are needed to ensure teams bring varied approaches to issues. The role the health LIS manager plays in managing the team includes dealing with the tensions that will undoubtedly occur when differences emerge. By encouraging the team's capabilities and encouraging creative thinking the health LIS manager will ensure the presence to the clinician of the 'added-value' in the service.

Staff development

The move to an increasingly information-centred and electronically dependent environment gives staff training and development a high profile (Walton and Edwards, 1999). This impact of technology is also underlined by Abbott (1998) who establishes that librarians need to extend their repertoire of skills and knowledge. It is interesting to note that it is not just information technology skills that are seen as important. Abbott (1998) also establishes that teaching, training, marketing and presentation skills are crucial along with the abilities to negotiate, manage teams and think strategically. A personal opinion is expressed by one commentator that if information workers fail to undertake effective training and development programmes the result may be the 'downfall of the information profession and its eventual irrelevance' (Barden, 1997, 4).

The health LIS manager needs to continually monitor their own individual skills' 'toolbox' along with those of colleagues to ensure the relevant attributes are present to contend with the rapidly changing environment. A study (Walton,

Day and Edwards, 1995) has underlined that staff at all levels need development activities. Doney (1998) observed that the feeling that staff do not have adequate time for continuing learning is a major deterrent to staff development activities. The health LIS manager has to develop a work environment where staff have the time and space to undertake staff development activities. In a national cross-sectional survey of attitudes of library staff to staff development, widespread apathy was identified (Farmer and Campbell, 1997). If health LIS staff are apathetic to development and feel they do not have enough time the manager has a major task to address. The concept of the 'learning organization' has been developed (Garvin, 1988) where systematic problem-solving, experimentation, learning from past experience, learning from others and transferring knowledge are seen as being the five main activities. The health LIS manager's role is to support these activities by addressing the negative perceptions surrounding staff development and training.

Conclusion

Appropriate strategic and staff management is proposed as central to the effective health LIS. There are other areas that are equally as important where skills need to be acquired and maintained. There is always pressure on health service providers to reduce costs and this driver is passed on to health LIS. With the dramatic developments in electronic health LIS, resources have to be found to fund them. For these reasons the health LIS managers' portfolio should include financial management. Various titles describe the necessary skills and knowledge (Roberts, 1998; Snyder, 1997; Schauer, 1986). (See Chapter 8.)

In researching this chapter, the dramatic influence of the rate and level of change is continually emphasized. No commentator has been able to identify a single coping approach relevant for the provider of health LIS. There are ranges of activities that can be undertaken that will increase the likelihood of the health LIS flourishing. At a strategic level, by undertaking strategic and internal analysis, by identifying and evaluating options and then implementing the chosen strategy the information service is likely to 'fit' its environment. This process is iterative and needs constant re-visiting. The manager must ensure that the colleagues who provide the service work together collaboratively with a shared vision of the direction in which the health LIS is heading. Appropriate change management processes have to be introduced and the workforce needs to display creativity, innovation and flexibility. Effective teamwork is to be encouraged and supported with individuals given the training and development that the modern health LIS will continue to require.

Key points

- Strategic management is concerned with the long-term survival of health information services. There needs to be an analysis of both the external environment and internal capabilities.
- Strategic options include consolidation, product development, market development or diversification and should be evaluated against criteria of suitability, acceptability and feasibility.
- Staff involvement, communication and adequate resources are among the factors related to effective strategic implementation. The influence of different stakeholders is also important.
- Change can be effectively managed if people are involved and informed. The rate at which change has to be implemented governs the management approach.
- Creativity, innovation and flexibility should be apparent in the workforce for the service to be appropriately developed. Teamwork is an accepted way of working in all sectors but teams do need managing and coordinating.
- The manager has to ensure that staff are given appropriate development and training to provide the necessary services.

7
Identifying users' needs

Andrew Booth

Introduction

Identification of users' needs is the first, and arguably the most important, step in setting up a library and information service (LIS). A service that is not attuned to the needs of its users may become underutilized, redundant or even obsolete. Additionally, health LIS managers seem more likely to pay attention to users' needs when starting a new service or project than in the equally important maintenance and ongoing review function. A provocative article draws an analogy between identification of information needs and diagnosis (Grover and Carabell, 1995). The LIS professional must diagnose needs, prescribe or recommend a remedy that meets those needs, implement that remedy, and evaluate the outcome of this interaction. An LIS professional's understanding of a client's information needs enables the customization of information services to address those needs.

This chapter begins by looking at problems around defining information needs before examining some of the ways in which they can be measured. Tools such as surveys, interviews and questionnaires are dealt with briefly before moving on to consideration of the information audit. Questions to ask when planning a survey or designing a questionnaire are outlined and then attention turns to methods for assessing group views: focus groups, group interviews and Delphi techniques. Methods are illustrated by recent examples from the literature.

Defining information needs

Definitions of 'information need' are often criticized as 'too vague or highly complex in nature – clouding further some already muddy water' (Nicholas,

1996). Line (1969) defined information needs as that 'information that would further this job or this research and would be recognised as doing so by the recipient'. Nicholas expands this definition by stating that: 'Information needs arise when a person recognises a gap in his/her state of knowledge and wishes to resolve that anomaly . . . it is the information that individuals ought to have to do their job effectively, solve a problem satisfactorily or pursue a hobby or interest happily'. Several methodologies have been developed to assess information need and use of these must be tempered by recognition of certain information 'pathologies':

- dormant needs – when people are unaware that they have information needs
- unexpressed needs – when the people are 'aware of their needs but do nothing about them, either because they cannot or because they will not'.

An increasing emphasis on evidence based medicine, and the resulting 'disintermediation' of the information retrieval process, has led to recognition that user needs not only include the resources and technologies required to meet a need but also the skills and competencies required to utilize these to best advantage. Thus a needs study commissioned in North Thames Region revealed wide variations in skill and self efficacy levels in using databases across professions, specialties and trusts (Pyne et al, 1999).

A number of considerations shape determination of users' needs – the objectives of the organization as a whole, the resources available to meet identified needs, the relative priority attached to differing types of need, and the legitimization of needs by the organization. To illustrate, a library service might score quite highly in satisfying user needs, but face a fight for survival because its Executive Board, who are not users of the library, do not feel that it contributes to the 'business' of the organization. Similarly, an organization might feel that its priority for LIS is to support clinical decision-making and yet users may be more concerned with the availability of resources for continuing professional development. Finally, there is the situation commonly encountered by trained nurses in that their needs, formerly catered for by resources provided for nurses in training, may not be formally legitimized by the allocation of a specific budgetary provision. An additional complication lies in the fact that a LIS usually finds it relatively easy to capture information on the needs of those who are already using a service, but finds it correspondingly more difficult to reach those who have no contact with the service. Reasons for non-use may be that non-users do not perceive a need or, more likely, because they have developed alternative formal or informal methods for information supply. Finally, LIS managers should be aware that they are not neutral data-gatherers where design and development of LIS is concerned. There are frequent instances when a survey will conclude 'All comments by respondents were supportive of the library' (Burton, 1995) when LIS staff are not separated from the collection process.

Measuring information needs

The concept of 'information needs' refers to a number of related dimensions. These may vary between professions but equally, variation can be seen within a professional group, eg comparing senior house officers with consultants or faculty with housestaff (Woolf and Benson, 1989). Even the same individual may exhibit variations according to whether the most important reason for seeking information at that point in time is keeping up to date, acquiring new ideas, developing competence in the field or supporting research work in progress. Psychological factors too play a role in the determination of information needs with some work having attempted to differentiate users by their personal characteristics (eg Pavlenko and Weinberg, 1990).

Another important consideration is whether to concentrate exclusively on information needs as they specifically relate to use of the library or whether to broaden the scope to include information derived from other sources. Furthermore is the focus to be on textual, processed information as housed in a library or will a more fluid definition of information be employed? Some surveys of information needs have successfully broadened their coverage to admit unpublished or statistical data sources. On the one hand this may result in a new and more revolutionary role for the library, yet, on the other hand, it may create a demanding role that the LIS is unable to sustain.

Surveys, interviews and questionnaires

The exact choice of data collection method, and indeed the actual collection instrument employed, should be determined by the objectives of the study. Is the emphasis on hard, quantitative data to provide a picture of patterns of potential demand? Alternatively, is the idea to develop an in-depth profile of how key users would use the services? Clearly techniques employed here would range from the survey method so popular amongst opinion poll companies to the in-depth interviewing more frequently used in research projects. A recent study of the information needs of life scientists utilized the broader approach drawing on the ethnographic methodologies used by anthropologists to study real life situations (Forsythe, 1998). Another approach, as exemplified in a study of nurses' perceptions of their needs for community information (Pettigrew, 1996) is to draw on qualitative techniques including the grounded theory approach and the critical incident technique.

The grounded theory approach was developed by the sociologists Strauss and Glaser as a way of formalizing the development of theory from empirical data. 'It is a methodological approach (entailing a cyclical process of induction, deduction and verification) and a set of strategies of data analysis to improve the reliability and theoretical depth of analysis. Particular attention is paid to the processes entailed in coding data' (Green, 1998). The critical incident technique was first developed in 1954 by Flanagan as a way of bringing together direct observations of human behaviour so as to make it possible for their potential to be realized in 'solving practical problems and developing broad psychological principles' (Flanagan, 1954, 327). Only observations meeting predefined criteria are included to minimize bias. The technique is best known in a health information context through its use by the National Library of Medicine to evaluate the impact of MEDLINE searches (**http://www.nlm.nih.gov/od/ope/cit.html**).

Another issue is the extent to which you already have data. If you seek to ascertain how many respondents fall into a number of pre-defined categories then a survey method will suffice. If, however, you are seeking to collect a variety of hitherto unknown responses then a more qualitative approach, using 'open questions' will be more appropriate. In practice, LIS professionals will seek a mixture of quantitative and qualitative data. This is one reason for the popularity of the questionnaire in seeking to reconcile breadth of response with validated findings using quantification of replies. Strictly speaking, surveys and interviews are contexts in which data is collected whereas a questionnaire is the data collection instrument. A survey, or indeed an interview, may be conducted using a questionnaire. However there will usually be differences in the context in which the questionnaire is administered. It is perhaps helpful to highlight instances of each methodology and to discuss those factors that may have led to its selection.

Case study

The interview: Information systems for nursing specialties (Bawden and Robinson, 1994)

This British Library Research and Development Department (BLRDD)-funded project aimed to determine the information needs and information-seeking behaviour of midwives and psychiatric nurses and to compare these needs and behaviours with those of general nurses, established by previous studies. The study was conducted by means of semi-structured interviews with practitioners, experts and information providers (45 midwives and 16 psychiatric nurses, concentrated at the senior nurse and tutor levels), in order to obtain an in-depth understanding of the factors involved.

The main purpose of this study was not to ascertain baseline data on the needs of midwives and psychiatric nurses but rather to characterize their needs in comparison with general nurses. The interview technique allows the investigator to explore qualitative differences and indeed to '*obtain an in depth understanding of the factors involved*' in differences between the two specialties. In fact Merry (1997a, 163) has observed that at first sight the two nursing specialties may seem to be opposites, midwifery being concerned with a single event and the events that precede and follow it while psychiatric nursing covers a wide range of persons with a wide range of disorders over a long period of time. The semi-structured nature of these interviews enables the investigator to achieve a degree of standardization between respondents and yet not deny them new avenues of investigation. The general structure of the interviews is likely to be determined by the pre-existing studies referred to yet the flexible methodology allows adjusting to new insights as new data is collected. An interesting sidepoint from this study is that the librarians interviewed were unaware of any significant differences in information use or behaviour between the two groups and had made no attempt to customize their services.

The information audit

The information audit or information needs analysis shares many features with the techniques mentioned above (St Clair, 1995). Derived from a special library context, it is characterized by the alignment of user needs with the business objectives of the organization. The Special Libraries Association (USA) has compiled a useful compendium of articles describing information audits (Special Libraries Association, 1996). A large-scale audit of 240 staff, ranging from the Chief Executive to the worker in the postroom, at the headquarters of a Regional Health Authority in one of the Thames regions featured use of an external team to oversee the audit and to train a team of internal auditors, a profile-raising information management day and the use of qualitative and quantitative data. Soft Systems Methodology was used to define four main information systems identified within the organization and a rich picture described pictorially the way information resources were currently perceived (Booth and Haines, 1993). Aside from the extensive data gathered in this way, organizational benefits included the development of a team of auditors, working across divisional boundaries, and placing information firmly on the agenda as a springboard for future developments.

The information audit typically looks at information needs, resources and flows *within* a single organization. It is equally important to look at information flows *between* organizations. An example from the NHS Executive Northern and Yorkshire Region (Banwell et al, 1994) looked at information needed in relation to the Research and Development (R&D) programme and channels and barriers to information flow within communication systems. Qualitative and quantitative data were collected through semi-structured interviews at six case study sites, representing a cross section of NHS organizations and professionals. In addition short questionnaires were employed with findings being presented as channels, barriers and suggested solutions to information flow.

Questions to ask when planning a survey

User needs analysis requires considerable thought about the process involved. Brief checklists provide only a limited awareness of the complexities of these issues. The following annotated questions are intended to give a more complete picture:

1   *How will I identify members of the target population that I am seeking to survey?* Consider staff listings, directories, mailing lists, key contacts, etc.
2   *What proportion of the potential study population am I seeking to target?* Blanket coverage (100%), a representative sample (a randomly selected subset of the total population), a stratified sample (ensuring coverage of all important subgroups), etc.
3   *What is the response rate likely to be?* Consider the perceived importance of the topic to potential respondents, the method of administration (in per-

son, by post, etc), likelihood of survey fatigue, etc. A study of the information needs and seeking behaviour of nurses (Wakeham, Houghton and Beard, 1992) had a response rate of 50.15% with 501 questionnaires being returned. This is considered higher than average with response rates typically falling between 35–45% even after prompts and follow-up.

4　*What factors are likely to impact either positively or negatively on likelihood of completion by particular subgroups?* Consider seniority within the organization, educational level or attainment, predisposition to the subject under consideration (eg users versus non-users of the library).

5　*What strategies might I use to ensure more complete coverage?* Incentives (eg a prize draw), follow-up postal reminders, telephone reminders, recruitment of opinion leaders, etc.

Questions to ask when planning interviews

1　*How many people do I need to interview?* Consider at what point 'data saturation' might occur (ie no additional important insights), organizational structure (ie different positions within hierarchy, different professional perspectives, distribution of numbers within each grade) and other opportunities to obtain supplementary data. In the study of nurses' information needs mentioned earlier, additional perspectives were obtained by comparing the findings of the survey with the perceptions that librarians have of nurses' information-seeking activity (Wakeham, 1993).

2　*What incentive is there for people to participate?* Consider the perceived importance of the topic to particular participants, how the interviews might best be marketed to participants.

3　*How long will the interviews need to be?* Consider the balance between the need to obtain data and the need to maintain the interest and cooperation of interview subjects.

4　*Should the interview be structured or semi-structured?* Consider the extent of your prior knowledge of responses, the requirement for additional elicitation and opportunities for follow-up.

5　*What is the logical sequence to the order of questions within the interview schedule?* Consider natural sequence of respondents' thoughts, placing of important questions, need for subsidiary questions, use of an 'icebreaker' question (to elicit involvement), elimination of duplicate or overlap questions.

Questions to ask when designing a questionnaire

1   *Is the data definitely not already available in a usable form?* Consider existing routine statistics, literature search request forms, ad hoc surveys, national data, etc.

2   *Is the balance right between quantitative and qualititative questions?* Consider how much data you already possess on the topic, how you are planning to present the results, the preferred data presentation styles of the main intended recipients of the results.

3   *Can the questionnaire incorporate unexpected responses?* For example, categories of response that are not itemized, selection of two or more valid responses, completion of 'don't know' or 'not applicable' responses, requests for clarification on meaning.

4   *How long will the questionnaire take to complete?* Is this time realistic, practicable?

5   *How long should respondents be given to return questionnaires?* Consider an actual return deadline, realistic timescale, but also likely distribution of response times (eg 75% within the first month).

6   *How can the return rate of questionnaires be improved?* Consider prominence of return address, subsidiary methods of collection (eg deposit boxes), provision of pre-paid or pre-addressed envelopes.

7   *How should the questions be laid out on the questionnaire?* Consider the use of (and balance of) multiple choice questions, tick boxes, free-text responses and Likert scales, etc.

8   *Is the terminology understandable and are the questions meaningful?* Consider the presence of ambiguous terms such as 'information' or 'information sources'. Are definitions of scope to be included or are responses to be at the interpretation of the respondent? Are categories comprehensive and mutually exclusive? Are questions realistic? For example, 'how often do you go on training courses – monthly, quarterly, semi-annually?' is not realistic given the ad hoc way training is usually offered; 'How many courses do you attend on average per year?' is more easily answered.

It is likely that a combination of techniques will be required. An in-depth investigation of the drug information needs of 40 people attending a rheumatology outpatients clinic in Aberdeen was followed up by a mapping exercise involving surveys of 230 rheumatology departments and 37 pharmaceutical companies

(Farmer and Peffer, 1995; Farmer and Peffer, 1996). Similarly 'triangulation', a technical research term referring to the use of two or more techniques to cross-validate data, was used in the ACUMEN study (Kempson and ACUMEN, 1984) which examined the need of the general public for health information in layperson's language. A detailed review of research reported was supported by a series of group discussions with members of the general public. Silverstein (1995) describes how the usefulness, impact and potential services of 11 hospital libraries in a four-county area in New York State were evaluated using two research instruments: a survey for hospital based medical professionals and a survey for hospital based information providers. Results from both surveys were compared to determine if users' needs were being fulfilled, and to develop plans for improved information services and products.

Focus groups, group interviews and Delphi techniques

Up to now the emphasis has been on mechanisms for collecting data from individual respondents, through survey, interview or questionnaire. A number of other techniques exploit group responses. An example from a marketing context is the focus group. Focus groups have enjoyed popularity for a number of reasons, not least for their democratic and political appeal. As a methodology for exploring user needs, however, they should be used with caution. There is a natural tension between the need to incorporate a variety of perspectives and the inhibition felt when practitioners of differing status are brought together in a group setting. Health organizations have a pronounced hierarchical structure with perceived 'pecking orders' in relationships between medical and nursing or paramedical staff. A vocal response may be adopted within a group, without objective consensus, and dissension with an expressed opinion is less likely than in a confidential setting. Nevertheless in a peer group setting, with a clearly defined remit and an explicit process of prioritization, useful data can be obtained. Focus groups have been used to discover health professionals' information needs in a marketing study conducted by the National Network of Libraries of Medicine (USA) (Mullaly-Quijas, Ward and Woelfl, 1994). Canning, Edwards and Meadows (1995) have described use of the focus group for the evaluation of library services and their user training programme. The methodology of focus groups in a health library setting is described at length by Glitz (1997).

An issue common to use of the focus group and its sister technique, the group interview, is the role that the LIS manager adopts in the process. It is difficult for a service provider to act in an objective way, and indeed for users to express candid opinions, when the service provider is involved in collection and interpretation of data.

Group interviews are at their most effective when the group is a convenience sample and therefore not imbued with prior power struggles or hierarchical challenges. A successful example was a study of the information needs of parents of children under the age of five (Nicholas and Marden, 1998). Parents were contacted through their library, clinic, nursery or church and their information needs studied using group and individual interviews. Once again the value of more than one data collection method can be seen. The chief sources of information that parents mentioned were local organizations (eg ante-natal classes), professionals (eg health visitors), and friends and books. Caution must be expressed here concerning the use of 'representatives'. It is rare for an individual to be completely enfranchised to speak on behalf of a group and representatives usually have a particular motivation for involvement in any consultative exercise. If a library or information service is to use representatives successfully this will usually necessitate cross-checking opinions for both validity (ie that they are interpreted in the way that they are originally intended) and applicability (ie that they express the thoughts or feelings of a significant number of the intended audience and not just a 'vocal minority'). An alternative approach, not claiming to be representative yet nevertheless with clear application to LIS planning, is to create a 'heavy users forum'. The Lister Hill Library at the University of Alabama (Pfeiffer and Algermissen, 1992) brings together the library's heavy users and the Director and Information Librarian for twice-yearly meetings. The goals are to find out what the users would like to see changed or added and to keep them informed of library plans. To date this has resulted in 35 changes or new services being recommended and subsequently implemented.

The Delphi technique is a very time- and labour-intensive methodology that comes into its own where there is an opportunity for user involvement (and commitment) over a pre-defined period of time. It usually provides an opportunity both to shape the initial stages of response (equivalent to 'open' questions) and to validate and prioritize previous responses. Dwyer (1999) provides an excellent example and discussion of the value of the technique.

Conclusion

The LIS manager has a variety of methods at their disposal in collecting data on the information needs of their users. Information needs analysis is usually iterative in nature and utilizing more than one method will improve validity. The LIS manager will be circumspect with regard to their own role in data collection and analysis and aware of threats to validity caused by existing power relationships or by vocal 'non-representatives'. Above all, information needs are dynamic and ever-changing and the LIS manager will seek to focus as much emphasis on the development of ongoing feedback systems, to allow continual realignment of service objectives, as on an initial baseline collection of data.

Key points

- Examination of users' information needs should include acknowledgment of, if not consideration of, both unexpressed demand and dormant need.
- A variety of methods of obtaining data on information needs exists and selection of the appropriate method will be determined both by the information manager's knowledge of the particular population and the purposes to which the analysis will be put.
- In practice it is likely that more than one method will be required both for 'triangulation' and for subsequent validation of initial results.
- Regardless of whichever method(s) are chosen the information manager should be aware of the potential for their involvement in data collection to have an effect, positive or negative, on the final results.

8
Making a case

Andrew Booth

Introduction

Development of local health library and information services (LIS) commonly depends upon the abilities of the manager to secure and maintain funding (Montanelli-Dale, 1987). Good housekeeping and the ability to balance a budget have always been prerequisite to successful LIS management. More recently, however, emphasis has shifted towards more dynamic interpersonal skills and an awareness of the politics of the organization and the environment in which it operates (see Chapter 6). Evidence on the effectiveness of different approaches to obtaining funds is scant, being based primarily on general LIS-focused 'how to do it' articles, a handful of case studies and a selection of personal observations. Central to any understanding of methods for obtaining funds is an awareness of the differences between the various sources of funding and the conditions typically attached to their use. Such differences exist both between sources of funding, for example service development versus research funds, and between types of fund, for example capital versus recurrent expenditure.

This chapter suggests how an LIS manager might set about 'winning friends and influencing people'. It starts by considering practical ways to 'know your patch' before proposing how the various professional, regional and national support structures, identified in Part 1, might be used appropriately to assist in making a case. Models for budgeting and costing are briefly outlined. Finally, success in securing funding depends not only on the individual merits of the case but also upon the way it is presented. This chapter concludes with sections on writing a successful proposal and making a presentation. Examples are UK based, but the principles have international application.

Operating in an entrepreneurial environment

A major change heralded by the National Health Service (NHS) reforms of 1990 was the introduction of a new approach to financial management. From April 1991 all NHS services were based on contracts and, in a microcosm of developments in the wider environment, LIS were forced to examine their mechanisms for collecting data, cross-boundary flows of information users and the resources required to support local information needs. For many health LIS managers it was the first time that they had been required to prepare a business plan. Despite this potentially threatening climate of justification and performance monitoring that pertained to the new NHS, many managers saw an opportunity to put their services on a more business-like footing. Postgraduate medical education funds, previously dispensed at the behest of the Regional Postgraduate Dean, started to be apportioned according to activity levels, formula funding and bids for development monies. This legacy is still in evidence with terms such as 'service level agreement' in common parlance and regional collection of comparative data, albeit in the form of crude performance and activity levels, an established fact of life.

As Godbolt, Williamson and Wilson (1997) state:

> An already complex and messy system of multiple funding streams for libraries was perpetuated in the transition to the new NHS with no possibility of virement between sources except at NHS ME (Management Executive) level. This left an incoherent system with no formal funding for several groups which included GPs (General Practitioners) and GP trainees, all hospital doctors not covered by PGMDE (Postgraduate Medical and Dental Education) funding and the largest group – qualified nurses and PAMs (Professions Allied to Medicine).

The new levy system, implemented from April 1996, did little more than perpetuate the fragmentation of funding. The main funding sources are described in Chapter 3. It is typical for a health LIS to have between five and seven different major streams of funding with other ad hoc funds and grants complicating an already confusing picture. These funds might variously include regional postgraduate education funding, nurse education funding (although decreasing with the transfer of nurse education from the NHS to higher education), local postgraduate trust funds, research and development monies, salaries from an acute trust and service level agreements with the community trust and the local health authority (Stewart, 1992; Hewlett, 1992). In addition there might be donations from pharmaceutical companies or equipment suppliers.

An illustrative example is the Cairns Library at the John Radcliffe Hospital in Oxford where, in addition to the grant from its parent body, the Cairns Library obtains funding from five other bodies, including National Health Service hospital trusts (Forrest and Cawasjee, 1997). Capel (1997) has demonstrated that funding arrangements for nurse education services are equally complex, with infinite variety in purchasing and contractual arrangements leading to problems of communication and access.

Another major development of growing importance is the library consortium. Jones and Cahoon (1998) describe a consortium in Trent Region offering networked subscriptions to MEDLINE, CINAHL and CancerLit with links to the full text of core medical journals via the BIOMED service. In the wider context, libraries of all types are looking to extend their purchasing capabilities and compensate for reduced budgets. Pye and Ball (1999) describe a study to investigate the activities of library purchasing consortia in higher education, further education, public and health libraries. Consortia provision of networked information services is often supplemented by bulk journal purchasing arrangements and the use of preferred library suppliers for books and other equipment. Such cooperative purchasing follows similar arrangements pioneered in North America. As long ago as 1975, Moulton discussed effective consortia under the headings (1) composite resources, (2) multi-institutional environment, (3) leadership, and (4) activities. Such consortia do not necessarily undermine longstanding regional library networks, rather they can enhance library resource sharing either across regions or within regions (Godbolt, Williamson and Wilson, 1997).

Some common principles of obtaining funding

Knowing your patch is not limited to being familiar with those people whom it is most important to influence. Prior to the preparation of any bid, it is important to determine the parent institution or community's receptivity to the request for finance. Little is gained from a losing sequence of poorly conceived and hastily constructed bids. Important factors to consider include the following:

- Sensitivity to the social/political/economic climate. This includes putting a current and topical 'spin' on the funding request (eg evidence based healthcare, clinical governance, or lifelong learning) and being realistic about competing demands within the organization (eg ward closure or redundancies versus a library automation system).

- Fitting the library's needs to its priorities. This includes gaining confidence in the library's 'bread and butter' services before trying to elicit funds for the 'jam'.

- Timing the request appropriately for the institution's budget process. In some organizations the last two months of a financial year signal attempts to offload projected underspends; in others the beginning of the financial year sees the start of a clean sheet. Many organizations operate a 'use it or lose it' policy whereby budgets have to be spent by the end of the financial year; others have a 'rollover' policy where monies are carried forward to augment the following year's funds; still others credit the 'rollover' to the following year's budget while keeping the overall budget in 'steady state'.

The key to obtaining funding is to see the project through the funders' eyes and to market it accordingly (Lapsley, 1995). Generally LIS professionals emphasize 'structure' and 'process' at the expense of 'outcomes'. A case for a new computer with a CD-ROM drive (structure) will typically aim to improve availability of bibliographic searches (process). Funders, particularly managers, will be more interested in the impact searches have on patient care, the behaviour of clinicians or in reducing risk through increased competence. However, it is often difficult to collect such data and even more of a challenge to prove causality between something as far removed as a library service and the outcome of patient care. Nevertheless it is helpful to think in terms of outcomes when preparing a case, particularly utilizing the following proposed framework:

KNOWLEDGE – ATTITUDES – BEHAVIOUR – (HEALTH) OUTCOMES

This continuum can apply to desired outcomes for any informational or educational process. As one moves from left to right it becomes progressively more difficult to measure change and to prove causality from the intervention. So one can measure changes in knowledge using a questionnaire, changes in attitudes using a Likert scale, changes in behaviour using observation and changes in health outcomes using clinical or resource outcome measures. The challenge is to select the measures most appropriate to the proposed intervention without becoming overly ambitious. So, for example, a proposal to introduce the Cochrane Library might feasibly aim to achieve a measurable change in clinical staff attitudes to use of systematic reviews or might possibly aim to improve uptake of literature searching services. It would stop short of claiming that a measurable amount of patient care is based on evidence from systematic reviews.

Enlisting support

Although it is common for health LIS professionals to find themselves acting in isolation, it is not true to think that they have no sources of support in making a case. Support may be found at a national level, a regional level or even from colleagues at local trusts. The skill lies in identifying the most appropriate sources of support for a particular case, clarifying what that support might entail, and in timing the most opportune moment for drawing upon that support. A Regional Library Adviser (see Chapter 3), for example, will be a ready source of advice and assistance in a number of professional issues, but may have little opportunity for input into an individual trust's Research & Development (R&D) Committee. A local librarian might therefore enlist their written support and request comparative data about funding linked to R&D or different models of librarian involvement either from within the region or from their regional librarian contacts. An alternative scenario might involve local disagreements over provision for postgraduate education where, as a mandated representative of the Regional Postgraduate Dean, the Regional Library Adviser might feel that more hands-on involvement is legitimate. Not that a librarian should only think in terms of *people* who might lend support to a particular case – there are a number of support structures that might perform a similar function. Trade unions such as Unison and professional groups such as the Health Libraries Group and its various subgroups can be added to a list that includes the NHS Library Adviser and the Special Libraries Adviser at The Library Association.

Models of budgeting

The two main perspectives of the library's contribution to financial management see the library as a cost centre and the library as a profit centre. If the library is a cost centre then it is not expected to make money itself, but is part of overhead expenses, necessary for the organization to deliver its product or service (Basker, 1997). If, on the other hand, the library is a profit centre, it has to generate income (Basker, 1997). A slightly different perspective uses two costing models: the resource based library model with the library as a central resource where levels of demand are anticipated and there is an incremental increase to the budget, and the information service based model which is customer-led and product-centred (van Loo, 1991). Users are targeted and may receive different levels of service, and income is maximized.

A library budget typically includes three main components: expenditure on materials (books, journals, databases); for services (computing, online subscriptions, etc) and for people (staffing, service contracts, etc). A typical line or formula budget will include the following items with approximate percentages of the total in brackets (Evans, 1976):

- books and materials (20–30%)
- salaries (60–70 %)
- utilities (1–2 %)*
- maintenance (4–5 %)*
- supplies (4–5 %)
- travel (1–2 %)
- insurance (1–2 %)*

Those items marked * are very often hidden costs absorbed by the parent organization. This will vary, however, as some libraries pick up maintenance costs for equipment such as the photocopier or the library computers. The indicative proportions given above will vary according to the exact nature of the library. A special library such as that at the School of Health and Related Research, University of Sheffield, pays a higher proportion of costs on staff, has a higher proportion of professional staff and, through reliance on university subscriptions and networks, has correspondingly less to pay on databases and the Internet infrastructure.

Formula funding

Formula funding has been the single most important issue in funding during the 1990s. Although, as Morgan (1992) points out, formula funding has a long pedigree in apportioning library services, this was primarily at a local level. More recently, national organizations such as the Higher Education Funding Councils and regional bodies such as the postgraduate medical education bodies have used formulae to decide apportionment at a macro level. As Morgan

(1992) states, 'Funding formulas offer one way in which library managers can hope to present a coherent case for funding which coordinates the different sources of financial support and the disparate needs within the library service.' An issue of *Health Libraries Review* (**9**, 2) pays much attention to this topic and is still timely despite the passing years (Morgan, 1992; Gove, 1992; Godbolt and Hewlett, 1992).

Other models of budgeting and costing

Other models of budgeting include programme budgeting and zero-based budgeting. Programme budgeting is where a LIS manager would look at the total cost for providing a particular service or portfolio of services rather than looking at the budget lines such as staffing, photocopying, lighting, heating, etc. It is particularly valuable in the context of service level agreements accompanying negotiations around volumes and unit costs. Zero-based budgeting is where the LIS starts with a blank sheet of paper in preparing a budget for the coming year. Each element in the service is assessed and justified without reference to historical data from previous years. Although consuming a great deal of time and energy this does allow the LIS manager to radically re-engineer the profile of the service (Sargent, 1978). Cooper (1997) challenges health LIS managers to move away from the current almost 'mechanistic' approach to one that looks at the library's worth in cost and qualitative terms.

Developing a service

Requirements for more sophisticated budgetary planning, prompted by serious budgetary constraints, technological change and shifting user demands, have led to a need for more detailed information, often obtained via ad hoc surveys rather than routine data. Rashid and Burns (1998) describe a survey that asked users to make choices between competing service priorities. In a UK setting (Carmel, 1991) the move towards contracts and service level agreements required an ad hoc survey of sources of library funding and precise spending details.

Obtaining research funding

The LIS manager will not only be alert to local opportunities for service development, but will also monitor the availability of research funding. Although the health LIS field has had no shortage of projects and programmes over the last decade, the main challenge is to continue services beyond the life of a project, integrating it into mainstream library services and passing the baton to similar projects. Several authors (Hannabuss, 1995; Clark, 1997) describe the research process and include advice on writing a research proposal. Books aimed at encouraging librarian participation in the research process will prove valuable for both professional and personal development (eg Powell, 1997).

Writing proposals

To apply for external funding, a LIS manager will write a proposal stating how they are qualified to conduct a project, what their proposal is, what resources they require and how they will use the resources. There are entire books on how to write effective proposals, but following a few basic principles will help you to get started. It is good practice to get into the habit of writing 'mini-proposals' even for internal use within your organization. They help to organize thoughts and rehearse any major arguments or justifications prior to discussions with a line manager or library committee. This process will clarify objectives, abilities, resources and an understanding of the problems that are to be tackled.

Although there are numerous directories of funding sources to yield potential sponsors, the skill lies not in identifying the source, but in presenting the project in a way that makes it desirable to the funding body. Even if the idea has been on your desktop for many months, you need to inject freshness into the proposal by adding relevance and urgency. The funding body needs to feel that it is the natural source of funding and to start to see benefits of association with a particular project. Some disease based charities approach the topic from a consumer or patient viewpoint, others have an explicit research agenda, yet others support the clinician treating the disease. Although an idea might be suitable for any of these approaches the way it is presented should differ markedly – the proposal should be worded so as to make it fit through the 'window' of the target funding source's interests.

It is very important to read carefully all guidance on eligibility, process and means of presentation for the proposal. If a scheme prohibits applications of more than three sides of A4 this should be observed without exception. A typical proposal starts with a covering letter, and is followed by a proposal summary, an introduction, a statement of the problem, the goals and objectives of the project, the methodology to be used, a proposed timescale and budget. Personal contact with the programme administrator will often prove valuable, but only if you ask questions not already answered in the documentation. Bear in mind, however, that they will only be a barometer of the funding body's prevailing opinions and will probably have little say in the actual selection of a successful project. Additional materials should be limited to those required by the funding source such as the curriculum vitae of key members of the project. It will be helpful to discuss the figures in the budget with another member of the organization, perhaps an R&D coordinator, prior to submission. Typically the novice proposal writer will underestimate the costs of organization. Overheads, postage, photocopying and accommodation are all items likely to be underestimated or even overlooked. If a funding source suspects that calculations are naïve they will have little confidence in associated abilities in project management.

Presenting your case

There is increasing awareness of the place of presentation skills in the professional development portfolio of the health LIS manager. Although a certain degree of success may involve the style and personality of the individual, there is no doubt that attention to presentation skills may make a poor presenter good and a good presenter better. Increasingly resources on the web assist by providing aide-memoires and practical tips. For example Kansas University has a Virtual Presentation Assistant that includes determining your purpose, selecting and researching your topic, analysing your audience, supporting and outlining your points, using visual aids and presenting your speech resources for presentations (**http://www.ukans.edu/cwis/units/coms2/vpa/vpa.htm**). There are also a number of books which cover presentation skills including Dunckel and Parnham (1984); Kenny (1983) and Zanna (1987).

Conclusion

The ability to make a case, develop a budget proposal and to present it effectively is essential to the LIS manager's armoury. The complexity of funding, the constant backdrop of change and the shifting priorities of health care organizations add to the imperative not only to 'fight your corner', but even to extend your boundaries. An LIS manager needs to demonstrate an entrepreneurial approach to winning funds while at the same time identifying allies to help win their case. Only if attention is paid to this area, alongside the technical skills that a LIS professional undoubtedly possesses, will they ensure that not only will there be a knowledge base for them to manage, but also that they will be the obvious choice by far to achieve that task.

Key points

- Many libraries receive funding from numerous sources with funding streams being difficult to identify.
- Library consortia have grown in importance with increasing pressure on resources and funding.
- Three key factors in obtaining funding are knowing the operating environment, fitting the library's needs to its priorities and sensitivity to timing.
- It is essential to understand basic concepts such as formula funding and zero-based budgeting as well as principles of costing.
- The most important factor when applying for funding is to present ideas in a way that makes them seem central to an organization's funding programmes.

9
Identifying resources

Sharon Dobbins

Introduction

Information professionals live in challenging times. The range of information resources available is increasing at an alarming rate while budgets decrease. Tough decisions are therefore needed to decide on which resources should be chosen so that good quality, up-to-date, relevant and useful information can be delivered cost-effectively.

This chapter explores the selection and evaluation of resources for health libraries and information services (LIS) and looks at some of the implications of the growing importance of electronic information. The chapter is informed by the gradual unfolding of a case study describing the process undergone by one hospital LIS in identifying appropriate resources for its users.

Case study 1

The start

A large acute trust has a small postgraduate medical library that does not provide services for nurses, paramedical staff or managers. The journal collection is adequate (about 150 titles) but due to a lack of funding, the book collection is out of date. There are two PCs, one for MEDLINE and the other connected to the Internet. The trust decides to invest in a multi-disciplinary library and provides funds to expand, renovate and re-equip the present library, and also to purchase appropriate stock and other electronic resources. So, how should the librarian go about acquiring all that is needed to provide an effective LIS? What decisions do they need to make? Where can they get the information needed to make those decisions?

This scenario will be revisited to see how the theory of the identification of resources is put into practice in a real situation

Effective management of selection

Increasingly, emphasis is being placed on planning the delivery of information services. NHS libraries, for example, were tasked to produce library strategies in HSG 97(47) (Department of Health, 1997a). Planning the acquisition of resources should be part of this process, giving the health information professional a structure in which to utilize the finite financial resources available. This can be achieved through the development of a collection management policy which 'is a necessary tool leading to consistent, informed decisions'. It will inform the library's governing body about directions as well as provide a clear and carefully articulated rationale for its collection, goals and practices. The library's ability to compete for resources will be improved and goals can be matched with available resources (Johnson, 1997).

Gorman and Howes (1989) are among many authors who give advice on what should be included in a collection development policy. Whether these areas are covered in a formal policy or not, they should be considered when acquiring resources. It is essential that resources purchased for the library reflect the mission of the wider organization (Corrall and Brewerton, 1999). For health libraries, it should be demonstrated that the library supports local and national NHS strategies and clinical governance together with other major policies. Key documents that should be referred to are HSG 97(47), the organization's business plan, and national strategies such as *Information for health* (NHS Executive, 1998).

Resources selected for the library should fully support the information needs of the user population (see Chapter 7). These should be considered in terms of what kind of information they need (ranging from clinical needs to education and research), where users are located (in the community or on split sites), and how many users there are. For health libraries, the support of evidence based practice and clinical governance is essential. Naidoo (1998) states that he wants information NUGGETS: 'I want information Now, Up-to-date, Grounded in Evidence, There (on my desk), and Specific to the problem'.

Library staff and other stakeholders should be involved with identifying and selecting resources. These could include:

- library members, through requests, interlibrary loans and feedback from user surveys
- library committee members, particularly if there are representatives from a range of staff groups
- teaching staff, who could identify appropriate materials to support their courses
- IT staff, who should be involved with the selection of electronic resources, particularly for those to be launched on an organization's network, or where technical support will be provided.

It is impossible for libraries to stock everything their users need, and there is pressure to share resources. HSG 97(47) makes this clear and tasks libraries to develop 'local strategies encouraging co-operation and value for money services via partnerships, contracts and service level agreements'. A number of regions have been successful in facilitating the sharing of resources, for example the Health Care Libraries Unit (HCLU) in the Anglia and Oxford Region (**http://libsun1. jr2.ox.ac.uk**). This kind of cooperation has major implications for the resources required in each participating library. Some NHS libraries have negotiated contracts with local universities, giving their members access to extensive collections and services available in academic libraries. City Hospitals Sunderland (CHS) and the University of Sunderland are a case in point. The contract allows all CHS staff full access to the collections and facilities in the university, and is supported by a linked automated catalogue and book collection service. Partnerships like this enable NHS libraries to concentrate resources (both printed and electronic) on special interest areas, avoiding unnecessary duplication.

Suppliers and a procurement timetable should be considered. NHS libraries and HE institutions must understand existing and potential supply arrangements and be aware of the best times of the year to purchase resources. Purchasing at the end of the financial year is fraught with difficulties. However, it is sometimes necessary to do so. Good relationships with suppliers, supplies departments and financial services will help to avoid major disasters.

The LIS should be as flexible as possible to respond to the ever-changing information scene. For NHS libraries, the development of the National electronic Library for Health (NeLH) is a good example. Some thought should be given to the implications of NeLH to present purchasing decisions as well as future plans. The challenge is to provide a complementary service now, and avoid duplication in the future.

Case study 2

Month 1 – the planning process begins

A project plan is drawn up for the establishment of the multidisciplinary library. This confirms the role and priorities of the library, identifies major suppliers (where known), outlines a project timetable and a budget. The plan is produced by the librarian in liaison with a library working party, the Supplies Department and with advice from the Regional Library Adviser.

Two months before the start of the following financial year, an annual collection development plan is produced. This specifies subject areas to concentrate on during the year with a timetable for purchase, ensuring that all funds are utilized well within the financial year. The librarian decides to collect extra orders as a reserve in the event of unspent funds being available at the year-end.

Selecting electronic information for the hybrid library

In this increasingly complex area and with so many choices available, it is necessary to make decisions on whether to choose electronic or paper resources and, if choosing electronic, the delivery mechanism. Finally the product itself can be considered. The overall strategy of the library and the balance aimed between electronic and paper resources will affect these decisions. Rowley (1998) does not believe that electronic information is the answer to all needs in the foreseeable future, and has a vision of a 'multimedia library which reflects the different forms and format that its community find convenient for communication and storage'. A range of factors has to be considered including publishing trends, functionality and access, culture and the delivery medium. (See Chapter 11)

Choosing a locally relevant solution

Each information service is unique and should choose the combination of delivery mechanisms that responds to their particular needs. Some may choose web/CD-ROM hybrids (Bradley, 1998), others will be looking at intranet solutions (Breeding, 1999). Some of the factors affecting that choice are:

- technical infrastructure and number of access points
- training available for library users and staff
- technical support
- budgetary constraints and pricing arrangements.

Before investing in electronic systems and services, thorough research should be done into the options available. This can be done by visiting other libraries, contacting suppliers, acquiring demonstration copies, getting users involved, speaking to experts, speaking to your IT department, finding out about networking capabilities, and so on.

Case study 3

Month 2 – starting to plan the delivery of electronic information

Finding this area difficult to make sense of, the librarian contacts the IT manager and they chat about the IT plans in the trust and explore possibilities of increasing the provision of electronic information. With the promise of finding out more about the options available, the librarian consults various contacts: the Regional Library Adviser, the librarian of a neighbouring trust who has launched a number of electronic databases and some of the suppliers of information systems. Early in the process, the librarian and IT manager visit the local trust to give them an idea of what can be achieved and the practical issues to bear in mind.

On the basis of this exploratory work, a plan is drafted for the way forward and work starts on selecting and purchasing the systems.

Selecting and evaluating information resources
Books

When selecting books there are a range of options to help with the process: core lists, online bookshops, traditional bookshops, library suppliers, book reviews in specialist journals, publishers and reading lists can be used. Core lists are valuable guides for stock acquisition containing resources selected by those with knowledge of health information. They include:

- *Books for primary health care: a core guide to collection development* (Donnugh et al, 1998)

- *Brandon/Hill selected list of books and journals for the small medical library* (Hill and Stickell, 1999) – mainly US coverage
- *Core collection of medical books and journals* (Hague, 1997)
- *Core list for nurses, midwives and health visitors* (Moore, 1998)
- *Dental books: recommended purchase by postgraduate libraries* (Stevens, 1998)
- *Mental health care: a core collection including further reading: The Derwen List* (Bisnath and Bolam, 1999)

Online bookshops have full searching facilities and can be a useful source to search for titles. Book records often consist of full bibliographic information and a review. MedbooksNOW.com (**http://www.medbooksNOW.com**) goes a stage further and provides weekly e-mail bulletins of new titles in particular subjects. This can be particularly useful when developing specialist collections. Other bookshops include Amazon, Blackwells and BMJ Bookshop. A list of bookshops can also be found at the NISS List of Bookshops and Publishers (**http://www.niss.ac.uk/lis/bookshops.html**).

Selecting books direct from a traditional bookshop, or doing a 'stock pick' can be a valuable way of making quick purchases or starting a new collection. There are limitations to this method however:

- Selection is limited to items in stock.
- It is difficult to avoid unwanted duplicates as it may not be possible to check existing stock
- Discounts may not be available or as attractive as with a library supplier.

Library suppliers offer discounts and a number of bibliographic services to assist in the selection of resources, including electronic services on the Internet, bibliographies, title slips, and so on. Increasingly NHS regions are entering into preferred provider arrangements, often involving bulk purchase of texts. Book reviews in specialist journals can be subjective, but it is worth scanning through them in the major journals. By contacting individual publishers, it is possible to receive catalogues, fliers and, in some cases, newsletters regularly. Many publishers also have websites, some of which can been found at Turpin – Links To Publisher websites. In support of continuing professional development and the needs of students, reading lists are an important selection tool. It is also important to find out the numbers of students and other trainees to enable the library to purchase an appropriate number of multiple copies.

Journals

The health LIS manager has various options to consider for providing help in choosing journal subscriptions. Included in these are core lists, other libraries' holdings, donations, resource sharing and electronic journals. Core lists are an excellent source of information for journal titles as well as books. A range of services is available from agents to help in the selection and management of serials. From an NHS library perspective, Claridge (1989) observes that the choice of a subscription agent is mainly based on the recommendations of other librarians. She then lists a number of areas to look at in detail. Added to this list would now be services relating to electronic journals.

Recommendations from other librarians and information on particular titles, including usage, popularity and timeliness can be useful. In order to build up back-runs and fill in gaps for binding, it is worth keeping an eye open for libraries or people that are disposing of stock. Before saying yes, the LIS manager would do well to consider the financial and opportunity costs of accepting such materials. Electronic discussion lists are a valuable source of information about offers from libraries, in particular lis-medical and lis-medjournal-duplicates. In addition, Bubl has recently developed the Journal Exchange Scheme (**http://www.bubl.ac.uk/org/dups/**). This enables people to scan through a list of issues on offer and e-mail donors direct (McMahon, 2000).

For less frequently used journals, participating in document delivery networks can be the most cost-effective option. Most regions operate these schemes, examples including Health Libraries North and Oxford and Anglia. Other schemes exist for particular subject areas, for example the British Medical Association, Royal College of Surgeons and the Nursing Union List of Journals. Information about e-journals is available from a number of sources. Web resources include the Electronic Journals Resource Directory and PubList.com, the Internet Directory of Publications. Subscription agents and electronic journal aggregation services also provide this information as well as supporting subscription services.

Cox, Godwin and Yeates (1999) have made a first attempt to establish criteria for choosing electronic journal services. Their suggested criteria are:

- cost of the licence, relative to its terms
- content
- access
- features
- SDI options
- performance
- user interface
- administration.

In this area of constant change, the e-collections discussion list is a useful source of information on current issues.

Reports, grey literature, statistics and audiovisual resources

There are a number of ways in which to build up a collection of *grey literature*, including visiting the websites of relevant organizations. Many include lists of hard copy and online publications. Many key organizations have mailing lists that will provide bibliographical details. It is also useful to ask colleagues and library users to pass on relevant information to the library.

Statistics are available from a range of sources. Local health and population statistics are available from local government, including the local health authority. Information on national statistics can be found from the Office of National Statistics, and the website Source of UK Facts and Figures, which provides a list of Government Statistical Service statistics including a range of health-related publications, with online versions where available. For example, the health and social services statistics can be accessed online and the site includes a list of other online and print statistical publications produced by the Department of Health. It should be noted, however, that in some cases, the online versions consist of key points only, and it is necessary to purchase the printed version to view the statistical tables.

A variety of health-related datasets are also available through Statbase@. This web based service provides information on statistics available and access to a comprehensive set of key statistics drawn from the whole range of official statistics. The Internet is also a good source for those searching for international statistics, giving access to sites like that of the National Center for Health Statistics and specific statistical reports, such as the Weekly Epidemiological Report from the World Health Organization.

Finding information on *audiovisual materials* can be difficult. The BMA library has one of the largest collections of medical films and videos in the UK, covering a wide range of subject areas. Catalogues of the collection can be requested and used to aid stock selection or to borrow videos from the library.

CD-ROMs and other databases

Information about databases available can be found from web sources like Medical CD-ROMs (**http://cdroms.go4it.net/medical.htm**), and from database suppliers. Free product trials are often available and demonstrations are given at trade exhibitions. An important area needing attention is the evaluation of the interface. Rowley and Slack (1997) emphasize the importance of a good-quality user interface for CD-ROM databases and propose evaluation checklists for interface and information retrieval features. These criteria can be used when comparing interfaces of CD-ROMs and other electronic resources, and include:

- input options available
- navigation within and between records
- communication, including screen titles and layout, prompts and terminology
- support
- quality of the index
- search structure, features and management.

As well as the interface, judgment is also needed about the database itself. There are a number of approaches to the evaluation of databases. Some libraries have developed standard criteria including Oxford University, where a CD-ROM/dataset evaluation form is available for users who are considering new datasets. Other libraries have set up committees who trial new products and make selection decisions for electronic information. Whichever approach is taken, it should be as standardized as possible, enabling decisions to be as objective as possible.

Internet resources

Muir Gray and de Lusignan (1999) point out that 'Simply providing access to the world wide web per se may exacerbate the problems of information overload, since every web browser has access to hundreds of millions of pages of information. However, the cost effective provision of access to timely, current, and high quality information is what internet potentially offers.' It is equally as important to evaluate Internet sites as it is to evaluate other information sources. 'Although the Internet can sometimes be a valuable source of information, it can also be a frustrating waste of time and the information which is available is often useless, outdated or difficult to authenticate' (Cooke, 1998). Much has been written on the evaluation of Internet resources. Cooke sets out evaluation criteria for general use, providing a number of useful checklists. Eysenbach and Diepgen (1998b) and Kim et al (1999), however, focus on health information: the quality of medical information on the Internet and key evaluation criteria respectively. Kim lists the following criteria that can be used:

- content of site (includes quality, reliability, accuracy, scope, depth)
- design and aesthetics (includes layout, interactivity, presentation, appeal, graphics, use of media)
- disclosure of authors, sponsors, developers (includes identification of purpose, nature of organization, sources of support, authorship, origin)
- currency of information (includes frequency of update, freshness, maintenance of site)
- authority of source (includes reputation of source, credibility, trustworthiness)
- ease of use (includes usability, navigability, functionality)
- accessibility and availability (includes ease of access, fee for access, stability)
- links (includes quality of links, links to other sources)
- attribution and documentation (includes presentation of clear references, balanced evidence)
- intended audience (includes nature of intended users, appropriateness for intended users)
- contact addresses or feedback mechanism (includes availability of contact information, contact address)
- user support (includes availability of support, documentation for users).

Case study 4

Month 3 – starting to acquire resources

The librarian begins to collect information about resources available by obtaining copies of selection tools, contacting other libraries, organizations and suppliers and becoming familiar with web resources available. In liaison with colleagues in the trust, and according to the project plan, the acquisition of resources begins.

Selecting furniture and equipment

When selecting and purchasing equipment and furniture, an understanding of procurement procedures and range of suppliers is invaluable. NHS supplies departments for example will be able to explain the Standards Enforcement in Procurement (STEP) policy (NHS Information Authority, 1996) for IT systems and will recommend suppliers for standard items, such as chairs and tables. It is prudent to identify as many potential suppliers as possible as three quotations are often required. Suppliers for specialist library equipment and fixtures are listed in the Buyers' Guide in the *Library Association Record* and may also be present at major library exhibitions together with examples of some of their wares.

Testing the goods is very important. Most suppliers will give purchasers the opportunity to visit a showroom, try out items of furniture or provide information on other libraries or offices where the item is in use. When comparing different items of furniture, the following should be borne in mind:

- cost
- health and safety, eg fire and VDU standards
- maintenance
- manual handling risks
- style and colour.

Case study 5

Month 4 – equipping the library

The librarian has to purchase both furniture and equipment for the new library. A list is made of all that has to be purchased, identifying specific library suppliers where appropriate (identified through the *Library Association Record* Buyers' Guide). The librarian goes through the list with Supplies Department and clarifies procedures and roles in the purchasing process. When costs and quotations are received, the librarian makes arrangements to borrow samples of chairs, visit showrooms to look at tables, and visit a local library to see a library counter and shelving. A few non-essential items have to be taken off the shopping list due to budget constraints. All of this takes a lot of time, and makes them feel more like an interior designer and systems analyst, but when all has been completed, they feel confident that the best choices were made when it was time to order.

Conclusion

In this changing world of health information, health service information providers need to be aware of the many types of information resources available and how to acquire them. If we are to provide high-quality, up-to-date, responsive information services, we need to listen to what our users need and respond by providing resources in the place and medium they require. The potential for accessing the wealth of electronic information available is overwhelming, as are the choices of how to deliver this information to the user. Thorough research and planning will enable the health information professional to make informed choices and provide the best service possible.

Key points

- Planning is essential to ensure that funds are spent wisely, the right resources are purchased in the right format at the right place and time and that the best combination of information delivery mechanisms for the particular information service is selected.
- Focus on users' needs to build up a resource that is relevant and accessible to them.
- Take time to research options, particularly when purchasing electronic information systems and equipment. Talk to as many people as possible, including colleagues and suppliers. Read as much as possible about options available.
- Develop an understanding of the issues and options surrounding elec-

tronic information so as to be in a position to take advantage of all it has to offer.

☞ Be as flexible as possible. The world of information is rapidly changing, and information services will soon become out of date if acquisition policies do not change with it.

Relevant websites

Resource sharing

Health Care Libraries Unit (HCLU), Anglia and Oxford region
    http://libsun1.jr2.ox.ac.uk/

Bookshops and publishers

Amazon
    http://www.amazon.co.uk
Blackwells
    http://bookshop.blackwell.co.uk
BMJ Bookshop
    http://www.bmjbookshop.com/
MedbooksNOW.com
    http://www.medbooksNOW.com
NISS List of Bookshops and Publishers
    http://www.niss.ac.uk/lis/bookshops.html
Turpin Links To Publisher Websites
    http://www.turpin-distribution.com/Turpin/PubDet/publinks.htm

Journals

Bubl Journal Exchange Scheme
    http://www.bubl.ac.uk/org/dups/
eBMJ
    http://www.bmj.com
Electronic Journals Resource Directory
    http://library.usask.ca/~scottp/links/
Nursing Union List of Journals
    http://www3.50megs.com/nulj

PubList.com, the Internet Directory of Publications
    http://www.publist.com/
Royal College of Surgeons and the Nursing Union List of Journals
    http://www3.50megs.com/nulj

Statistics

UK

Department of Health statistical publications
    http://www.doh.gov.uk/public/hpssspub.htm
Health and Personal Social Services Statistics
    http://www.doh.gov.uk/hpsss/index.htm
Office of National Statistics
    http://www.ons.gov.uk/
The Source of UK Facts and Figures
    http://www.statistics.gov.uk
Statbase@
    http://www.statistics.gov.uk/statbase/mainmenu.asp

International

National Centre for Health Statistics
    http://www.cdc.gov/nchswww
Weekly Epidemiological Report
    http://www.who.ch/wer/

Videos

BMA Library
    http://library.bma.org.uk/html/servicesf.html

CD-ROMs and multimedia

Medical CD-ROMs
    http://cdroms.go4it.net/medical.htm

Web resources

He@lth information on the Internet
http://www.wellcome.ac.uk/en/1/homlibinfacthii.htm
Netting the Evidence: A ScHARR Introduction to Evidence Based Practice on the Internet
http://www.shef.ac.uk/~scharr/ir/netting.html
OMNI: Organising Medical Networked Information
http://www.omni.ac.uk

Electronic discussion lists

e-collections
http://www.mailbase.ac.uk/lists/e-collections/
lis-medical
http://www.mailbase.ac.uk/lists/lis-medical/
lis-medjournal-duplicates
http://www.mailbase.ac.uk/lists/lis-medjournal-duplicates/
lis-nursing
http://www.mailbase.ac.uk/lists/lis-nursing/

10
Organizing information resources

Andrew Booth

Introduction

The physical layout and arrangement of stock and services is the most immediate feature of a health library and information service (LIS) and yet it is often overlooked. Although a comparatively few LIS managers have the privilege, and stress, associated with planning and designing a new library, numerous scenarios necessitate knowledge of the principles of library planning. These include:

- refurbishment of an existing building (McDonald, 1994)
- changes in functions or operations
- movement of the library within an existing building
- installation of new equipment (Crockford, 1993).

Many considerations discussed under planning will have some equivalent in other scenarios. It is important to consider the logical organization of the stock at the same time as considering the library's physical features (Kjaer, Tseng and Lucas, 1997).

This chapter examines factors to be taken into account when organizing or even reorganizing a library. It starts by considering practical issues around the physical layout and environment of the library before exploring particular challenges around refurbishment and removal. Classification and cataloguing is briefly covered before extending the discussion to more topical issues such as special collections and the organization of electronic resources. Finally, the chapter concludes by recommending further sources that might inform the planning and physical layout of the knowledge base.

Planning the library

Emergent roles for libraries require flexibility in building design for moving collections, services, functions, and equipment. Staffing is being restructured, new services and new technologies are being introduced, unnecessary or non-affordable services are being eliminated and other departments are being integrated within the structure of the 'new' library (Ludwig, 1995). Planning a new LIS building is an important and complex undertaking. Building design should be done well because it can be altered only with considerable difficulty and expense. Achieving the best organization and arrangement of resources at the time that the building is planned should be done in as flexible a way as the physical structure allows. Creation of a multiple use facility may allow the library to evolve with each change of use, but may require compromises that cause the new facility to function below optimum capacity. Similarly, operating costs depend in large measure upon how well the facilities are designed (Cohen, 1994).

A building is a costly undertaking and will exceed any other area of library expenditure, even installation of a sophisticated network configuration. Unless the librarian operates a 'steady-state' or 'self-renewing library', the need for additional library space will doubtless occur during their tenure. Whether this is manifest in the need for an entirely new building, in the relegation of materials from the open access shelves to a journal stack, or just as an annual 'move-around' of journal holdings will depend on the recent history of the library. A postgraduate medical library with 100 current journal titles will need an additional shelf space of about 25 metres per year.

In a library context, planning is often the responsibility of people with little or no knowledge or experience of this task. A LIS manager is unlikely to have overseen the planning of a library before but will be able to use their professional knowledge to foresee the specific needs of their users. An architect may have extensive experience of a wide range of buildings but may not have presided over the building of a library. A good dialogue and working relationship between the architect and the LIS manager is essential (Cohen, 1989; Simon and Yourke, 1987). It should be recognized that each brings a different perspective, and possibly conflicting values, to the dialogue.

Architects and LIS managers often disagree on what constitutes a successful library building: architects work on a big scale and view light as an aesthetic component, LIS managers are concerned with reading light, security and functionality. An architect may make assumptions about the load-bearing requirements of a library floor, but an LIS manager will know from experience the not inconsiderable weight of a run of bound journals. However, it is also worth acknowledging that architects and LIS managers may also share a number of perceptions (Foote, 1995). They will both recognize that print collections will remain a primary function of libraries for the foreseeable future, flexibility in shelving arrangements is essential, adjacencies must be fluid, floor to floor heights should be generous, the need for compact shelving is commonplace, print and electronic media must coexist, and technology has not reduced library space requirements.

It is helpful if the LIS manager can identify a professional ally to act as a sounding-board for ideas and to add support when there are differences between architect and LIS manager or when appeals to economy meet with wider acceptance than those to functionality. Compromise will be required in terms of the space desired, the space needed and the space received. In many cases the NHS Regional Library Adviser will be a natural point of referral and will bring with them a ready reference source of library design issues from around their region (Collins, 1995).

However, each library's planning considerations should be governed in the first instance by its specific objectives. Planning should therefore involve consideration of user requirements, design of libraries serving similar purposes and a feasibility assessment of the design. The library brief, in effect a user specification, is particularly important in this context (Clarke, 1989). Consideration of design requirements for a new library, although pressing at the time, should not obscure the fact that a new health sciences library provides an excellent marketing opportunity (Walker, 1995). A well-designed library will continue to market itself through its convenience, attractiveness and ease of use. A marketing approach to library planning takes into account needs of users and of library staff and considers the LIS manager's relations with hospital employees. This will be particularly important in view of the fact that library users are likely to suffer considerable disruption and inconvenience during the refurbishment or building of premises and the relocation of an existing library service.

Physical layout and environment of information resources

There are five main components to the space needed in a library setting: personal space, equipment space, storage space, display space, and public space (Crockford, 1993). Personal space will require consideration of both the operating requirements of the main enquiry desk and the various behind-the-scenes workplaces for technical processes, managerial processes and communication. Equipment space may require a specific controlled environment such as cooling for the not inconsiderable heat given off by massed banks of computer terminals or an electrically isolated room for a library file-server. Storage space can be maximized by use of rolling stacks and other intensive storage arrangements. Display space will need to be used selectively as it will tend to take up a more than average allocation, but with dividends in terms of use and promotion of facilities. Several compromises exist such as the facility to store up to a year's journal issues behind the current displayed copy.

Public space will need to take into account the library's policy on noise, eating and drinking and its patterns of use. For example, the widely documented move to problem based learning (PBL) may legitimize small group working in the library, but will also require provision of quiet study areas. Marshall et al (1993) found that more medical students in PBL curricula use the library than in traditional curricula and that when the PBL students use the library, they do so more frequently, for longer periods of time, and as a source of a greater proportion of their study materials. PBL students also use the library more than their counterparts as a place to study and meet other students. Students in the problem based curriculum also use end-user MEDLINE searching library journals, reserve or short term loan materials, photocopy services and audiovisual materials more extensively. It is clear that all these findings have implications for space planning.

LIS managers will also need to establish if there are any recommended standards for their user groups, whether laid down by the parent organization or by accrediting bodies such as professional colleges. They will consider the arrangement of the stacks, the layout of the reading room and the design of library furniture, together with optimal levels for environmental factors such as lighting, temperature, humidity and noise for both library staff and users (Rooney, 1994).

Furniture and interior design

There are three specific aspects to library space planning, namely, the distribution of individual service areas within a library building, the layout of furniture and equipment within library service areas and the value of particular library furniture and its design characteristics.

Kaser (1995) proposed that the internal layout and equipping of library buildings could be made much more user-friendly than they are now and that the library profession should pay more attention to making them so. Users' views should be taken on board particularly in connection with preferences as regards study carrels, lounge seating and group study rooms. The environment of the library has tremendous power to either make people satisfied or put them off. Light, aspect, colour, layout and furniture all have an effect on library visitors and staff. Reading and studying is an intense intellectual activity requiring concentration, often for a considerable time period. Even when the reader is merely walking through the library, the design of book exhibitions or even posters will have a marked effect on their perception of the working environment. Unfortunately libraries are not immune from 'sick building syndrome' even when they may be associated with a healthcare facility (Simon, 1990; Hay, 1995).

Security

The security of library collections, library staff and library buildings is of growing concern for managers of all types of libraries (Jones and Larkin, 1993; Shuman, 1996). Security is most effectively tackled as an integral part of the design process, whether for a new or renovated library, rather than as a bolt-on extra. One approach is 'passive security' which includes siting, perimeter security, after hours return book drops, library entrances, lifts, outdoor public areas and fire exits, as well as more active measures such as panic buttons and security alarms. A security-minded layout for library areas, including attention to the line of sight, can often be achieved without adding significantly to overall project costs. A regular process of self-audit is the best line of first defence, performed at least annually to ensure sound maintenance and attention to faults that could cause harm, injury or death (eg trailing power leads). Safety policies should be produced and housed in an immediately accessible place such as the enquiry desk or the staffroom.

Signposting

Signposting in the library involves the combination of three important ideas: the layout space, the orientation of the users and the image of the library. As well as pragmatic considerations it will need to reflect the cultural and institutional values of the users. To be effective, signposting must be visible, readable and intelligible. It should start outside the library and should include both directional guides ('Where is the photocopier?') and instructional guides ('How do I use the Online Public Access Catalogue (OPAC)?'). It will include diagrammatic devices such as a map showing the layout of the library, end of stack signs giving a concise summary of contents and on-shelf indicators such as location of specific classmarks. Collins (1995) provides some useful practical guidance on signposting, including the exhortation to keep negative instructions to a minimum, rephrasing where necessary (eg 'Thank you for not smoking').

Planning for special needs

It is a popular misconception that planning for those with special needs will require an inordinate amount of extra time and effort. It should be remembered that 'handicap' characterizes a situation that prevents someone from doing something, not the person themselves. An environment that has not been designed with the needs of the user in mind will handicap many of the user population. LIS managers must therefore aim to diminish the difficulties in using their library, and in doing so will benefit everyone. Specific provisions will include wheelchair access, screens that allow magnification of text, generous space through main thoroughfares as well as a more general need to be attentive to improved signing and layout.

Refurbishment

The refurbishment of libraries has recently become increasingly popular with rising building costs and greater concern for the conservation of buildings. Although an excellent location is in itself a prime reason for refurbishment, it is important that the LIS manager evaluate how well the space available can be refurbished and converted for library use. Particular considerations will include size, flexibility, accessibility, communication, ease of use, variety, environmental conditions, lighting, provision for information technology, security, provision for the disabled and value for money (McDonald, 1994).

If members of the planning team think only in terms of the redeployment of existing resources and the acquisition of more space, then it is likely that a valuable opportunity will be missed. Considerations during refurbishment should be broadened to include new kinds of material added to the library since its initial specification; changes in the quantities of varying kinds of materials (less paper and more computers); changes in power and data distribution into the building, within the building, and in the furnishings and relocation of computers as the interior layout changes (Brown, 1995). Optimally, scenario modelling should be included to take into account both future technology and new products, new user groups and changes in staffing patterns and, at the most strategic level, changes in the mission, goals, objectives and service plan of the library. A recent example of a renovation and expansion project is described by Shedlock and Ross (1997).

Moving the library

Planning for the physical movement of the library, whether to a new building or, as with the Royal College of Nursing Library in London, a double move to a temporary home during refurbishment and then back again, should be started as soon as the plans for building have been proposed. Rationalization of stock is something that should be considered at this time, as it is unlikely that it will be of high priority either during the move itself or in the subsequent rush to get items onto the new shelves. Labelling and the physical location of the stock should command urgent attention as portering staff, even with the best will in the world, are unlikely to appreciate the niceties of subject classification. Some form of colour-coding (for location) and numbering (for sequence) has been found effective under such circumstances.

Discussions with those who have undergone such a traumatic upheaval will prove invaluable, while assistance is on hand in the form of a number of articles on this topic. Henexson (1994/5) offers advice on collection, evaluation space planning, library layout, setting out timelines and deadlines, and using software. He goes on to describe how to plan for the actual move covering working with the mover, moving the collection, moving library shelving and scheduling the move. He rightly indicates the need to 'celebrate' the move as a reward to both the staff and library users.

Compton-Ellis (1988) describes a major building project in Pennsylvania in which the entire collection of over half a million volumes had to be moved twice. She identifies considerations such as measuring the collection, assessing staff and equipment needs, calculating the shelf space required, planning the collection layout, assessing the logistics of the move and preparing the shelf space for the move.

Brogan and Lipscomb (1982) describe the relocation of the entire journal and book collections within their library. They discuss the problems involved in planning such a move, the gathering and analysis of relevant data, the formulation of an overall plan based on the data analysis, and the actual move. Much of the move was greatly enhanced by the use of specially written computer programs to help in both planning and execution with a useful by-product being a wealth of quantitative data describing the characteristics of the collection. Finally a book in the Aslib Know-How Guide series entitled *Moving your library* (McDonald, 1994) provides a clear exposition of other important considerations.

Classification and cataloguing

With the increase in computerized record-keeping and the development of regional cataloguing cooperatives, the physical layout of the stock has assumed lesser, although by no means negligible importance. It should be borne in mind that many users still go straight to the shelves in their quest for a book on a particular subject and browsing the shelves is still a popular option. Subject indexing allows multiple access points so apparent dilemmas over the exact placement of a book have, at least to a certain extent, become more academic. The driving rationale for any logical arrangement of stock should be where the users are most likely to look for a particular subject. At the same time long runs of books with a single class number (eg WY 100, the National Library of Medicine Classification Scheme Number for 'Nursing – general') should be avoided at all costs. Many books now have Cataloguing in Publication data, although the discriminating LIS manager will often wish to check the catalogue for the location of previous books on the same subject.

A systematic sampling of the most recent edition of *Directory of Medical and Healthcare Libraries in the United Kingdom* (1997) reveals that the National Library of Medicine Classification scheme is the most commonly used means of arranging stock. This uses the Library of Congress schedules for subjects outside the fields of medicine and related topics while classmarks for healthcare topics begin W (eg WE – Orthopaedics, WG – Cardiology, WP – Gynaecology, WQ – Obstetrics) followed by a number of up to three digits, possibly followed by a decimal point and further digits. Second comes the Dewey Decimal Classification system so common in public libraries. Between them these two schemes account for approximately two-thirds of all UK healthcare LIS. Other systems include faceted classifications such as Bliss and the Barnard system (as used by the King's Fund Library). Table 10.1 shows the full breakdown. Decisions as to the choice of classification scheme will now more usually be determined by membership of cooperative cataloguing arrangements, a significant factor in the move towards standardization. Broadly speaking, however, the National Library of Medicine scheme is most suitable for the 'medical' library while more general purpose schemes such as Dewey are appropriate for those libraries covering a range of disciplines (eg education, social sciences, etc).

Table 10.1   *Prevalence of classification schemes in UK healthcare LIS*

Classification scheme	No of LIS	Percentage using system
Barnard	21	3.6%
Blacks Medical & Dental Classification	2	0.3%
Bliss	15	2.6%
Cunningham	2	0.3%
Dewey	111	19.0%
DH/DSS Data Thesaurus	1	0.2%
Garside	1	0.2%
Library of Congress	39	6.7%
National Library of Medicine	272	46.5%
Own	92	15.7%
Royal College of Psychiatry	1	0.2%
Royal College of Nursing	6	1.0%
Science Reference Information Service	2	0.3%
Thesaurus of Disability Index	1	0.2%
Universal Decimal Classification	19	3.2%
TOTAL	585	100%

It has been estimated that it can take, on average, 20 minutes to catalogue a book (Godbolt, 1995). Clearly, the emphasis should be on enhancing the catalogue record by providing additional access through subject headings. Typically, these might be provided according to the same Medical Subject Headings (MeSH) used to index the journal literature. However, books are, by their very nature, more comprehensive in their coverage than journal articles, and selectivity will need to be used in the number of subject headings one is going to assign. For example, some cataloguing systems follow a principle of not assigning any more than six subject headings per record. Additional entry points can be offered through use of subheadings (eg \statistics or \history).

Increasingly, cooperative cataloguing is featuring as a mainstay of resource sharing and effective utilization of resources across NHS regions. Through such arrangements it is only the first library to receive and catalogue a popular medical or nursing text that has to invest effort in the intellectual process of cataloguing and classification. Once a record has been added to the cooperative database other libraries simply add their location code to 'claim' a record for their local catalogue. Ironically this does provide a perverse disincentive, in that those libraries that hold back from cataloguing an item are likely to be saved time and effort by their colleagues across their region. Concern has necessarily focused on consistency of cataloguing and the development of regional standards. Whereas, in the absence of a logical classmark for a new item, a librarian might previously have felt able to make an arbitrary decision on behalf of their own library, this new collective responsibility requires that such a choice becomes subject to the scrutiny of other colleagues. In fairness, however, the librarian is also given access to a much larger dataset of cataloguing precedent to assist in making such decisions. Mechanisms to improve quality control include electronic worksheets with classmarks linked to subject headings (as used by the former South East Thames Region), annotated subject headings (as used by former South West Thames) and the establishment, in a number of regions, of Cataloguing Advisory Groups. By-products from such cooperative schemes can include the complementary process of regional stock withdrawal policies, whereby a librarian can signal a candidate for withdrawal for consideration by their colleagues. Another source of data, on which there is an increasing dependence, is the cataloguing in publication record, supplied by publishers, although transatlantic differences may limit the direct applicability of classmarks or cataloguing terms for books of North American origin.

Special collections

Most libraries will house special collections according to the interests of the local users and the historical pedigree of the library or its parent organization. Reasons for special collections can include an archival function, the availability of a discrete donor or funder, a regional or national reference function (eg WHO documentation centres), subject specialization or patterns of user behaviour (eg heavy use of a numbered report series).

A number of considerations arise in connection with the physical layout and the logistics of a special collection. For example is the special collection to be physically separate from the main collection? Is it going to be organized in a different logical arrangement (eg by date or by report number)? Is it subject to different reference or loan restrictions? Is it to be accessible through the library catalogue, as an integrated or separate file?

As with any decision about the organization of resources there will be no right or wrong answer to such dilemmas. However it will suffice to record here that LIS managers should resist temptations to handle a special collection as if it were the main collection without due consideration of the attendant issues involved and that they should be alert to factors that may change either the rationale or even the necessity of housing such a collection.

Electronic resources

Libraries spend a great deal of time planning the hardware and software implementations of electronic information services, but pay scant attention to the human factors. Computers and electronic tools have changed the nature of many librarians' daily work, creating new problems, including stress, fatigue and repetitive strain disorders (Thibodeau and Melamut, 1995). Users too are affected by the growth in library based workstations and 'microlaboratories' with an increasing number of design and ergonomic considerations (Baymann, 1992). Some of the common problems of the digital workplace can be addressed by paying attention to basic ergonomic issues when designing workstations and work areas. Proper monitor placement, lighting, workstation organization and seating prevent many of the common occupational problems associated with computers. Staff training can further reduce the likelihood of ergonomic problems in the electronic workplace.

Factors to be addressed may be itemized as follows:

- Location. There is a need to balance factors such as security and user support with those of noise, heat and availability of light.
- Layout. There will need to be adequate provision and location of terminals, and decisions will have to be taken about whether frequently used electronic titles are to be stored and possibly archived (in which case copyright must be considered).
- Workstation design. Purpose-built workstations may optimize current use but may provide a later barrier to the flexible introduction of newer tech-

nologies. Staff who work in front of a terminal throughout the main part of the working day will have different needs from a user with a five-minute enquiry.

- Suitability of furniture. Chairs positioned at workstations will need to be adjustable. It is unlikely that ordinary chairs will suffice for anything more than a brief interrogation of a public access catalogue. When the computer is for the permanent use of a member of staff other provisions may be required such as foot-rests, wrist-supports and document holders.
- Lighting levels. This will not only include provision of adequate artificial light but will also extend to ensuring that glare from bright sunlight is not reflected on the screens of visual display units.
- Environmental factors. The amount of heat given off by a bank of computer terminals is often underestimated. A dot matrix printer may be cheap and appropriate to high-volume use, but the noise factor may prove unacceptable if in close proximity to a study area. A high-volume photocopier may have the required capacity, but again may give off high levels of both heat and noise and will require careful positioning.
- Health and safety factors. Printer and power cables can cause direct injury while poor positioning of screens or furniture can induce chronic problems affecting either back or neck.
- Human factors. Readers may wish to work for long sessions at a terminal, particularly during exam time or when an assignment deadline approaches. However, food and drink can cause physical harm to the workings of keyboards or other computer equipment.

Hyatt (1990) has produced a useful checklist for library automation including such factors as planning and budgeting for installation and maintenance, choice of hardware and software, training and health and safety aspects.

Planning for automation within the library building, particularly the physical layout of the reception desk, requires particular attention to detail. This includes ensuring that applications to telecommunications suppliers for communications lines are made well in advance of need, together with other specific installation requirements. These will include cabling and electrical wiring, determining the workflow, terminal locations and desk layout, and special design considerations at the circulation desk. Library staff will need to maintain a high standard of customer service if the user is not to feel subordinate to the technology (Barraclough, 1993).

Specific software requirements need to be addressed. Texts may look different to readers depending on the software they are using (for example Adobe Acrobat (pdf) versus Hypertext Markup Language), which is not a problem with printed journals. Then there are problems of access if the network goes down. However, printed journals in their turn have always had problems of access associated with theft or mutilation. As technology changes, systems become obsolete and require updating, with attendant costs. Libraries need to consider whether archived electronic material can still be read as technology changes and consider having a system of backups held in a reliable format. Kahin (1996, 292) points out that if the library cancels a subscription, 'the lack of an owned copy means that if the library decides to terminate a subscription to a database service or a CD-ROM, it has nothing to offer its patrons'. If a site is closed, no access to its documents will be available, and there could be problems if a printed journal subscription is cancelled in favour of an electronic service which then no longer covers a particular title. King (1993) has cautioned against uncritical acceptance of the concept of the electronic library. Lucier (1995) describes a more far-sighted three-pronged strategy, where the physical, paper based library is refined by continuously introducing new technology for functional improvement while, at the same time, a free standing digital library focuses on innovative applications. To ensure complementary interaction, technology is focused on the interface between paper and digital libraries as the library attempts to become an integral whole. The hybrid library is explored elsewhere (see Chapter 11). Developing countries have particular requirements for establishing automated LIS, some of which are addressed in guidelines from Fenn, Weatherby and Pasquariella (1990).

Conclusion

Although the physical layout of resources rightly commands a place in the LIS manager's planning and management toolkit there is very little information specifically within a health context. Interested readers can do no better than refer to an excellent chapter by Collins (1995). The review by Doran (1989), though now over ten years old, is a most useful source, discussing general principles alongside specific planning for the new library for the Royal College of Surgeons in Ireland. Clarke (1989) gives further brief guidelines specifically for those planning a new hospital library for patients.

Two comprehensive textbooks that offer an insight into the issues involved are *Planning Library Buildings and Facilities From Concept to Completion* by Holt (1989) and *Designing Better Libraries: Selecting and Working with Building Professionals* by McCarthy (1995). Occasionally a published account of the planning of a health library appears in the information literature, providing useful and transferable lessons (Weise and Tooey, 1995; Cohn, 1995).

It can be seen that, notwithstanding the rapid development of virtual or electronic libraries, the physical layout of the library or information unit remains one of the fundamental principles of knowledge management. Although the consequences of bad decisions can be minimized by the increasing versatility of electrical equipment and communications and the modular design of library furniture, such choice may still impact adversely on users and can also have important cost consequences. In particular the occasional nature of opportunities for redesign or relocation requires that the health information professional treat these as a 'special project' and avail themselves of the resources described above. In doing this they will demonstrate that their facility is well equipped for the effective organization and subsequent exploitation of the knowledge base.

Key points

- In planning a library one should aim for the best available configuration to meet current needs without compromising flexibility for future requirements.
- A good dialogue between librarian and architect is essential.
- Changes to new educational paradigms, such as the shift to problem based learning, often require adjustments to library layout and facilities.
- Choice of classification scheme will be determined by knowledge of user needs together with any constraints imposed by cooperative cataloguing arrangements.
- Electronic resources place specific planning requirements on the organization and delivery of library services.

11
Delivering and accessing resources

Andrew Booth

Introduction

In an environment of expanding information needs, spiralling journal costs, and curtailed financial resources, healthcare libraries must take advantage of the rapid evolution in document delivery services. There have been exciting developments in transmission technology, from fax machines to scanners to the Internet. Health librarians are witnessing a shift away from traditional reliance on library networks toward use of commercial vendors as document providers. These changes require re-evaluation of interlibrary loan (ILL) and document delivery systems on many levels, including pricing structures, workflow and impact on collection development. As commercial vendors develop increasingly effective products, health library and information (LIS) managers can test, evaluate and incorporate them into their ILL operations to enhance their services to users and relieve the pressure to acquire new resources. In this way, LIS managers move from the 'just in case' practice of building an on-site collection to the 'just in time' model of providing timely delivery of materials to users as needed.

This chapter begins by looking at how the 'just in case' and 'just in time' models impact on healthcare libraries. It then looks at the options available for document delivery, including networks, national libraries and professional associations and commercial providers. It briefly discusses the implications of the so-called hybrid library before looking at the specific case of the UK National electronic Library for Health (NeLH). The chapter then assesses how the dilemma between end-user and intermediary access, acted out in healthcare libraries over the last 20 years, is currently being resolved. Finally it examines the specific contribution of the Internet as a document delivery mechanism and associated issues such as Internet access policies.

The current climate for health LIS is causing traditional collection development philosophies to be re-examined. The rising cost of journals, coupled with steady or declining budgets, necessitates that LIS managers review how they provide local access to information. Where once the local collection was all-important, the focus now has widened to other sources. Many libraries are beginning to shift collection development funds to document delivery services. Librarians are being forced to re-evaluate usage levels against subscription price, to examine increased use of document delivery services as a cost-effective alternative to traditional interlibrary loan, and to cater for greater demand for electronic information products and services. While the move from 'just in case' to 'just in time' has commanded the most attention, the ultimate destination of such a shift is likely to be services customized for the individual user – a 'just for you' service. The future shape of this type of service, corresponding to the personalized selective dissemination services more usually associated with special libraries, is explored briefly in Chapter 21.

Document delivery

The health LIS manager must decide on an optimal mix, based on cost-efficiency, between continuing with journal subscriptions versus document delivery via the various sources open to them. Typically these will include network options (regional or subject specialist schemes such as the Anglia and Oxford Regional Scheme and the Nursing Journals Union List), national document supply sources (British Library) and membership schemes (either formal, eg British Medical Association, or informal, eg Royal College of Surgeons or King's Fund). An additional option, appearing on the scene in recent years, is the commercial provider. Services such as UnCover (**http://uncweb.carl.org**) are supported by a huge bibliographic database where the individually priced article is the unit of payment rather than the journal title. Delivery can be by fax providing guaranteed delivery within 24 hours. Payment is particularly problematic as such systems are set up for individual users with credit card payment. For health LIS which have had difficulty in the past persuading their accounts departments to let them purchase large stocks of prepaid vouchers, the prospect of approval for an institutional credit card is extremely unlikely. However with the recent move of the largest British interlibrary loan provider, the British Library, to encourage a deposit account system for prepayment against interlibrary loans (with a minimum £1000 balance), it is likely that the LIS manager will increasingly move to a 'shoparound' value for money approach. It is arguable, too, whether the concept of document delivery as separate from the bibliographic function will persist as a valid one. Certainly the boundaries between these two functions are becoming blurred with subscription agents getting into the supply of bibliographic information, database providers offering full-text collections and journal publishers offering searchable archives of their back issues alongside the current issue. The temporal distinction of current journals and back-runs is also likely to become more fuzzy. Readers are likely to follow themes through strings of related references linked by hypertext, and so the prospect of reading a complete article, as opposed to some key relevant paragraphs, will increasingly recede. As Odlyzko (1994) observes, 'Although the transition may be painful, there is the promise of a substantial increase in the effectiveness of scholarly work. Publication delays will disappear, and reliability of the literature will increase with opportunities to add comments to papers and attach references to later works that cite them.'

Such a pattern can already be discerned in the eBMJ, the electronic version of the *British Medical Journal*. This journal creates hypertext links to previous articles, subsequent articles citing an article of interest can be pursued and electronic correspondence can be added to the journal website. Two additional developments being pioneered by the same journal are the availability of longer electronic versions with more complete reporting only on the website and not in the printed edition (Delamothe and Smith, 1998) and the facility to post preprints in advance of, or as an alternative to, the peer review process.

Another issue concerns the technical method to be utilized for document delivery. Converting documents into Hypertext Markup Language (HTML) is relatively straightforward but is not suitable for replicating complicated textual arrangements or technical figures and illustrations. Current examples, such as the Ovid full-text service and the eBMJ, embed thumbnail illustrations in the page with the option to enlarge images as required. Documents with many embedded images can take a long time to print out. On the other hand portable document format (pdf) files preserve the typographical layout, but as they are images and not text documents they are not searchable. Shipman et al (1998) describe a local experiment conducted by the University of Washington Health Sciences Libraries where journal articles were scanned into portable document format and sent as MIME e-mail attachments to remote faculty members. Such e-mail options utilizing file attachments provide a user-friendly alternative to the more technical file transfer protocol (FTP), but have attendant problems with file size and network capacity. Interestingly, the popular electronic BMJ service acknowledges the dual formats by offering a pdf option – it remains to be seen which option is the VHS equivalent and which the Betamax.

Interlibrary loan networks

Most LIS managers have access to local or regional networks for the purpose of interlending or photocopying. Some of these are administered by a regional coordinating unit with administration and updating of holdings records being a tangible deliverable of the regional library network. Such schemes are usually in a position to secure certain agreed standards in relation to response and delivery. Other network schemes, eg the Nursing Journals list administered by the Glenfield Medical Library in Leicester, are set up on a voluntary basis and participating libraries can opt for one of a variety of response levels, including post only, telephone requests and fax delivery. Increasingly, Internet technology provides a means of offering otherwise bulky union lists of holdings as searchable web databases, such as that used by the Anglia and Oxford library network. It surely will not be long before all maintenance of individual libraries holdings will be distributed, with libraries being given password access to amend their own holdings remotely. Recent years have seen a continuing trend towards formal cooperation schemes with vouchers or cross-charging mechanisms, although, amongst libraries working in a common narrow specialist area, reciprocal arrangements in mutual interest are still to be found.

Institutional memberships

The last two decades of the 20th century have seen national centres of excellence and professional associations having to make difficult decisions in connection with their relationship with NHS libraries. Some libraries have had to accept that their first priority is to their members and have cut back on their support to local libraries. Others have argued persuasively that it is an important component of their support to members to operate through a national network of local branch libraries. Still others, with the British Medical Association at the forefront, have made positive efforts to develop a customer-oriented philosophy to those libraries which subscribe to institutional membership. In the case of the BMA participating libraries can purchase prepaid vouchers, check holdings on a web based catalogue and submit requests through a web interface. They receive a printed list of journal holdings and are regularly kept informed through the library newsletter. The origins of this scheme are described by Bonnett (1992).

The hybrid library

Healthcare LIS managers have managed the delicate balance between locally held resources and regional network provision for many years. Most healthcare libraries today are, in fact, hybrid libraries: they own and subscribe to a range of resources and services which are supplied in a variety of formats and media – print monographs and serials, electronic journals, abstract and indexing services on CD-ROM – the list can be expanded to include computer-assisted learning packages, etc. Many electronic resources are accessed on remote servers. An increasing number of end-users access these services from outside the home institution. Faced with such demands a health LIS manager might consider, for example, offering password-controlled access to the world wide web version of the Cochrane Library rather than merely purchasing a network licence on a hospital intranet.

The management challenge is to optimize use by end-users, in a variety of formats and from a number of local and remote sources, in a seamless and integrated way. The hybrid library should be 'designed to bring a range of technologies from different sources together in the context of a working library, and also to begin to explore integrated systems and services in both the electronic and print environments' (Rusbridge, 1998).

Observers of the development of the hybrid library in a healthcare context watch with interest commercial developments such as SilverPlatter's Electronic Reference Library (ERL). Features include links to electronic journals, support for display of local holdings information and the creation of selective dissemination of information (SDI) tools. As an alternative model, Davis and Stone (1998) describe WebCat (an additional module of Sirsi's Unicorn library housekeeping system), a technical solution to integrate electronic journals with the print collection, provide hypertext links to journal home pages from within catalogue records and offer access using the Z39.50 protocol across the five sites of Imperial College School of Medicine in London. The National electronic Library for Health (NeLH) (Muir Gray and de Lusignan, 1999) brings debates around the hybrid library into sharp focus. The NeLH provides a unique testbed for the use of such libraries in a professional clinical setting.

Case study

National electronic Library for Health

The mission of the NeLH is to provide easy access to best current knowledge and, by doing so, to improve health and healthcare, patient choice and clinical practice. A single Knowledge and Know-How Platform will underpin the NeLH, a series of linked databases interrogated by a single search engine via a world wide web interface. Virtual branch libraries (VBLs) will provide special collections that organize and display information in a way most appropriate to the VBL user. Local LIS managers are seen as central to the development and delivery of the NeLH's aims and objectives (Fraser, 1999b).

Findings from the digital and hybrid library projects of the UK academic-funded Electronic Libraries programme (eLib: **http://www.ukoln.ac.uk/services/elib**) are germane to the NeLH – they are as much about cultural change as developing new processes and technologies. Health LIS managers need to acquire new skills and new mindsets in their work (Fraser, 1999b). Decision-makers within their institutions (managers, postgraduate tutors, continuing professional development managers and directors of R&D) need to recognize the potential of these developments for supporting teaching, learning and research. Commercial providers need to develop more open, customizable products. Finally, a considerable training agenda is needed to assist information users to acquire skills in seeking and exploiting information sources.

Accessing electronic information sources

Many issues relating to electronic document delivery have been rehearsed in the provision and delivery of electronic information services (Ray and Day, 1998). Hersh and Hickam (1998) review the effectiveness of electronic information retrieval (IR) systems for physicians. They evaluated such systems against frequency of use, purpose of use, user satisfaction, searching utility, search failure and outcomes. Significantly, most physicians use IR systems for bibliographic rather than full-text purposes, but even then overall use occurs just 0.3 to 9 times per physician per month.

End-user versus intermediary access

CD-ROM systems are heavily used in health LIS with a number of authors suggesting that end-user searching is of poor quality. The increasing concern over doctors' legal liability for their patients (as stimulated by the clinical governance imperative) and the requirement for evidence based healthcare, presuppose that the information retrieved is of high enough quality. Retrieval of good-quality information may be compromised by poor end-user searching. Mediated searching is not without limitations, as Muir and Oppenheim (1995) have stated. The likelihood of healthcare LIS managers being held liable for their service depends on critical issues such as whether the recipient is relying on the information you provide and whether this reliance is reasonable, whether money changed hands, and whether the institution is under a statutory obligation to provide the information.

Reassuringly, Dyer and Buckle (1995) found, in a small-scale study in Nottingham, that, while end-user searching is inelegant, it is not necessarily ineffective. They identified an attendant need for training in the use of CD-ROM systems: an increasing body of evidence suggests what the components of such training should be. Nelson (1992) analysed transaction logs and found that although 84% of end-user searches were judged successful, use of Medical Subject Headings (MeSH) to obtain optimal results was low; only 20% of all successful subject searches employed MeSH. Starr and Renford (1987), in a study that predates the new generation of search interfaces, found that their users had particular difficulties with appropriate use of explodes and subheadings, as well as locating appropriate search terms.

McKibbon and Walker-Dilks (1995) found that, although end-users appreciate and value training along with feedback on their searching techniques, practice is the biggest single factor in improving the quality of searching. Ikeda and Schwartz (1992) conducted a four-year follow-up study of end-user search training in pharmacy students and found that the training appeared to impact on the continued use of computerized literature searching even several years after the formal educational programme had been undertaken. This theme of training is picked up in greater detail in Chapter 14.

What makes users more likely to use end-user services rather than mediated search facilities? Ash (1999) examined 15 putative factors clustered into three attribute sets (innovation attributes, organizational attributes and marketing attributes). Although management support may impact on *introduction* of end-user services it had a negative relation to the extent of *uptake* which perhaps can be increased despite top-level management actions. Marketing was not seen as an important factor in promoting uptake. Healthcare LIS managers should concentrate on identifying advocates for the service from within professional groups rather than simply using traditional marketing techniques.

Marshall (1995) illustrates total quality management (TQM) and continuous quality improvement (CQI) in an end-user search programme. The quality of an online search programme may be measured through determinants such as reliability, consistency, competence and credibility; responsiveness and timeliness; access and approachability; courtesy, communication and understanding customer needs; and security and physical factors. These criteria may then be further tailored to meet the specific needs of end-user programmes. End-user search services have led to an expanded information management and technology role for the healthcare LIS manager. Implementation of such services can represent a major shift in the strategic direction of a service and must be planned carefully. Klein and Ross (1997) describe such a plan focusing on software, hardware, finances, policies, staff allocations and responsibilities, educational programme design and programme evaluation. This plan can then be used as a springboard for future development, including the delivery of electronic document services.

The role of the Internet in delivering information

Cost, geographic location, technical illiteracy, disability and factors related to the capacity of people to use these technologies appropriately and effectively provide barriers to equitable delivery of health information. Although few would argue with a goal of universal access to health information, coordinated efforts by both public and private-sector stakeholders (government agencies and private corporations) are required to bridge the gap between the health information 'haves' and 'have-nots'.

As has been mentioned above, this will require a technical infrastructure supporting health information technology access, not only in the workplace but also in homes and public places. However, simply providing access to the world wide web per se may exacerbate the problems of information overload, since every web browser has access to hundreds of millions of pages of information (Muir Gray and de Lusignan, 1999). The large amount of electronic information available makes filtering a vital component of contemporary information work. The filtering mechanism requires both quality and relevance criteria.

Chapter 19 covers some of the issues associated with filtering materials, not just specific to information from the Internet but also to other information sources.

Although the focus of this chapter has been on electronic document delivery, a major contribution of the Internet is delivery of information via interactive technologies such as new 'push' technologies (discussed in Chapter 21) and online conferencing.

There are several ways to conference online. Three of these are 'chat', bulletin boards and electronic discussion lists or 'listservs'. Chat, currently more popular in the leisure domain, allows communication with another person or group online, in real time. Bulletin boards can either be within an organization (via the intranet) or in the public domain (over the Internet) as with 'newsgroups'. Montgomery and Keenan (1995) describe how they created a bulletin board to facilitate communication between faculty and staff and their colleagues at other institutions. An attraction of such systems is that they do not clutter up a user's e-mail folders. They provide a natural expertise-sharing medium for interest groups where local users can post announcements, questions and answers.

A listserv is an automated mailing feature that brings people together from other online services. In the UK it is most familiar through the Mailbase service which, until the end of 1999, provided services for academic discussion lists such as lis-medical and evidence based-health. However there are thousands more listservs on the Internet, some private and some public, and these can be identified from the web at Liszt (www.liszt.com). Listservs can be either 'participatory' or 'one way'. In a participatory network, you send a message to an address, which then sends a copy to everyone on the subscription list. When someone replies to your message, they can either reply directly to you, or back to the listserv, so everyone receives a copy. Conferencing in this manner helps brainstorm issues among a group that is separated by distance.

Internet access policies

Provision of a computer with an Internet connection in the library and, increasingly, direct access to the world wide web via the NHSnet, increases the imperative for healthcare LIS managers to develop an Internet access policy (Sherwill-Navarro, 1998). It is clear, however, that preferred solutions will operate at an organizational level rather than in policing individual terminals. Most universities have an acceptable use policy governing Internet access, whereby an employee or student can be dismissed if they use the equipment to access pornography or if they place inflammatory materials on a website. It is clear that NHS organizations must also proceed down this route. 'Net-nannying' software is both impractical (consider the gynaecological surgeon trying to access technical materials) and, probably more importantly, creates an unwelcome image of the relationship between a library and its patrons.

A more significant problem concerns malicious viruses that, either deliberately or unintentionally, are introduced on to library machines. Protective options include virus checkers, locks for floppy drives and automatic boot-up programmes with hidden escape keys to prevent the user accessing the operating system. However it is true to say that these will avert the accidental and discourage the curious, but will have little effect on the purposive hacker.

Raitt (1998) discusses issues involved in developing a systematic approach to Internet use and Lingle and Delozier (1996) have compiled a collection of policy documents that can act as a template for in-house policy development.

Conclusion

It has often been argued that professional publishing contains a fundamental absurdity in that a university and its faculty produces a wealth of content, freely supplied to commercial publishers who profit from it by selling journal subscriptions to the university library. Emerging digital library technology holds promise for allowing the creation of digital libraries and digital presses that can allow faculty and universities to bypass commercial publishers, retain control of their content, and distribute it directly to users, allowing the university and faculty to better serve their constituencies. Such approaches, pioneered at a local level by the University of Iowa with its Virtual Hospital digital library (D'Alessandro et al, 1998b), are now crystallized by the challenge posed by the PubMed preprint services. A new paradigm for academic publishing is in the process of being created and it is this that holds a prospect for the realization of the vision of the hybrid library epitomized by the National electronic Library for Health.

It can be seen from the foregoing that although it has been developments in information retrieval via the Internet that have commanded the most attention it is arguably document delivery that is witnessing the most rapid and pervasive progress. Although interlibrary loan networks and institutional memberships continue to handle the bulk of requests, and will continue to do so for the foreseeable future, the advent of electronic services adds impressive versatility to the delivery mechanisms available to health LIS. The traditional boundaries differentiating bibliographic control and access to actual documents are becoming increasingly blurred as, indeed, are the roles of the end user and the intermediary. Effective management of the knowledge base in health care requires the identification of an optimal blend of traditional and developmental services, epitomized in the concept of the hybrid library.

Key points

- As library services move from a 'just in case' to a 'just in time' paradigm, the eventual destination is likely to be 'just for you', ie personalized information services.
- Although interlibrary loan networks, national document supply sources and membership schemes continue to be important, the most likely growth sector for the remote supply of documents is the commercial provider.
- Developments in electronic publishing are making traditional boundaries such as those between bibliographic control and document access, and those between current and archival journal holdings, increasingly indistinct.
- The health information provider needs to develop skills in managing a hybrid paper/electronic resource.
- The development of the National electronic Library for Health crystallizes debate about the balance between distributed electronic and local paper based resources.

12
Marketing a service

Andrew Booth

Introduction

Marketing is a long-established feature of the special library (Coote, 1997; Batchelor, 1997). Its entry on to the health library and information service (LIS) agenda was signalled in the first issue of *Health Libraries Review* (van Loo, 1984). As the health LIS moves from the 'service' ethic towards cost-consciousness, this topic merits greater attention. Healthcare LIS operate in a competitive environment where precedence is often given to other demands, not only from patient care, but also from other information providers within the organization (Bonnett, 1997). Health LIS have moved from comfortable monopoly to almost an open information market. Challengers include IT departments, R&D support personnel and clinical effectiveness staff. The library must focus on 'niche' marketing, on value-added services rather than the traditional 'brand awareness'. Furthermore the LIS should develop a portfolio of information products to emphasize different features of the service, letting go of non-essential services or, at least, acknowledging the value of complementary partnerships with other providers.

After briefly discussing the concept of marketing, this chapter examines techniques for marketing services such as professional events and open days, posters, leaflets, newsletters, press releases and the provision of a web page within the specific health context. The chapter concludes with a discussion of how the success or impact of such strategies might be evaluated.

Marketing and its importance

A popular view would have it that marketing is 'selling goods that don't come back to people that do' (Anon). The most prevalent of many definitions of marketing is probably that preferred by the Chartered Institute of Marketing: 'The management process responsible for identifying, anticipating and satisfying customers' requirements profitably.' The concept of marketing has been extended from the traditional commercial world to include service organizations, charities and not-for-profit bodies. In this context 'profitable' represents a form of exchange where both parties feel that they gain benefit (Adcock et al, 1995). This is appropriate to a library setting where LIS manager and client engage in a number of transactions (borrowing, information requests and even training) which aim to satisfy the user and to contribute to fulfilment of organizational objectives.

The marketing strategy must complement and support the global strategy the organization has chosen. Jobber (1995) distinguishes between a market-driven approach and an internally oriented approach. Do all your library services reflect a customer concern or are certain services at the convenience of the library staff (eg opening hours)? Do you formally obtain feedback on library services or do you rely on anecdotes and received wisdom? Do you always look out for new markets, reaching non-users or unmet user needs, or are you happy to stick with the same services?

The so-called 'marketing mix' describes those elements that can be manipulated in order to maintain competitive edge: product, place/distribution, pricing and promotion (the 4Ps). Typically libraries focus on product, using the traditional image of the library as their 'brand identity'. Attention is now being rightly diverted to the other elements. Are products distributed from a physical place, or is the intranet, or even Internet, used as a delivery medium? How do prices for library products or services compare with electronic Internet based current awareness, document delivery or bibliographic services? Price can be seen in terms of a fee based service or in how individual users 'value' the service, the focus of 'value and impact' studies. Finally, will the library actively promote its services or risk losing business to new information providers? With the expansion of marketing into service delivery, the 4Ps have been augmented by a further three Ps (Dibb and Simkin, 1994):

- people – staff selection and customer care training
- physical evidence – décor and ambience
- process – the efficiency of the process, eg it is not enough to deliver inter-library loans but the library should ensure that they arrive, at worst, no less than one day before they are no longer required.

With an increasingly customer-orientated approach the 4Ps are losing their appeal. The marketing mix is now commonly expressed as the 4Cs: customer value, cost to the customer, convenience for the buyer and communication. All these emphasize what the customer really wants – for example, the one-way push of information known as promotion is replaced with the two-way dialogue of communication.

Marketing services

Marketing services, as opposed to products, presents particular problems given the *intangibility* of what is provided, the *inseparability* of production, consumption and distribution, the *variability* of quality and the *perceived risk* of use. How can one quantify benefits to a doctor who walks into the library, looks up a textbook or electronic text and is thus equipped with the knowledge to treat a patient effectively? How can one compare the quality of two literature searches, one with a large amount of information and the other with very little?

It is perhaps artificial for a health LIS to talk of a single 'product' as they usually operate through a portfolio of services. A diagrammatic representation of a portfolio, the growth-share matrix, was constructed by the Boston Consulting Group in the early 1970s. This plots products against popularity and demand (see Figure 12.1).

In an example of such a grid, used for an information audit in Thames region, existing information services such as the library, e-mail and the Videotex system were positioned in the grid for a presentation to the region's directors. So, for example, the library was a cash cow in that it was quite heavily used but demand was now static.

Marketing is associated with the ability of the LIS manager to identify, or even create, opportunities. This quality, known as entrepreneurship, is characterized by a willingness to be proactive rather than reactive. LIS managers use their special knowledge of their own organization, the information needs of their users and their preferences for format and method of delivery to identify

	Static demand	Growing demand
Unpopular	Dogs	Problem children
Popular	Cash cows	Rising stars

Fig. 12.1   *Growth-share matrix*

new opportunities to emphasize their particular contribution to organizational objectives. Much of the success of the entrepreneurial approach is down to personal characteristics and not learnt through textbooks. Nevertheless, descriptions of this approach, though few in number, are informative. Vine (1998) uses the market for 'classroom instruction' to generate a list for aspiring entrepreneurs. Lemkau, Burrows and Stolz (1991) explore the nature of entrepreneurialism, defined as 'when an innovative solution involves calculated risk taking', and describe two entrepreneurial programmes in a traditional library setting.

Successful marketing at a local level

What are some opportunities for using marketing techniques? The list is almost endless. However, contrasting contexts might include the building and/or refurbishment of a library (Walker, 1995) or the production of a new database or electronic service (Cox, 1995). The LIS might target a particular professional group such as doctors (Cooper, 1991) or nurses (Bunyan and Lutz, 1991), either because a group is already a heavy user of some services and not others or because they are poorly represented among the library's membership. It might target external bodies such as commercial organizations as a means of generating income.

For an LIS manager the first practical step, after using the above conceptual frameworks, is to conduct a marketing audit. A marketing audit provides a structured approach that allows an LIS to look at its audiences, services and products (Olson, 1993). The audit examines LIS activities and provides a framework for ongoing decision-making, evaluation and long-range planning. Wakeley, Poole and Foster (1988) present a case study of such an approach. Hernando (1997) describes a similar 'community profile' approach by which she was able to find out:

- what proportion of the community uses the library service
- whether use is related to status/job title
- whether use is related to location of base
- which particular services are used for patient care services.

This study demonstrates the benefit that a local library can derive from applying marketing principles. The use of focus groups (see Chapter 7) is another technique from the marketing sector gaining popularity in the health information field (Robbins and Holst, 1990; Mullaly-Quijas, Ward and Woelfl, 1994). In fact any exercise to establish LIS needs may heighten awareness among users being surveyed – a process measure independent of any actual outcome (Crabtree and Crawford, 1997).

Examples of successful marketing in a health library context are regrettably few. Accounts from related settings merely highlight the potential. Hilton and Gold (1998) describe how the Wellcome Institute for the History of Medicine created a working party to look at how the library could be promoted. Its remit included the potential for attracting new readers from areas other than the history of medicine (diversification) and whether the user-base could be extended beyond its geographical concentration (expansion).

Specific marketing techniques

The range of techniques available to the health LIS manager, either to promote their service as a whole or a specific service or product, is, in fact, impressive. Selection of appropriate techniques will be governed by a knowledge of the local context, the LIS manager's ability to seize opportunities as they present themselves and the need to keep approaches innovative and fresh. Certainly it is important to be aware that even tried and tested methods that have proved successful in the past can become stale and ineffectual if repeated without modification. The following techniques are presented as exemplars but represent a small proportion of the potential toolbox available. Regional networks, features in the professional journals and visits to neighbouring services, possibly even in other information sectors, will all serve to augment the techniques described briefly below.

Organizing an open day

Health service staff will not normally choose to go to a library event in preference to other demands on their precious time. Open days should, therefore, be carefully designed and used selectively. It is good to accompany existing events or opportunities (perhaps in conjunction with a regular lunchtime meeting slot or major study day) and to offer something for both the serendipitous and the purposive visitor. An open day could have displays or posters that will be available throughout the day and also have a timetable of demonstrations. Printed reminders will not normally suffice so posters and, more importantly, personal contact should be used to recruit visitors to the event. Many healthcare LIS managers have used National Libraries Week (facilitated by The Library Association) as a focus for local initiatives and many imaginative thematic displays have been developed in response to this.

Getting your message across with posters, resource guides and leaflets

The design of posters, resource guides and leaflets requires the LIS professional to combine generic information processing skills with those specific to a LIS context. There is a ready supply of books and materials of a 'how to do it' type (Wolfe, 1997; Maxymuk, 1997) whilst the health literature often includes useful features on marketing and publicity, especially in health education. The LIS manager must manage the balance between informational content and presentation – leaflets or posters with a large amount of text impair the visual aspects of display. On the other hand a visually stimulating poster is of little use if people cannot recall what it is for.

Posters are usually most effective when associated with the launch of a new service or a special event. The wealth of graphic content available in electronic form, as clipart for example, makes production of posters so much easier today. However posters should be reviewed regularly to make sure that they are not out of date, that they have not outstayed their welcome and that they have not become crumpled and dog-eared.

The challenge of producing a *resource guide* is whether it is to be resource-led or user-led. A single guide will have to make assumptions about people's use of the resource and will perhaps choose a familiar example to illustrate its use. In contrast a range of guides for the same resource aimed at different user groups can be time-consuming but will have heightened appeal to each group. Many libraries compromise by having a house style and some standard paragraphs while inserting user-specific text in appropriate sections. The availability of word-processing and desktop publishing (DTP) packages makes this option all the more feasible.

A common mistake made by LIS managers when designing *leaflets* is to try to incorporate too much information. Frequently, this makes the text time-limited and requires more frequent updating. Lists of databases held or types of stock acquired are of little interest to a user who wants a work-related question answered. Here a customer or market focus will require that the leaflet indicates the sort of purposes for which the library or information unit may be used or the sort of questions it may answer. Many LIS managers now purchase 'blanks' of leaflets in a standard style, often with bright colours, and with colour printers, a variety of fonts and desktop publishing equipment they produce leaflets that compare very favourably with those of professional printers. Some form of local logo or motif is desirable – an early attempt at the William Harvey Hospital involved a redesign of one of William Harvey's original drawings with library facilities incorporated into the various veins and the caption 'Keeping you in Circulation'.

Exploiting a library newsletter

DTP, or even the quasi-DTP facilities of the standard word-processing packages, have opened up imaginative prospects for newsletter production. A typical Microsoft Word newsletter template with clipart can meet many purposes of monthly newsletter publishing. However, it is often good to experiment with additional clipart or logos where available as the overuse of the same packages can lead to a new symptom of 'clipart fatigue'. Maxymuk (1997) provides a good overview of the main issues to consider.

Writing an effective press release

A press release is an opportunity to present information to the media in the way that you want it. It can also be useful for keeping other stakeholders informed of what you are doing. Writing a press release is an acquired skill – it should be professionally written, and communicate effectively. Nevertheless a few key principles can be followed to increase the likelihood of success. An effective press release should be:

*   *Brief.* No more than two pages in length, typed double-spaced, and with a wide margin for notes.
*   *Well-introduced.* Begin with an opening sentence or short paragraph summarizing the contents. This is called 'the lead,' and should answer the basic questions 'who, what, where, why, when and how'.
*   *Structured.* Stick to only the basic information in a logical sequence. Further information should be available through follow-up with a well-briefed contact.

- *Personalized.* One or two very short quotes from someone who can speak with authority (eg Chief Executive, NHS Library Adviser, etc) will help authenticate your story. A good news release includes a strong quote in the second paragraph to support information given in the first paragraph.
- *Informative.* In addition to the main statement, it is helpful to give, very briefly, any critical factual background. This might include details of you or your library, the political importance of the context and facts and figures that illustrate the context. This is illustrated in Department of Health press releases where accompanying notes usually contain supportive factual information.

Finally, a press release should include clear and reliable contact details. It is helpful if the contact has experience of being interviewed. The aim of the press release is to tempt journalists to follow it up with a more detailed investigation so your representation is critical. A follow-up phone call to journalists will further stimulate a response.

Designing and promoting a library web page

Health LIS managers have already established a distinctive presence on the world wide web and there is every reason to believe that they will continue to do so. Although many of the initiatives are small-scale and dependent on local enthusiasm and acquired skills, the web is an important shop window – one that primarily attracts the local browser but which, as an attractive by-product, allows access to serendipitous viewers from the other side of the world. The Internet particularly lends itself to being a public relations medium. Whereas in the past libraries would issue printed resource guides, or possibly a library newsletter reporting current service developments, it is now feasible to broadcast to a far greater audience through publicly accessible web pages. What is more, the incremental effort involved in migrating from the parochial to the global is almost non-existent. A formatted Microsoft Word document can be saved as a Hypertext Markup Language (HTML) document and, with a minimum of revision, be loaded on to a web server. Although it is arguable whether products designed for the printed page should merely be translated into a machine-readable version rather than transformed, the development of 'what you see is what you get' (WYSIWYG) browsers such as Netscape Composer means that would-be web authors no longer have to experiment with text files and coding tags. The development of this cheap dissemination technology allows other powerful marketing options. For example, publications can be placed on the web – forestalling the need to cover postage, production, distribution and administration costs – available as downloadable Microsoft Word documents. Such an approach does, however, bring into sharp focus the raison d'être of an organization and the tension between income generation and public profile.

What are some of the purposes for which a healthcare library might use the world wide web? In their analysis of academic medical centre libraries in the USA, Tannery and Wessel (1998) summarize numerous present uses and give suggestions for future applications. Examples range from basic information such as description and access to library services, through access points to commercial databases, to use of interactive forms (such as for literature search, interlibrary loan or photocopy requests). Chu and Chan (1998) have focused on the tremendous potential of the world wide web in the design and creation of applications specifically for medical education. They rightly caution that these should not be seen merely as a means for translating traditional modes of collaborative medical education (eg voice, presence, print, motion) into web applications. Similarly the LIS manager should try to evaluate the potential of a website, not merely in terms of 'How can we do what we do now' over the web but rather 'How can we do what we do now more effectively or more efficiently', or even more 'How can we do what we can't currently do by using the web'? The three dimensions to innovation that can facilitate this type of development are information (the types and formats available), interface (how it presents to the user) and interactivity (how the user relates to the system).

Halub (1999) describes how users value web based library services because they save time while the library appreciates its increased visibility within the hospital system and the facility to provide a 24-hour service. In creating and maintaining a website, LIS managers should be mindful of the following: consider the design carefully, weigh the advantages of providing services against the time required to maintain them and make the content as accessible as possible. A website, although itself a medium for marketing, should be promoted at every opportunity, including putting its URL on stationery, letterheads and other printed products (Kerr, 1999).

Published instances recording the use of websites for marketing purposes are becoming increasingly plentiful (Shedlock et al, 1996; Stephenson and Fowler, 1997). Donaldson and MacKay (1997), for example, describe the development of the important web presence for the Health Education Board for Scotland (HEBSWEB). Significantly, the skills needed to manage a website are not confined to those of a technical nature, such as interactive media production, HTML programming, and server management. The web manager also needs to possess a better than working knowledge of marketing strategy (Savard, 1998). Increasingly, there is an emerging consensus concerning criteria for a website to include content, design and aesthetics of site, disclosure of authors, sponsors or developers, currency of information (including frequency of update, freshness, maintenance of site), authority of source, ease of use, accessibility and availability (Kim et al, 1999). Several authors (Quintana and Bardyn, 1996; Harvey, 1998; Schnell, 1997) provide a basic introduction to principles of web design in a healthcare context. Hukins (1995) describes the practical steps by which Hope Hospital Library, Salford, UK, set up a home page on the world wide web while McGowan (1997) describes how library staff can use their organizational, indexing and cataloguing skills to establish an effective institutional web presence.

Evaluating your market strategy

As with all the areas covered in this book, there is a need for ongoing monitoring and evaluation. A marketing plan, drawn up around the dimensions mentioned above and accompanied by a small number of specific key success indicators, will be the basis for establishing the relative progress of the information service. Achievements should relate to the objectives of the service, but should also be aligned with those aspects of the service that are important to the customers (Pinder and Melling, 1996). If the service is deviating significantly from the marketing plan, then the information manager will need to take corrective action to realign it with the objectives. Questionnaires, surveys and focus groups can all be used in the context of evaluation as well as in those previously described.

Conclusion

Marketing, though previously a neglected area in the health information sector, is now well and truly established as crucial to the success of any service. A major key to such success is for marketing not to be seen as a bolt-on extra, a luxury that is done when the LIS manager has the time, but rather as an essential component of service delivery. With the growth in expertise and the sharing of know-how through informal and published experiences it is likely that marketing will become one of the essential defining characteristics of management of the knowledge base of healthcare.

Key points

- Marketing is beginning to command its rightful place in the management of all types of health information service.
- The traditional 'marketing mix' comprises product, place/distribution, pricing and promotion (the 4Ps), with libraries, typically, focusing on their product.
- Contemporary marketing has an increased emphasis on the customer and this can be used to realign all types of library service.
- Successfully designed printed publicity materials will pay attention both to informational content and presentation.
- A library web page can be used not only as an effective marketing device, but also to enhance service delivery.

13
Evaluating information services

Linda Banwell

Introduction

Managing the modern health library and information service (LIS) is about managing change, which gives evaluation a central role: are we still in touch with our users' changing needs (assuming we know what they are), and are we servicing their needs and the organization's goals effectively?

This chapter provides a practical guide to evaluating an LIS. It starts by contextualizing evaluation to provide a basic understanding of what evaluation is, and where it fits in the health LIS manager's toolkit. The chapter concludes with a case study of Nonsuch Hospital, illustrating how evaluation can be designed and implemented to underpin the organization's wider aims and drive for continuous improvement.

The context of evaluation

Evaluation does not exist in isolation. It is associated with a range of other concepts: performance measurement and benchmarking, quality, validity, effectiveness, value for money, best value, audit. These are essentially the management tools for the adaptive and flexible organization; they locate evaluation activity, of which LIS evaluation is part, as a central and accountable function within the organization's core management. To this list should also be added the concept of learning: evaluation underpins a learning organization.

Although the explicit evaluation of the LIS is fairly new, evaluation has been embedded in the culture of both education and computer science for some years. In education, evaluation has historically been at the core of initiatives at both central and local government levels, and is also built firmly into the practice of individual teachers. Teachers are encouraged to become reflective practitioners which involves thinking about practice in order to facilitate learning (Loughran, 1996).

> Reflection is an important human activity in which people recapture their experience, think about it, mull it over, and evaluate it. It is this working with experience that is important in learning (Boud, Keogh and Walker, 1985).

These same concepts lie at the heart of evaluation as seen by computer scientists, where it is one activity in the life-cycle of information system development. To perform and implement user-centred information system design requires the developers to collect data on users and their needs, and to evaluate their experiences of using the system in order to inform subsequent redesign (Allen, 1996). User based evaluation requires the extension of evaluative criteria from the quantitative to incorporate the qualitative aspects of the service.

Education and computer science are amongst many disciplines which converge on and contribute to information service design and delivery. From management science come the techniques and vocabulary of project management. Information services are increasingly being viewed as projects for all or part of their lives. For example, the electronic literature resources provided through the JISC (Joint Information Systems Committee) data centres began their lives as projects and have become longer-term services where funding, probably through commercialization, is forthcoming. Evaluation is a central concern for JISC, and to that end the eLib projects were encouraged to evaluate themselves following guidelines developed by the Tavistock Institute (1996). This formative evaluation studies the development of individual projects through continuous feedback on organizational and technical aspects. The emphasis is on the value of feeding learning back into project decision-making (Shaw and Payne, 1998). In addition, JISC has its programmes evaluated externally. Consequently, the culture of evaluation is increasingly embedded in the theory and practice adopted by LIS managers to underpin and monitor continuous improvement.

Predating JISC, important work had been undertaken on developing evaluation for information services. Lancaster has been at the forefront of such activity since the 1960s, and has now taken up the challenge of developing techniques suited to the digital library (Lancaster, 1997). He sees evaluation criteria as needing to be different for the digital library given that use itself will be different, but that it is still the quality of the human service provided which will continue to be the most important criterion for evaluating the service a user receives. The work of McClure also makes a major contribution to developing the theory and practice of evaluating networked information services, with the author being especially interested in the development of qualitative performance measures to facilitate user-centred evaluation (McClure, 1999; McClure and Lopata, 1996). The work of Lancaster and McClure serves to contextualize and inform the development of service evaluation for a trust or other local health sector library.

Other projects offer a wider perspective for practice at the local level. The EU-funded project EQUINOX: Library Performance Measurement and Quality Management System is developing international agreement on standard performance measures for the electronic library. A set of 14 quantitative performance indicators has been produced, each to be supplemented by qualitative survey data (Clarke, 1999). From the public library domain, there is work on the Best Value framework as applied to library services (Heyes, 1999). The case is made, by using the same framework applied to other council services, for continuing library support. This theme of integrated services has a clear message for the health sector. Hemsley (1999) warns of the pitfalls of using misleading statistics with an example from the DCMS (Department of Culture, Media and Sport) applied to the public library sector.

Evaluation in the context of health library and information projects and services

In its *Information strategy for the modern NHS 1998–2005* (NHS Executive, 1998), the NHS Executive recognizes that 'better care for patients, and improved health for everyone depend on the availability of good information, accessible, when and where it is needed'. The agenda set for the NHS includes the requirement to evaluate – care, health improvements, evidence, every aspect of a trust's performance – and that explicitly includes information, and hence LIS, provision. A new attitude is required which espouses the concepts of effectiveness and value and therefore implies the need for benchmarking. Work on the auditing of LIS is reviewed by Merry (1997a): 'Audit of a library and information service implies a systematic critical analysis of the business of that service, looking at the procedures used and the outcomes for the customer.'

Following work on the value to clinicians of NHS library services, Urquhart and Hepworth (1995a, b) produced *The value toolkit*, a practical package to guide information managers through the process of evaluating the quality of their own services. The toolkit provides a set of templates to be used as a basis for surveying the performance of an LIS, and the findings of the Value project are incorporated into the toolkit as a set of benchmarks against which to assess tool performance. Guidance provided includes checklists of questions, to be tailored for use as part of a questionnaire or interview.

The LINC (Library and Information Co-operation Council) Health Panel has also been working on quality development and has produced a checklist and toolkit as the basis of a national framework for quality development in health libraries. This could form the basis for activity to help the library succeed in inspections of the organization when seeking accreditation from bodies such as the royal colleges. The LINC checklist 'focuses on basics: contribution to the parent body's goals; keeping in touch with users' needs; resources needed; performance measurement; future development' (*Library Association Record*, 1998). The toolkit maps directly onto sections of the accreditation checklist (LINC, 1998a, b).

Against a background of new initiatives and changing cultures (Swaffield, 1999) health LIS professionals must ensure the quality of all aspects of their service and of the service as a whole. The usual evaluation method is the brief questionnaire – teachers use them to evaluate a course of teaching sessions; librarians use them to review particular aspects of their activity, such as the reference interaction. Whittlestone, Low and Pope (1999) write about a new training initiative in the West Midlands. Initial evaluation was by questionnaire, on a fairly informal basis, although there are plans to conduct a formal evaluation after the pack has been used for some time. Local ad hoc and piecemeal evaluation work is often not reported outside an organization, despite the fact that it could inform other practitioners interested in evaluation.

Forms and levels of evaluation

Marshall (1995) explains the difference between two forms of evaluation, formative and summative. Formative evaluation is 'a type of evaluation that continues throughout the life of the programme with the goal of providing monitoring and feedback'. Summative evaluation 'typically results in a written report assessing the extent to which the programme's objectives have been attained in the specified time period'. Both types of evaluation, building on the Tavistock model, are seen in the JISC-funded HyLiFe (Hybrid Libraries of the Future) project. HyLiFe seeks to establish, test, evaluate and disseminate a knowledge of operating practices for the hybrid library (**http://www.unn.ac.uk/~xcu2/hylife/**). Demonstrator tailored interfaces are being established in a consortium of sites – one interface, called HyLiFe for Health, is specifically designed to serve health students on work placement. Evaluation is being used to give formative feedback, provide ongoing quality control, ensure that deliverables are as promised and demonstrate project impact on the wider community.

Three levels of evaluation were initially planned to provide formative and summative feedback on both usability and usefulness of the interfaces:

1   *Performance evaluation* of processes at the overall project level to inform system design iteratively, undertaken at local project level and then aggregated across the whole project. Data collection methods proposed were: measurement of progress against task lists and Gantt charts by monitoring documentation, transaction log analysis, focus groups with users to elicit views on gaps between their requirements and the reality of the service, structured interviews with key individuals to gain deeper insights, and general input from the Project Board.

2   *Impact level evaluation* to monitor both formatively and summatively what is happening as a result of project activities. This would focus on a wider community than the performance level evaluation and would seek to gauge reaction from the sector and locate it within the institution's organizational and educational context. Methods proposed for obtaining such were: in-depth interviews with interface users and institutional stakeholders (eg library and computing managers, institutional senior managers), observation of interface use, analysis of institutional documentation (eg information strategy, learning and teaching strategy, staff training programme) and a questionnaire to users.

3   *Synthesis level evaluation*, looking beyond the project interfaces to draw together the learning that has resulted from the overall project. Methods proposed for use were a summative review of evaluation data collected throughout the project and an ongoing study of current literature and developments.

The reality of practice during the project has resulted in these three levels of activity being repackaged and presented for future iterations of the project as evaluation of project progress, interface performance and project impact

(HyLiFe project, 1999). The health interface is currently being developed into a service for all health students and will become embedded in the University of Northumbria at Newcastle's LIS portfolio. The original ethos of evaluation is to be embedded in practice – hence the need to see both project and service as one.

A practical guide to evaluation methods

This section provides a brief overview of methods, which can be used to evaluate information services and projects. Reference to a good text such as *Qualitative research for the information professional* (Gorman and Clayton, 1997), or *Qualitative data analysis: an expanded source* (Miles and Huberman, 1995), will provide a detailed account of qualitative techniques, whilst *Simple statistics for library and information professionals* (Stephen and Hornby, 1997) guides the reader on the use of quantitative techniques.

The design of any investigation will be underpinned by at least a basic application of research theory. One of the first decisions the investigators must make is whether the study will be essentially *quantitative or qualitative* in approach. Broadly speaking, the qualitative approach follows an *interpretist* paradigm, which seeks to understand those being studied from their perspective, believing that theory will evolve *inductively*, using a bottom-up approach to data analysis. The quantitative approach follows the *positivist* paradigm, where the world is seen as a set of observable events, which can be measured, with data analysed according to a *deductive* model. In practice, the use of elements of both approaches provides the most robust and flexible analysis of a situation, with both used in evaluation, and the emphasis depending on the broad context of the work.

The choice and use of research methods will be governed by the broad approach chosen: qualitative investigation is generally undertaken using a *case study* framework, whilst a quantitative approach demands the rigours of *statistical analysis*. Some research methods can be used in both qualitative and quantitative frameworks. The case study is particularly suited to investigation in the health sector given the complexity of the field and the rate of change – the case study is uniquely able to access and interpret the depth and richness of the situation. A defence of the use of the method is provided by Preston and Hayward (1998).

The evaluator has a wide choice of research techniques from which to put together a toolkit (see Chapter 7). The most popular techniques are as follows:

1   *Questionnaires* are used most frequently, and can collect quantitative data in the form of facts and figures (eg why?), thus opening the way for an

2   *Interview*, to probe particular areas of interest. These may be one-to-one, or group (a *focus group* is moderated with a light touch to promote exploration within the group), and can be face-to-face, or electronic. The number conducted and their length generally depends on time and resources available – very brief, directed interviews, conducted 'on the hoof', are a good way of cornering notoriously reluctant students and other non-users of a system. Long, in-depth interviews will yield an unparalleled richness of data but are very time-consuming for the participant and for the investigator who must analyse the data obtained.

3   *Observation* is a good opening technique. Descriptive material can be collected to set the context for the subsequent use of other techniques; in addition, the unobtrusive observation of behaviour can be a valuable tool in its own right, which can provide and enhance understanding.

4   *Critical incident techniques* are becoming more popular and are successful in capturing details relating to behaviour by describing specific experiences (eg please describe the last time you used the . . .). The technique can be used in verbal or written form, and permits a level of comparison if all participants are 'set' the same task to solve (eg please describe how you would find out about . . .). Such problem-solving scenarios are termed *vignettes*. Comparisons can lead to local generalizations, which add rigour to the picture being built up.

5   The collection of *quantitative performance measures*, such as those underlying the annual SCONUL (Standing Conference On National and University Libraries) statistics collected by each university library, is facilitated by various techniques designed to provide data which can be counted and then manipulated statistically. *Transaction analysis* records automatically the use made of a system. Users can be asked to provide *activity logs*, or *diaries*, although these are often hard to interpret and are unreliable. Questionnaires also provide data which can be counted.

6   *Literature surveys and documentary analysis* (eg of in-house reports and manuals) will generally be used in addition to a selection of the techniques outlined above, to set the wider context of the investigation.

Case study

Evaluation of Nonsuch Hospital library and information service

Nonsuch Hospital's library has undergone a succession of changes – services are now concentrated into one, multidisciplinary, LIS under the management of the hospital with funding from several sources. Hospital management has embarked upon a programme of continuous improvement in order to meet the demands of the new NHS and the accreditation requirements of the professional bodies. The library must participate in this programme and work within the overall framework set out in the programme. This means identifying evaluation criteria and benchmarking all aspects of the service through five stages of development: baseline, change, congruence, embedding, and full integration (Banwell, Day and Ray, 1999). The requirements are to understand the library's context within the hospital and the type of data required to feed into the programme. There is a need to understand the library's users and their changing needs. Evidence of the service's performance against identified needs has to be provided and the future development path indicated.

The hospital management proposes to build up evidence and then introduce benchmarking on six themes to provide their view of the wider context of the organization and its strategic management, and on the service issues of user needs, communications, quality and resources.

Planning activity for the library's evaluation consists of a literature review and analysis of documentation (reports and in-house documents) to set local context. There will be an audit of existing resources and identification of user groups. Information use will be observed at present and there will be interviews (face-to-face, one-to-one) with key stakeholders of the service (hospital senior managers; university/professional body contacts) about their perceptions and expectations of the service.

A combination of data collection methods is proposed. A questionnaire (brief, not more than two pages if possible, piloted) will be sent to as many users as resources allow, to provide background data using closed questions (what sources used? how often? your background?); it will also include a few open-ended questions to go beyond the background (why? how satisfied? problems? desired improvements?). Gaps between user expectations and the reality of the service will be identified. Interviews will take place with a stratified sample of users along with vignettes produced to provide objective and comparable data. There will be some transaction logging, if systems permit it, to collect figures.

There will be five stages to data analysis and interpretation:

1 Prepare data for analysis – code questionnaires, transcribe interview data.
2 Generate statistics where possible (count responses to individual questions).
3 Categorize (ie systematize) qualitative responses from questionnaires and inter-views.
4 Interpret analysed data in light of development framework for each theme (at what stage are they?).
5 Prepare development plans for each theme.

The product will be a report that will be able to be fed into the wider hospital evaluation. It should indicate how the Nonsuch Hospital library is helping the hospital to achieve its broad aims and objectives.

Conclusion

The chapter has sought to contextualize and describe evaluation in such a way as to support its practical use in healthcare libraries. Choice of research method will depend on the degree to which the appropriate data can be delivered. Evaluation is as a key activity to underpin the future success of libraries and it is hoped that it will have enthused librarians who are encouraged to 'do it for themselves' in a positive and outgoing way.

Key points

- The need for internal and external cooperation and partnership between health LIS and other departments and LIS increases further the need for the explicit evaluation of the service.
- Evaluation must be within the context of organizational goals and not exclusively library-focused; the increasing drive for mission statements facilitates the process.
- The evaluation of information services can be seen as the development of the reflective practitioner concept from the field of education.
- The increase in market-driven services and the rise of the concept of services as 'projects' has increased the closeness between services and projects and embedded the principles of evaluation into service management.
- Shortcomings in the traditional data collection methods used in support of evaluation require methodology to be developed to address the derivation of the value ascribed to a service by all its stakeholders.

14
Training the users

Alison Hicks

Introduction

Information professionals have long provided help and instruction to their clients, but many now experience rising demands for information skills training. A number of factors are encouraging a move towards greater self-sufficiency. Technological developments enable health professionals to access information resources at a time and location convenient to their needs. New approaches to working, such as evidence based practice, place an emphasis on information and knowledge. Health professionals need information skills training more than ever and information professionals need to provide services to meet this demand as effectively and efficiently as possible.

This chapter considers the impact of health policy and technologies on the training and learning needs of health professionals. A systematic approach to training provision is essential and a framework for planning is suggested. A case study is included, describing an innovative training programme at the Royal Cornwall Hospitals NHS Trust. Lastly, the impact on information professionals is discussed with suggestions for equipping library staff with the skills and knowledge to provide effective training.

The current environment

Against the background of developments outlined in Chapters 1–6, the roles and responsibilities of health professionals are changing. The move in 1991 to reduce junior doctors' hours was a driving force for new roles for nurses (Shewan and Read, 1999). Increasingly, nurses are utilizing research evidence, but are finding it difficult to keep up with new technologies and new sources. Royle et al (1997, 20) surveyed nurse administrators to obtain a picture of information resources and skills available to nurses; the study found that 62% of respondents required information skills training. Many health professionals are also undergoing formal education and training programmes. As more professions become degree based, so the knowledge base grows. Increasingly, health professionals are undertaking their own research, from small audit projects through to large randomized controlled trials and systematic reviews. Typically, health professionals work irregular hours and often have little time for information research during office hours when help is at hand. New skills are required if health professionals are to stay current, to pursue educational programmes and to provide quality patient care.

Within this environment, health professionals are faced with a wealth of information, which, without adequate training, can resemble a maze. The Internet has quickly become a valuable tool for accessing and publishing information but remains difficult to navigate. Its use is likely to rise as we move towards sources such as the National electronic Library for Health which only exist in electronic form (Muir Gray and de Lusignan, 1999). The amount of material published each year is increasing, and without training health professionals find it difficult to select relevant and quality material to inform their practice. With the introduction of clinical governance, health professionals have a greater responsibility to keep up to date with developments in their chosen specialty. Scally and Donaldson (1998, 63) describe the potential impact of clinical governance and recognize the importance of information skills to achieve this: 'accessing and appraising evidence is rapidly becoming a core clinical competency'.

The move towards evidence based practice has heralded a new role for information professionals and brought with it a reinforced need for information skills training. Librarians can provide support and training for evidence based practice, in particular, question formulation, searching and critical appraisal (See Chapters 15–19). Critical appraisal is a relatively new area for librarians, but many librarians see this as an opportunity to further expand their role and are currently involved in providing critical appraisal training. Davidoff estimated that a doctor working in the field of adult internal medicine would need to read around 17 articles a day every day of the year to keep up with the published literature (Davidoff et al, 1995). There is an obvious need for health professionals to learn how to recognize information which is of good quality and of relevance to their practice. In addition, health professionals also need support in developing information and communications technology skills, particularly training and awareness relating to the Internet (e-mail and web). Pyne et al (1999) provide a useful list of training needs based on a survey of health professionals.

Above all, what health professionals need is training which is timely, relevant and accurate. Rose (1998) outlines the problems faced by primary healthcare professionals: increased workload, isolation, less access to information than acute care professionals, explosion of information. Even where primary care professionals are aware of sources of information, they may not have the time or access to use the sources regularly to support their clinical decision-making. Rose (1998, 172) suggests that a core role for information professionals is as trainer and educator, in particular to 'maximize levels of self-sufficiency' in the use of information sources. Information skills training delivered at the appropriate time and level can help health professionals to find and use the best available evidence and, subsequently, to make more efficient use of their time.

The learning process

To plan and provide effective training, we must consider how adults learn and what methods can be used to facilitate the learning process. The education sector is moving away from the traditional 'information transfer' style of teaching and for some time has advocated active learning. This is defined as 'a method of instruction which involves the students/attendees in the learning process by having them participate and reflect on that experience' (Francis and Kelly, 1997, 25). Many librarians are developing training to promote active learning: Snowball (1997) describes training to teach search strategy; Earl and Neutens (1999) describe case based exercises; Francis and Kelly (1997) quote several examples, including courses to teach searching and netiquette. Many different methods can be used to introduce active learning: brainstorming sessions, buzz groups, small group discussion and role play exercises.

This approach to training does involve more work for the instructors. However, the benefits are widely recognized. Snowball (1997) acknowledges that this approach can make learning more relevant for the learner and can help to motivate learners, making the process of learning search skills more enjoyable and more interactive. The reflective approach has also been tested by Martin (1998) who developed, with nursing tutors, a novel approach to induction training for diploma-level nursing students. Students are assigned a reflective essay, requiring them to use and evaluate library based sources. This has proved an effective exercise and Martin notes in particular the improvement in users' confidence. Active learning encourages constant reflection and feedback, enabling participants to monitor their progress. Borger and Seaborne (1982, 168) recognize this feedback as crucial: '[there is] a need for information along the way, which can be used to confirm successful progress so far.'

One other issue of particular relevance to the health sector is the timing and scheduling of courses. Health professionals often cannot find the time during office hours to receive training. Although the concept of the virtual library has greatly helped users to access information, it has resulted in greater training needs. Many health professionals use information resources outside of office hours and cannot access support services when they most require them. One solution is to use IT to deliver training and support. Jensen and Sih (1995) outline a project undertaken to deliver training for researchers via e-mail. The experiment proved popular and has now been expanded to deliver materials via the web. Clay, Harlan and Swanson (1999) outline the use of a web based electronic workbook to provide training within an academic setting; it was found that the main disadvantages were technical (eg the package had to be designed for the lowest common denominator), but that the benefits outweighed the hard work. Garland et al (1999) outline a similar project undertaken in a UK university which proved less effective. In this project, students were split into three groups where they received either face-to-face teaching, computer-assisted learning or web based learning; those who received face-to-face teaching appeared to have learned more. In the UK, the use of IT in training is still in its infancy (Cox, 1997); many NHS based libraries do not yet have the resources to provide this level of service; however, it is something to consider for the future as library services are collaborating more and more.

Planning a training programme

Planning a new training programme can seem overwhelming. The following section is a brief guide to the steps typically involved in the design of a training session.

Identify the group's training needs

It is important to start by considering the users' needs as it will be a waste of time to deliver a course which is not ultimately useful. As well as identifying the subject areas to cover, it is equally important to obtain an idea of existing skills and knowledge.

Develop aims and objectives for the training session based on the needs identified

Aims and learning objectives help to structure a training session. Ramsden (1992, 130) defines aims and objectives as follows: 'Aims are best thought of as general statements of educational intent, seen from the students' point of view, while objectives are more specific and concrete statements of what students are expected to learn.'

Determine how you will know if the learning objectives have been met

There needs to be some method of assessment; this does not necessarily mean examinations or tests, but could involve a group discussion covering the main points of the session.

Plan the learning activities and decide on the delivery methods and content of the session

Once training needs have been identified and aims and objectives developed, an outline of the session can be drawn up. Many authors describe the content and delivery of local training (Hepworth, 1992; Hicks, 1998; Adams and Plosker, 1997).

There are several methods of delivering training, some of which are discussed in Table 14.1.

Develop the learning materials

This involves writing and producing presentations, handouts and exercise sheets for the session. It is important that any exercises are piloted to make sure they work. Materials should be updated and, if possible, tailored to the specific group. Any equipment required should be identified at this stage.

Table 14.1   *Training methods*

Method	Benefits	Drawbacks
Presentation/ Lecture	Can reach large numbers of people therefore an efficient use of time. A good method for providing an overview of a subject.	A passive method of learning. Does not allow for individual needs or requirements. Can be difficult to listen for long periods of time.
Demonstration	Can be used to show the correct procedure. Useful for supplementing a presentation.	Can seem contrived if prepared examples are used. Would require a back-up should equipment fail to work on the day.
Discussion	Promotes active learning and participation. Can help to identify new ideas and new issues.	Group may be reticent and reluctant to contribute. Alternatively, it may be difficult to control discussion.
Small groups	A less intimidating environment for shy learners. Facilitates discussion and collaborative learning.	Can be time-consuming. Groups may use the time allocated for social chatting.
Practical	Promotes learning by doing. Useful for training searching, eg of the Internet. Focused to individual needs and can be self-paced.	Requires access to reliable equipment and facilities. More time-consuming. Staff-intensive.
Handout	Easily distributed to large groups. Can be used to reinforce points made during a session. Can be easy and cheap to produce.	Will require regular updating. Many people need face-to-face contact to learn so cannot be used to replace a session.
Web based tutorial	Can be made available to a wide audience. Can be self-paced. Anonymous. Can be used at a time convenient to the learner.	Involves a lot of time and effort to produce. Difficult to make inter-active. Will only be as good as the access to it.

Table 14.1 *continued*

Method	Benefits	Drawbacks
One-to-one	Highly personalized sessions which are focused on the individual's needs. Individuals are approaching library staff for training therefore motivated to learn.	Very staff-intensive. Not all users can attend instruction during office hours. Requires private space to avoid interruptions.

Determine how the session will run and decide on the timing and scheduling of activities

Although it is vital to be flexible and tailor sessions around the participants, it can be helpful to start with a basic structure. This can be amended during the course as required.

An aid similar to Figure 14.1 can be used to produce a brief session outline.

Time	Key points	Delivery method	Resources	Duration
0930–0950	Evidence based practice and associated study designs	Presentation	Handouts of slides	20 minutes
0950–1010	Use of method-ological filters to retrieve therapy studies	Presentation	Handouts of slides	20 minutes
1010–1055	Use of filters in literature searching	Practical session on computers	Exercise sheets	45 minutes
1055–1100		Feedback session	Flipchart	5 minutes
1100–1115	BREAK			
1115–1200	Use of filters in literature searching	Practical session on computers	Exercise sheets	45 minutes
1200–1210		Feedback session	Flipchart	10 minutes
1210–1225	Summary and general feedback	Discussion		15 minutes

Fig. 14.1 *Sample session outline* (Based on a session from a training programme designed by ScHARR Information Resources to train librarians in the use of methodological filters)

Decide on the venue and location

Health professionals can find it difficult to find the time to attend courses held in the library. It is possible to take the training to small groups although the local facilities determine the activities which can be undertaken.

Publicize the session

Some of the media available for publicity include newsletters, noticeboards, letters to interested parties, e-mail announcements, meetings, web page announcements and word of mouth.

Plan the feedback mechanisms which you will use

It is important to evaluate both the session itself and the trainer. Methods of evaluation are discussed below. LaGuardia et al (1996) discuss approaches to observe or self-evaluate training and teaching techniques.

Develop ideas for future training based on the feedback received

It is absolutely vital that any evaluative information collected is used to inform planning of future training provision.

Evaluating training provision

The provision of training is a cyclical process; all training should be evaluated to identify any problems and to assist planning for future provision. Hepworth (1991, 98) stresses the need for formal evaluation to obtain a realistic view: 'a vital corollary is that training programmes of all kinds must be evaluated to discover what indeed has been achieved, rather than what it might be convenient to believe has been achieved.'

There are a number of methods available for collecting evaluative data. A popular method is the questionnaire distributed at the end of the session which can be used to collect both quantitative and qualitative data. The questions could relate to the original learning objectives (Earl and Neutens, 1999) or to the delegate's level of satisfaction with the course (Hicks, 1998). The main problem is in obtaining a high response rate. Hicks (1998) outlines methods developed by the Trent Institute for Health Services Research to encourage feedback: a simple design, Likert-scale questions to start, time during the session to complete forms, anonymity, analysis of data to inform future planning.

Burrows and Tylman (1999) describe an approach used to evaluate the search proficiency of students and residents following literature search training. The participants are given a scenario from which they must develop a search strategy, which is evaluated against criteria developed by library staff. Those deemed to have poor strategies are offered follow-up training. Other methods include the use of focus groups and the use of surveys.

Case study

Royal Cornwall Hospitals NHS Trust

This case study describes training provision at the Library Service of the Royal Cornwall Hospitals NHS Trust (RCHT). The approach is innovative and proactive and is responsive to recent changes in health policy (eg clinical governance) and technological developments (eg National electronic Library for Health). The following is an account of the design and delivery of training within the RCHT.

The library service not only runs its own programme of training, but also contributes to wider programmes within the trust. Regular, scheduled sessions are organized and library staff also respond to ad hoc requests. Current training activity can be summarized as follows:

- One-to-one training within the library for individuals on an ad hoc basis.
- Regular sessions forming part of the trust's Training Department programme. This covers database searching, information retrieval and critical appraisal, lasts 60–90 minutes and is held once every two weeks. The sessions are held in a specially designed training room with ten networked computers.
- A schedule of library service training sessions in community hospitals, one in each of the five local primary care group (PCG) areas. These are designed both as an induction for new staff and a refresher for existing staff. A library-funded computer is available in each hospital and training is usually focused there.
- On-demand training at the workplace, within the RCHT. This is usually held at a venue convenient to the requesting group; a notebook computer and LPG projector are used.

Library staff aim to provide 'hands-on' training as much as possible. An active and reflective approach is used, where participants are encouraged to learn by doing and to reflect on their experience. A great deal of preparation is involved to keep sessions fresh and as active as possible. Instructors are flexible and act as facilitators or enablers rather than as teachers in the didactic sense. Each formal session is evaluated, using feedback forms; this form is also available electronically on the library's intranet site.

A typical session:

- Brief outline of the context of information retrieval – where does it fit in relation to evidence based practice and the relevance to clinical governance.
- Introduction to the library service site on the intranet (Cornwall Managed Network) and its five sections: User Guide, News, Databases, Journals, Request Form (10 minutes).
- Use of databases – comparative search using the same term on Cochrane, MEDLINE, BNI, demonstrating differences in searching, output, expectations, critical evaluation and appraisal of articles (30 minutes).
- Same search on web search engines including meta search engines, demonstrating variance and limitations (15 minutes).
- Round-up setting each element in context, reminding users of value of Journals, News, Request Form and Feedback Form (icon on every page) (10 minutes).
- Free search time, if any left.

(Times are approximate and there is some flexibility depending on the user group and their level of IT awareness.)

Demand for training is managed by booking group sessions via the Training Department and by scheduling community hospital visits according to a rolling programme. In-house and ad hoc sessions are organized according to demand at times convenient for library staffing.

This approach to training is influenced by local and national factors. Locally, the user population is widely dispersed and so a totally library based training programme could not be successful. The establishment of the Cornwall Managed Network (the electronic linkage between acute, community and primary care sites) has provided new opportunities for library services, including training. The library service identified a gap in the training market and developed training ideas to meet this need. Training provision has since evolved and the library manager is now on the official trust training programme. Other related departments have been made aware of the role of the library with regard to training and this has cut down on the duplication of effort, where several departments may be offering similar training.

The library staff have identified opportunities from the continually changing environment of the NHS and developed an innovative and effective programme of training. The library manager's philosophy is 'that by training end users, we empower them to our mutual benefit. They use library resources more effectively and we spend less time assisting them in future . . . Training is one of the highest priorities on our agenda – both training end users and training library staff to carry this out effectively.'

The implications for librarians' roles

Having considered the growing demand for information skills training within the health sector, what are the implications for library and information professionals? If library staff are to support growing demands for training, they themselves will need training and support. All library staff in contact with users will require some training in order to support evidence based practice and clinical governance. Those involved in training users may require teaching and communication skills. Within the academic sector in the UK, a number of projects were established as part of the Electronic Libraries (eLib) programme. Two projects in particular aimed to provide librarians with the skills to support new methods of learning: Netskills (**http://www.netskills.ac.uk**), based at the University of Newcastle, which provided training in technical skills; and Edulib (**http://www.tay.ac.uk/edulib/index.html**), based at the University of Hull, which provided training in teaching and communication skills. The websites are still active.

Several programmes have been established to provide LIS professionals with new skills (Hicks, Booth and Sawers, 1998; Palmer et al, 1997). One of the most imaginative is the Librarian of the 21st Century Project (Palmer et al, 1997; Palmer, 2000). The programme, concentrating on skills for evidence based healthcare (EBH), was planned during 1994 and implemented in the Anglia and Oxford Region. Five workshops included a review of the trends affecting library services and librarianship, critical appraisal, teaching and training, retrieval and handling skills and managing information. The final workshop reviewed the programme with an extensive evaluation by participants identifying gaps and experience on which to build. The project showed librarians *how* to improve and enhance their skills, it provided a cohort of librarians with training, and it provided a package of learning events 'whose content has wider applicability and significance than for health care alone' (Palmer, 2000, 164). The package has been extended to other regions.

The project was matched by the Critical Appraisal Skills Programme (CASP), which was launched in 1994 to teach the skills to healthcare professionals; more than 3000 people have now attended CASP workshops. Finding evidence is another area where trainees wanted to learn more, and the CASP Finding the Evidence Workshops (CASPfew) were developed to answer this need. The results of these two projects have been published as a workbook and CD-ROM for further teaching and training in EBH (Critical Appraisal Skills Programme and Health Care Libraries Unit, 1999) and have been used by other regional library units.

Project APPLE, 'a programme of professional development and training for librarians in evidence-supported healthcare', established during 1998 in the West Midlands Region, is accredited by the Open College at the University of Wolverhampton (Whittlestone, 1998). It uses online study packs available through the Apple website (**http://library.hsrc.org.uk/projectapple**) and promotes networking through a closed discussion list 'Applenet' (Whittlestone, Low and Pope, 1999).

Other work has extended the librarian's role beyond identification of the literature into involvement in practising and teaching quality filtering and critical appraisal. Scherrer and Dorsch (1999) describe a professional development programme for health librarians from university and hospital sites. Hicks, Booth and Sawers (1998) developed a programme to deliver training materials for EBH using a mixture of workshops and distance learning formats, as a joint initiative between a specialist EBH information unit and a regional library unit.

Conclusion

Training is a major part of library and information work and this looks set to continue. It can be time and resource-consuming to design and deliver training, and collaborative working is the sensible route to take. McCray and Maloney (1997) outline a state-wide collaborative effort to improve access to the healthcare knowledge base in Arizona; a state-wide education team is responsible for determining aims of training, developing new materials and coordinating classes and sessions. Training is consistent throughout the state and duplication of effort is eliminated.

Training provision should be proactive, not reactive, but should always consider the needs and requirements of health professionals. Heseltine (1995) emphasizes the need for a totally new approach to teaching and learning in response to the information revolution: 'people will learn how, where and when they want.' Librarians must adapt to the changing environment and deliver training which is effective and evolving. To quote Tiefel (1995, 336): 'Librarians must move fast to seize the opportunities and break out of the molds of the past. They must be visionary, innovative, and flexible in meeting the challenges of the future.'

Key points

- The training needs of health professionals are growing following the introduction of evidence based practice and clinical governance, and technological developments from *Information for Health*.
- Ultimately, health professionals require training which is timely, relevant and accurate.
- Active learning has been shown to encourage learning and has been used by many librarians to teach searching and Internet sessions.
- A planning cycle can be used to develop and design training programmes, for a more systematic approach.
- Evaluation of all training is crucial; even more crucial is that the information collected is used to inform future provision.
- Developing training can involve a lot of resources but can help to make users more self-sufficient.
- Collaborative working with colleagues locally, regionally and nationally can help to make better use of training resources.

Part 3

**Skills needed to make effective use
of the knowledge base**

15
Formulating the question

Andrew Booth

Introduction

Successful interaction with information retrieval systems, whether accessed directly by an end-user or mediated through a health information professional, requires a number of skills. These have been identified by Proud et al (1993) as the abilities to 'formulate a question, retrieve current information, critically review relevant articles, communicate effectively, and use these skills to contribute to patient care.' Rightly this list begins with 'formulate a question', a much neglected science commanding increased interest with techniques developed and promulgated by the practitioners of evidence based medicine (EBM). This chapter begins by discussing clinicians' generation and use of questions as they reflect on their information needs. It then looks at how clinicians interact with information services. From here it examines what EBM has taught us about background and foreground questions and the technique of focusing the question. The chapter concludes by looking at how these skills can inform the practice of information retrieval and the development of the role of the health librarian.

Studies of clinical questioning behaviour

Clinicians ask one question of medical knowledge for every two patients seen (primary care physicians (Gorman and Helfand, 1995)) or two questions for every three patients seen (office practice physicians (Covell et al, 1985)). A pragmatic study of Australian general practitioners found that they asked 2.4 clinical questions for every 10 patients seen, finding satisfactory answers to just over three-quarters of these questions (Barrie and Ward, 1997). Of these questions a consistently observed 30% (Covell et al, 1985; Gorman and Helfand, 1995) are pursued for an answer through a wide variety of information sources. Sources consulted will include humans (eg colleagues and pharmacists), printed materials (eg textbooks and personal reprint collections) or computer systems (eg MEDLINE). Only a minute proportion, possibly less than 1%, of the original set of patient-derived questions present to computer systems (Barrie & Ward, 1997), extrapolated from Gorman and Helfand, 1995)). Two factors that will have a bearing on whether a topic is pursued across a number of sources will be whether or not the patient's problem is perceived to be urgent and whether the doctor believes a definitive answer exists (Thompson, 1997).

The reference interview

Excluding 'quick reference' enquiries, the healthcare librarian most frequently encounters questions in the context of the pre-search reference interview. White (1998) has devised a typology to represent the content of such questions:

- problem (the reason for soliciting the information or underlying context for the question)
- subject (what the question is about)
- service requested (what the client wants to know about the subject)
- external constraints (situational constraints which may affect choice or packaging of information)
- internal constraints (characteristics of the questioner which may influence choice or packaging of information, eg knowledge of the subject matter)
- prior search history
- output (characteristics of the search output, eg number of items, elements in the format)
- search strategy (eg Boolean logic, database characteristics)
- logistics/closure (information related to the logistics of doing the search).

Typically forms used to record literature requests contain open-ended elements (eg a free-text description of the problem or subject) and closed, limited response items (eg language, year-range, types of material). Debate continues as to how exactly the advent of online services has changed the reference interview and the relationship between the librarian and the client (Hurych, 1982). More scientific methods for dealing with users' online search requests can arguably be directly applicable to traditional reference services. Yet some commentators

(Auster, 1983; Somerville, 1977) have argued the converse, that the traditional reference interview is the source of the skills required to make computer search strategy more effective. Although a number of authors have proposed a more structured approach to the reference interview (Somerville, 1982), few have applied this to health information practice.

The librarian–clinician interaction

Optimally a search is conducted with requester and intermediary working in tandem – the former supplying detailed clinical knowledge and immediate relevance feedback, the latter using information skills in command language, search logic and methods for limiting search results. Morris et al (1982) found that having the user present increased precision, recall and user satisfaction for a search. It is often impractical for both clinician and librarian to conduct a 'real-time' search either at the point of request or on a subsequent occasion. Typically, therefore, a clinician–intermediary interaction involves a brief interview (less than five minutes), conducted either face-to-face or over the telephone, with details recorded on an unstructured, or minimally structured, literature search request form.

The interaction between healthcare librarian and *clinical* staff is more complex than most. A study of 59 information exchanges between a librarian and hospital staff (Schulz, 1996) revealed that 29% contained some sort of jargon, either acronyms, books and periodicals identification, online searching or eponyms. The healthcare librarian supports clinical practice through intermediary searching in three principal ways:

- by maximizing the relevance and utility of search results
- by optimizing retrieval of high quality research studies to answer a patient-centred clinical question
- by making the pre-search interview and interaction with database sources as efficient and productive as possible.

The contribution of evidence based medicine

The recent emergence of evidence based medicine (EBM) (Evidence Based Medicine Working Group, 1992) has reawakened interest in the questioning behaviour of clinicians. EBM seeks to isolate that small proportion of the knowledge base (estimated as no more than 1% of the whole) that is required for the practice of patient care; hence the maxim 'drowning in information, thirsting for evidence' (Booth, 1996). Information needs are focused on scenarios of immediate concern to an individual's own practice (Rosenberg and Donald, 1995).

Background and foreground questions

The study of questions provides an 'insight into the mental activities of participants engaged in problem solving or decision making' (White, 1998). Satisfying a clinician's information needs can lead to accurate diagnosis, selection of the most appropriate course of treatment and, ultimately, to improved health status.

Richardson and Wilson (1997) differentiate questions as being either foreground or background. Background questions ask 'What is this disorder?', 'What causes it?', 'How does it present?', 'What treatment options exist?'; so an unfocused or 'background' question might be 'What are the available treatments for respiratory syncytial virus (RSV)?' Foreground questions are more detailed and specific so a focused or 'foreground' question, in contrast, would be 'In a 12-month-old child with cyanotic congenital heart disease and severe bronchiolitis caused by RSV, how would nebulized ribavirin compare with other treatments in terms of morbidity, mortality, length of stay and avoidance of side effects?' A lack of prior knowledge or experience of a particular condition or situation characterizes background questions, whereas foreground questions relate to a need for advanced decisions between treatment options.

In differentiating between the information sources that might answer the two types of question, one finds that a background question is more likely to be answered from a textbook or a traditional review article while a foreground question will either be fortuitously answered by a systematic review or, more likely, by a randomized controlled trial or similarly focused study. Thompson (1997) observed that, for patient-specific questions, physicians most often seek medical facts or medical opinions. Stavri (1996) classified questions into 'quantification' questions which tend to be asked under urgent conditions and 'verification' questions which tend to be asked when the least amount of information is presented.

Focusing the question

The first stage of EBM is to convert information needs from practice into 'focused, structured questions' (Sackett and Rosenberg, 1995). The goal of this primary stage, variously called *focusing* or *formulating your question* (Richardson et al, 1995), is to convert a precise, yet possibly vaguely expressed, information need into an 'answerable question' thus shaping the subsequent search strategy and selection of materials. Questions most commonly centre on therapy ('Is the treatment of interest more effective in producing a desired outcome than an alternative?') or diagnosis ('How likely is a patient who has a particular symptom, sign or test result to have a specific disorder?'). They might also involve other domains such as aetiology ('What has caused the disorder?'), prognosis ('What is the probability of a specific outcome in this patient?'), cost-effectiveness ('Which of two available treatments or procedures yields the greatest benefit per pound spent?') or even the interpretation of clinical findings ('What is blood in the urine likely to signify?').

The four elements that make a question focused comprise an 'anatomy' of a question which include the Patient or Population, an Intervention or Exposure, measurable Outcomes and, optionally, a Comparison (Richardson et al, 1997).This is often called the PIOC framework or the 'anatomy' of a clinical question. These elements can be variously defined as follows:

- *Patient or population* answers the question '*Who* is the particular treatment or diagnostic test or other process of care being delivered to?'. This will either be an individual *patient* (for clinicians) or *group of patients* or a *population* (for those involved in an audit, management or public health context).
- *Intervention* answers the question '*What* is the procedure, agent or manoeuvre that is being administered to either a single patient or a group of patients?' Interventions can be therapeutic, diagnostic, managerial, organizational or behavioural and are characterized as being planned activities, eg administering a particular drug.
- *Exposure*: This also answers the question *what?* but, in this case '*What* is happening to the patient or population?' The *exposure* is alternative to an intervention in that it is either the unplanned or unintentional action of a harmful agent, eg carbon monoxide, or the accidental adverse effect or side-effect of an intervention that has otherwise been planned, eg thromboembolism as a result of taking a contraceptive pill.

- *Outcome(s)*. These answer the question '*How* is the effect of an intervention or an exposure on a patient or population actually measured?' Outcomes can either be actual endpoints or targets in themselves, eg smoking cessation, or they can be surrogate endpoints, eg biochemical confirmation of absence of nicotine, that indicate progress towards a particular target or goal.
- *Comparison*: This helps to answer the questions '*How much better?*' and '*Better than what?*' In each case the comparison provides a frame of reference (eg an alternative intervention, a different method of administration or pattern of dosage or a different timescale) against which the outcomes might be measured.

This technique was originally proposed as a self-help tool for clinicians, most specifically medical students (Booth, 1995). It has been found to translate easily to a number of other contexts including nursing (Flemming, 1998), the therapy professions (Booth and Madge, 1998), mental health (Geddes, 1999) and healthcare purchasing (Dixon et al, 1997).

Several information services have redesigned their search request forms to take these methods into account. These include the Aggressive Research Intelligence Facility (ARIF) in the West Midlands and the Primary Care Sharing the Evidence (PRISE) project in Anglia and Oxford. The British Library-funded Automated Retrieval of Clinically Relevant Evidence (AuRACLE) project compared structured request forms with unstructured forms. They found statistically significant correlations demonstrating that the structured form encouraged a more complex search strategy and that clinical requests handled by the structured form retrieved fewer items, but a higher proportion of relevant ones. Practice necessitates that librarians can handle the full range of clinical questions within a three or four-part structure; not merely the more 'classical' therapy and diagnosis question types but also those for aetiology, prognosis, clinical quality and cost-effectiveness (Hicks et al, 1998).

Implications of formulating the question for information retrieval

Formulating the question offers a new clinician-friendly method of explaining information retrieval. Snowball (1997) has shown that the process of setting a clear search question, breaking it into search concepts, and then trying out a range of search terms for each major concept, fits elegantly into an EBM-initiated PIOC framework. Indeed there are clear parallels between the two processes. Firstly dissecting a question into the PIOC anatomy bears a clear relation to Boolean logic (AND, OR, NOT) making it easier to explain these unfamiliar concepts in user education sessions. The intersect *between* elements of the anatomy, for example, Patient and Intervention corresponds to the Boolean term 'AND'. The conjunction of terms *within* an individual element (eg synonyms such as learning disabilities and learning difficulties) corresponds to the Boolean 'OR'.

Formulating a question improves the precision of the search strategy. Clinical questions demand very precise answers and so, if this level of detail is not present in the abstract, the searcher runs a risk of retrieving zero results. It is likely that the growth of full-text databases and journals will make this technique even more valuable. Although narrowing searches in this way may run the risk of missing relevant records, and of losing the serendipity that broad search results can yield, developments in database design (for example the 'Records Like This' feature of the National Library of Medicine's PubMed MEDLINE interface) minimize these effects.

PIOC and abstracts

The focused question is clearly useful in clarifying clinicians' information requests. A second and related line of thought is that this technique can enhance the information content of a document (Harbourt et al, 1995). Increasingly structured abstracts are being used to organize descriptions of research studies within a meaningful framework. Journals such as the *British Medical Journal*, the *Journal of the American Medical Associaton* and the *Annals of Internal Medicine* now insist that research studies are accompanied by abstracts containing subjects, interventions, outcomes and a description of the study design, including any comparators (Haynes, 1987; Haynes et al, 1990). Secondary evidence based journals such as *Evidence Based Medicine, Evidence Based Nursing, Evidence Based Healthcare* and *Evidence Based Mental Health* have replaced the objectives section of their structured abstracts with a structured clinical question that the research was primarily designed to answer (Richardson, 1998). Value-added databases such as the Database of Abstracts of Reviews of Effectiveness (DARE), Best Evidence and the Cochrane Library (all of which are described more fully elsewhere) use structured abstracts to speed up the match between originating question and the potential source of an answer.

Again, a study from the British Library AuRACLE project found that structuring abstracts according to the PIOC anatomy improved the precision of searches for clinical questions when compared with unstructured single paragraph abstracts (Booth and O'Rourke, 1997). However the same study found considerable variation in the ways that these individual components might be described, eg the Population field might equally be labelled 'Participants' or 'Subjects'.

Implications of focusing the question for the role of the health information professional

Work on focusing the question has concentrated on the 'user need' end of the information chain while structuring abstracts, in both journals and databases, approaches the problem from the 'information source' end. These two approaches are complementary. Structuring in retrieval, as exemplified by the AuRACLE project, lies at the interface between these two components. Using focused questions for end-user training (Snowball, 1997) is a further related, yet conceptually distinct, application.

Why is the context of the structured question so important? There are at least two reasons: first, the types of structured question and indeed proportion of each typology (eg diagnosis, therapy etc) may be different in different contexts. For example, there is an attrition in questions from the two for every three patients seen as experienced by the clinician, to those pursued to any information source, to those that are pursued to the library, to those suitable for MEDLINE (McKibbon et al, 1995). Very little is known about how and why questions get lost along the way.

At the same time libraries receive a large proportion of non-patient-related questions that are completely inappropriate for the PIOC structure. These may involve interpersonal, educational or management issues, not concerned with effectiveness *per se*. In responding to the stimulus provided by EBM, healthcare librarians are becoming increasingly aware of the importance of understanding the clinical context in which questions are generated.

Conclusion

This chapter has demonstrated that the traditional 'art' of conducting a reference interview using carefully chosen questions has been invested with new importance as a result of the EBM movement. It has examined the usefulness of a structured approach to question formulation against a backdrop of published literature looking at clinicians' questioning behaviour. It concludes by acknowledging the different contexts in which questions might be posed and the limitations of a structured approach to non-clinical questions. An understanding of the usefulness and limitations of such an approach is clearly seen to be a prerequisite for the successful management and exploitation of the knowledge base of healthcare.

Key points

- The emergence of evidence based medicine (EBM) has resulted in renewed interest in the questioning behaviour of clinicians.
- Questions can be divided into 'background' questions (characterized by a lack of prior knowledge or experience of a particular condition) and 'foreground' questions (which relate to a need for advanced decisions between treatment options).
- The four elements that comprise an 'anatomy' of a question are the Patient or Population, an Intervention or Exposure, measurable Outcomes and, optionally, a Comparison.
- Focused questions can be used in literature search instruction, information retrieval and the structuring of abstracts and improve the precision of retrieval results at the expense of sensitivity.

16
Selecting appropriate sources

Andrew Booth

Introduction

Users of the knowledge base face a bewildering array of information sources. Never before have the domains of 'information' (the material used to answer clinical queries) and 'information about information' (the bibliographical details used to locate source material) been in such close juxtaposition. This is illustrated by so many formats of information delivery: in hypertext links from bibliographic references to cited material; in the increasing numbers of full-text collections and compact library products; and, epitomized by the Cochrane Library, a hybrid product placing full-text reviews alongside a register of trials. Where can the user turn for assistance in navigating the ever more complex path to answering clinical questions? How indeed can the health LIS professional choose between conflicting sources to use time and effort most effectively?

This chapter aims to assist the user in selecting the most appropriate source, or range of sources, for the question in hand. It begins with the concept of an information-seeking protocol by which information professionals define a preferred route for particular types of enquiry determined by importance and likely yield of available sources. It surveys the range of primary, secondary and tertiary sources available for answering users' information needs before discussing strengths and weaknesses of each type of source. For example, a consideration of the usefulness of paper based journals discusses limitations such as publication bias and the merits of the peer review process. This evaluative approach leads to consideration of solutions to identified limitations, for example, those of full-text electronic journals and electronic archives of unpublished papers. The chapter includes an overview of studies indicating which sources practitioners, researchers and librarians actually use.

Information-seeking protocols

Recently a number of librarians have experimented with 'information protocols' or 'information pathways'. These work on two levels: first, at the macro level by helping the user to judge which sources suit which type of question (eg a diagnosis question) based on potential yield; secondly, at the micro level in charting the decision processes for a particular topic or subject area. In this latter case they correspond to the clinical algorithms used in selecting a diagnosis or treatment for a particular patient. Information protocols, and even more so information algorithms, are very much in their infancy. To date attention has focused on the 'absolute' content of sources and not on relative factors such as their ease of use and availability. For example, it is not useful to place a source in the front line for a particular type of an enquiry if it has an interface that neither user nor intermediary can master. However in these days of increasing 'disintermediation' such protocols or algorithms have tremendous potential:

- to provide easily comprehensible assistance to help users select sources of relevance to a specific enquiry
- to assist in teaching a logical approach to retrieval for a particular topic
- to make explicit decisions taken by an experienced health librarian
- to pass on enquiry-handling skills to junior and non-professional staff
- to arrive at consensus among groups of health information professionals working in a specific subject area, and finally
- to assist in the development of expert searching systems (Cimino et al, 1993).

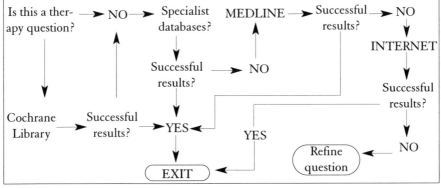

Fig. 16.1   *A simplified information protocol*

A simplified information protocol is shown in Figure 16.1. Answering a specific clinical question from information sources in a library is a complex process that challenges mapping in such a simplistic manner. However, these protocols equate well with the health information professional who, once suitably experienced, draws on past experience and knowledge to match new enquiries to those previously encountered. It is also an important stepping stone in progress towards evidence based librarianship.

To map subject queries in this manner requires a number of discrete components:

- a knowledge of the patterns of *information need*, and potential information need, of the user community (eg what types of questions are my users asking and what are the main categories into which they fall?)
- a comprehensive awareness of available sources, their *coverage*, their strengths and weaknesses and their relative merits when faced with choices between sources (eg what items are covered in a database, how are they selected and how even is the coverage across subject areas?)
- a knowledge of patterns of use for particular types of resource and their *acceptability* to users (eg how do doctors use electronic information retrieval systems and what is their preferred order of using different types of resource?)
- a clear understanding of the specific *characteristics of a particular subject area* or topic and how it might differ from any perceived 'norm' (eg what particular requirements, if any, does the literature of diagnostic radiology impose compared with radiotherapy and how should this affect selection of sources?).

The interrelationship of this chapter with others is clear. Issues around the information needs of users are flagged up in Chapter 2. The characteristics of different sources are examined in Chapters 9 and 11 while the importance of obtaining an accurate picture of the enquiry (Chapter 15) and filtering results for relevance and quality (Chapter 18) is incontrovertible.

What are some broad principles of source selection?

1   *Currency* requires that 'live' Internet based versions of databases such as MEDLINE (which include the PRE-MEDLINE fast tracking service for core journal citations) via PubMed or Internet Grateful Med are given pri-

ority over CD-ROM, which can be up to four months behind. On the other hand some databases, eg the Cochrane Library, are no more up to date in their Internet version than in their CD-ROM version.

2   *Specialism* requires that a librarian prioritizes databases with a particular scope or emphasis over more general sources. For example, Cancerlit takes priority over MEDLINE for a cancer enquiry as would HealthSTAR for a health technology enquiry. The Cochrane Library now contains more randomized controlled trials than MEDLINE and so is the first port of call for therapy questions which utilize this optimal design.

3   *Coverage* requires that a librarian be aware of the merits of particular data sources. This is not the same as scope (as defined by the database) but is more pragmatic knowledge. So, for example, EMBASE has stronger coverage of pharmaceutical interventions than MEDLINE while Science Citation Index has more comprehensive indexing of correspondence in journals than MEDLINE.

4   *Added value* requires that certain sources be selected because they offer additional features over a basic bibliographic record. Examples are the Database of Abstracts of Reviews of Effectiveness (DARE) and Best Evidence which offer appraised summaries of key articles to be consulted even when source journals are likely covered on MEDLINE.

5   *Facilities* are a specific form of added value relating to functionality and content. For example, the facility to link basic MEDLINE bibliographic records to full-text articles impacts on source selection. So too the Cochrane Library Internet version is more basic than its established CD-ROM counterpart where greater sophistication of the interface gives it pre-eminence.

McKibbon, Richardson and Walker-Dilks (1999) demonstrate how such factors work at a practical question-answering level. By taking into account these and other factors, the healthcare LIS professional can develop locally relevant protocols for information seeking.

Patterns of information need

This section maps major features of the information needs landscape and different approaches that have been taken. Two important observations can be made:

1   Certain professions have been researched more thoroughly than others. For example Haug (1997) conducted a meta-analysis summarizing 20 years of studies on physicians' preferences for information sources. He reviews 12 studies published between 1978 and 1992, categorizing and ranking the physicians' preferred information sources reported in each study. Despite an oversimplistic analysis where he aggregates and counts the frequencies of the top six preferences, together with associated first and second preferences, the results indicate that physicians prefer to obtain information from journals and books. They will often consult colleagues to answer clinical and research questions.

2   As Urquhart states in Chapter 2, information needs for clinical problems have distinguishing features that set them apart from questions arising in the context of research and education.

Our understanding of clinicians' patient-related needs was greatly extended by the Rochester study (Marshall, 1992), in which 208 respondents in the Rochester area (New York) requested information related to a current clinical case and were asked to evaluate its impact on patient care. 80% said that they probably or definitely handled some aspect of patient care differently than they would have handled it otherwise. They reported changes in diagnosis (29%), choice of tests (51%), choice of drugs (45%), reduced length of hospital stay (19%) and advice given to the patient (72%). Information provided by the library helped avoid hospital admission (12%), patient mortality (19%), hospital-acquired infection (8%), surgery (21%) and additional tests or procedures (49%). Osheroff and Bankowitz (1993) looked at 50 questions from eight clinically active internists and medical subspecialists (between three and 11 per participant). Using a workstation with electronic texts, participants satisfactorily answered 20 questions (40% of the total), partially answered 16 questions (32%), and did not obtain useful information for 14 questions (28%). Significantly, however, participants found answers outside the workstation to eight of the 14 questions (57%) not answered by using the software. The most common question topic was drug information (16 questions, or 32% of the total).

Following in the steps blazed by Rochester, two studies from Aberystwyth – the Value project (Urquhart and Hepworth, 1995c) and the EVINCE project (Urquhart and Davies, 1997) have further contributed to our understanding, particularly in their UK context. These studies have been covered in detail in Chapter 2.

Gorman, Ash and Wykoff (1994) examined whether 'native' questions asked by primary care practitioners could be answered using the journal literature. The average total time spent searching for and selecting articles for each question was 43 minutes and the average cost per question searched was $27.37. For 28 questions (56%), clinicians judged the material relevant; for 22 questions (46%) the information provided a 'clear answer' to their question. They expected information to impact on their patient in 19 (40%) cases and on themselves or their practice in 24 (51%) cases.

Studies classifying information need

Several studies categorize or classify types of information need. Florance (1992) analysed 60 questions, based on actual online search requests and identified four contexts in which literature searching could contribute to patient care: pre-diagnostic assessment, diagnosis, treatment choice, and learning. She concludes that clinical problem-solving requires a blend of declarative and procedural knowledge, but that procedural knowledge is either absent from the journal literature or, at the very least, difficult to identify. Dee and Blazek (1993) reconstructed patient care questions from rural physicians' patient charts. Of the questions they came up with, 75% were on treatment, 14.7% on diagnosis, 8.3% on aetiology, and 2.1% on the psychological aspects of disease. Ely and colleagues (Ely et al, 1999) conducted an observational study of 103 family doctors in Iowa and attempted to characterize their information needs by collecting their questions and classifying them according to question type. Although it is difficult to make comparisons across very different studies (Dee and Blazek = absolute percentages, Ely et al = Top ten categories, Urquhart and Hepworth = non-exclusive categories) a similar pattern sees domination of therapy and diagnosis questions. The predominance of therapy over diagnosis is by a factor of between two and five times across three studies from three continents. Table 16.1 summarizes the three studies.

Table 16.1 *Summary of types of questions originating from doctors' information needs*

	Dee & Blazek (1993)	Ely et al (1999)	Urquhart & Hepworth (1995c)
Staff group	Rural physicians (US)	Family doctors (Aus)	Doctors (UK)
THERAPY	**75.0%**	**(28%)**	
Dosage of drug		8%	
Management of disease		7%	
Treatment of disease		7%	
Drug of choice		3%	
Drug indications		3%	
Identification of alternative therapies			35%
Improved quality of life for patient and/or family			33%
Confirmation of proposed therapy			32%
Minimization of risks of treatment			27%
Revision of treatment plan			25%
DIAGNOSIS	**14.7%**	**(12%)**	
Presence of disease or condition		4%	
Is test indicated?		4%	
Cause of test finding		4%	
Recognition of abnormal or normal condition			36%
Differential diagnosis			31%
Choice of diagnostic test			22%
AETIOLOGY	**8.3%**	**(9%)**	
Cause of symptom		9%	
PSYCHOLOGICAL EFFECTS	**2.1%**		
AUDIT OR STANDARDS OF CARE			26%
LEGAL OR ETHICAL ISSUES			16%

Challenging some assumptions

In looking for patterns of information need it should not be assumed that a professional group is homogenous enough to be a unit for analysis (eg 'doctors'). Several studies have shown significant differences in information behaviour within groups. Woolf and Benson (1989) found information needs of house staff differed significantly from faculty physicians across a number of dimensions. House staff more frequently needed information for patient care and preferred the use of textbooks and handbooks as information sources. Faculty more frequently needed information for activities unrelated to patient care and placed greater importance on basic science information.

Neither should it be assumed that the library is the first port of call. As mentioned in Chapter 15, a large number of questions are filtered off without finding their way to a formal information service. Veenstra (1992) showed that physicians generally research a question prior to presenting it to the librarian. This was true even when a clinical medical librarian (CML) was readily available. Nevertheless the CML provided house officers with information that affected patient care (defined as diagnosis, diagnostic tests or treatment) between 40% and 59% of the time. Wildemuth et al (1994) found that users often prejudge the types of questions to ask a librarian according to their expectations. First-year medical students were asked to imagine that they had access to a medical reference librarian and a toxicologist. Students were more likely to address questions on the identity of a toxin and supporting references to the hypothetical librarian and more likely to ask the toxicologist about symptoms and treatment.

Coverage of sources

Tables 16.2 and 16.3 (pages 216–7) give some comparative information about the different kinds of sources and list key examples of each.

Journals

Scientific journals have traditionally published primary research, often of variable quality and written primarily by researchers for researchers. Researchers collect data and produce information, but for many users the information that is published in scientific journals is not particularly helpful: it is often biased (NHS Information Authority, 1999a), with the bias being very difficult to detect

(NHS Information Authority, 1999b). Interpretation may require sophisticated skills in critical appraisal while information may not be expressed in the way most useful to users. For example, results may be presented as relative risks, whereas many users would also like to know absolute risk and benefit. In the context of evidence based healthcare, advocates recommend that, in view of the vast quantity of the primary research base and its rate of increase, the primary literature should be accessed only after attempting to find the evidence from systematic reviews. However, questions addressed by reviews tend to be broader than those required for clinical practice and the clinician will often gravitate to primary research. Traditional review articles and articles containing tables and graphs are more likely to be important for teaching than for a specific aspect of patient care (Sievert et al, 1996).

Peer review

One of the purported strengths of the scientific journal is the peer review process. However recent history has seen increased understanding of this process leading to a number of misgivings (Smith, 1997). Eldredge (1999) has documented five fundamental variations between journals:

- the extent of 'peer review'
- the point at which decisions are made
- blinding practices
- acceptance rates
- guidelines stating editors' expectations of reviewers.

It is therefore difficult to relate the peer review process *per se* to journal quality. Wood (1998) has extended the debate to electronic peer review by looking at the eLib Electronic Submission and Peer Review (ESPERE) project.

Publication bias

Publication bias, that is 'the tendency of investigators to submit, and of reviewers and editors to accept, manuscripts for publication based on the direction or strength of study findings' (Dickersin et al, 1992), has commanded an inordinate amount of attention over the last decade. While undoubtedly an issue for those producing systematic reviews, it is something of a red herring to clinical users of the literature. In truth, so many biases are associated with the uptake of research findings (eg bias in selecting and citing references, bias in deciding which journals to submit manuscripts to, bias in selecting which journals the library will stock, bias in deciding which journals will be included in a database, bias in deciding which journals to read, and bias in deciding to which articles and authors to give credence) that it is artificial to single out just one or two.

An immense amount of effort is expended in addressing publication bias. Examples include the electronic preprint services, such as Netprints (Delamothe et al, 1999) set up by the *British Medical Journal*, trials registers (Horton and Smith, 1999), the trend to fuller publication and the opportunity (in both the *British Medical Journal* and Cochrane Library) to submit instant comment or criticism. None of these techniques makes journal articles easier to read or comprehend. However improved search engines and retrieval facilities may make the paragraph the unit of information delivery rather than the journal article.

Electronic journals

It may seem artificial to treat electronic journals separately from paper based ones yet we still know very little about readers' use and preferences in relation to electronic journals. The SuperJournal project, though in an academic and cross-disciplinary context, supplies some initial assumptions (Norman and Hibbott, 1999). Users' requirements focused on accessibility, a wide range of journals, easy searching/browsing, links to other primary and secondary sources and a back-file of issues. Dawson (1999) used the BUBL Journals Service to measure usage of electronic journals and suggests that browsing, reading and searching may require different means of access. A distinction should be made between journals used for research and reference and those for current awareness and casual browsing.

Full-text searching is very powerful, particularly as it can retrieve items from words in a paragraph or in a citation from the references. Effectiveness of full-text sources is still constrained, however, by the ability of users to utilize a retrieval interface effectively. Studies of full-text retrieval have shown readers miss relevant articles because search strategies are too restrictive or because they overlook natural language variants.

Table 16.2 *Advantages and disadvantages of different types of resource*

Type of resource	Advantages	Disadvantages
Textbooks		Expensive
		Time lag to production
Electronic textbooks	Updateable	Require equipment
Journals		Expensive
		Publication bias
		Unhelpful structure
Electronic journals	Non-location dependent	Lack of specificity
		of search interfaces
	Multiple retrieval points	Quality of graphics
		Insecurity about
		archival function
Secondary journals	Explicit selection criteria	Patchiness of coverage
	Added-value of appraisal	Delay in publication
		Limited amount of
		detail
Handbooks	Portable	Limited detail
CD-ROMs	Cheap to produce	Require equipment
Internet		Delays in downloading
		Complex to navigate

Table 16.3 *Examples of each principal type of resource*

Type of resource	Examples
Textbooks	*Bailey and Love's Textbook of Surgery*
	Davidson's Principles and Practice of Medicine
Electronic textbooks	*Scientific American Medicine*
	UptoDate
Journals	*Annals of Internal Medicine* (also electronic TOC plus some articles)
	British Medical Journal (also fully electronic)
	Journal of the American Medical Association (also fully electronic)
	Lancet (also fully electronic)
	New England Journal of Medicine (also fully electronic)

cont.

Table 16.3 *continued*

Type of resource	Examples
Electronic journals	*Online Journal of Knowledge Synthesis in Nursing*
	Online Journal of Current Clinical Trials
Secondary journals	*ACP Journal Club*
(covered in detail in	*Evidence Based Healthcare*
Chapter 19)	*Evidence Based Medicine*
	Evidence Based Nursing
Handbooks	*Clinical Evidence* (updated 6-monthly)
	Oxford Handbook of Clinical Specialities
CD-ROMs	*AIDS Compact Library*
	Cochrane Library
	Oxford Textbook of Medicine
	WHO Library of Reproductive Health
Internet	*Medscape*

Books

Textbooks consistently appear high in lists of users' preferred sources. Cogdill and Moore (1997) looked at first-year medical students' information needs and the information resources they used to answer a clinical scenario and found MEDLINE and textbooks as the most popular resources. Cullen (1997) investigated three major information sources (textbooks, colleagues and medical specialists) used by family practitioners in New Zealand. Thirty-four practitioners rated these information sources for clinical decision-making against five criteria: availability, searchability, understandability, credibility and applicability. Textbooks were consulted most frequently, but were rated less valuable than colleagues and specialists as a source of information. D'Alessandro et al (1999) carried out a prospective, descriptive study using a modified critical incident technique to gather data from on-call radiology residents. Residents sought answers to 138 of the 182 questions (76%) by using a wide variety of resources, with staff members and textbooks being the most common. D'Alessandro et al's study was consistent with an earlier report from Woolf and Benson (1989) who found the most commonly used sources of information were again textbooks and colleagues.

In the context of evidence based healthcare, it may take years for an effective intervention to be mentioned, let alone recommended, in a textbook. An oft-cited instance, the study by Antman et al (1992), reports delays of at least ten years between evidence of the effectiveness of thrombolytic therapy appearing and its inclusion in textbooks. In line with such limitations, Burdick et al (1993) found that the literature of internal medicine cited an average of 88% serial references and 12% monographs while physicians on ward rounds cited 89.5% serials and 10.5% monographs to student teams. Although physicians make heavy use of textbooks for their own reference purposes they seem to feel it more important to use journal literature in teaching or in academic communication. It will be interesting to see whether, with the growth of evidence based medicine, this trend is accentuated even further, or indeed whether secondary sources such as *Clinical Evidence* and the evidence based journals initiate a shift to yet another preferred source.

CD-ROM services

MEDLINE and other bibliographic sources are given great emphasis by librarians as sources of evidence to answer clinical questions. However they have two major limitations: they provide indicative information in the form of abstracts without necessarily providing full answers and they can take almost 30 minutes to obtain a satisfactory answer (Haynes et al, 1990; Chambliss and Conley, 1996).

Then there are the idiosyncrasies and complexities of database indexing policies. Wakiji (1997) used a bibliometric analysis to determine the extent to which the references cited by two core physiotherapy journals were covered by the primary indexing sources. MEDLINE rated highest as the indexing tool of choice for these 109 journal references.

The Internet

There has been very little published research on the use of the Internet by health professionals in practice, although much effort has been expended in speculation and discussion. Farmer and Richardson (1997a, b) have looked at the potential of the Internet, and other networked information resources, to improve access to information for trained nurses working in remote areas. A questionnaire survey of UK postgraduate centres, conducted in September 1997 by Jordaan and Jones (1999), asked participants to rate various reasons for having Internet access. Top of the list came having access to latest research information, then support for evidence based medicine, then information not available in the printed information and fourth, formal continuing medical education. There is a need for much more research, not only on why users wish to use the Internet, but also in how they use it and whether they find it useful.

Patterns of use and acceptability to users

As mentioned above, relevance of sources is not measured simply in terms of coverage of a particular topic area. Hersh (1993) has separated relevance factors into 'topical' and 'situational'. Topical relates to the subject content and situational to the 'impact of the system on the user'. Johnson, McKinin and Sievert (1992) give a good example of the importance of 'situational' factors: 'A nursing student writing a five-page paper on gastric bypass would define a quality article differently than a surgeon preparing to perform the procedure.' The same team (Sievert et al, 1996) later looked at those factors beyond relevance that influence a clinician's decision to satisfy an information need with one article in preference to another. Factors influencing the decision of clinicians included evidence based criteria such as methodological rigour, but also non-evidence based features such as the identity of the authors and their institutional affiliations. Other factors included document types and applicability, and the population studied. These factors will determine preferential selection of sources, for example, in prominence accorded to evidence based databases such as *Best Evidence*, but also in preferences for national sources where available. Thompson (1997) found that primary care physicians required that information resources for answering clinical questions should be readily available, familiar, and quick to use. They should offer opportunities for lifelong learning and require a minimum of time, effort and expense.

Another factor influencing health information users' preferences with regard to sources relates to their familiarity and degree of comfort with computer based resources. Short (1999) found that computer ownership is inversely related to years in practice. The shorter the physicians' years in practice the more likely they were to own a computer. Although entertainment was the predominant use for their CD-ROM (52.6%), medical textbooks (44.9%), literature searching software (25.6%), drug information (17.9%), continuing medical education (15.4%), and journals on CD-ROM (11.5%) all figured prominently. Such patterns can inform the development of information protocols. If, for example, there is widespread familiarity among a user group with CD-ROM textbooks, their enhanced retrieval capabilities might be a reason to give them greater emphasis than printed counterparts. If the converse is true then electronic textbooks might be relegated to a less prominent place in the protocol or, in the case of a particularly unfriendly interface, omitted altogether.

Characteristics of a particular subject area

There are a number of ways to identify the characteristics of a particular subject area. The most common is to use bibliometric studies. Walcott (1999) describes how they attempted to identify core journals in diagnostic medical sonography and determine how well these were indexed by MEDLINE, EMBASE/Excerpta Medica, and CINAHL. The analysis suggests that echocardiography, a special area of diagnostic medical sonography, is indexed much more completely by MEDLINE and EMBASE/Excerpta Medica than by CINAHL. As part of the same project Wakiji (1997) identified core journals in physical therapy by analysing cited references from *Physical Therapy* and *Archives of Physical Medicine and Rehabilitation* between 1991 and 1993. In this study, 14 journals were found to supply one-third of all references studied with 95 journals providing an additional third of the references.

Conclusion

Although the choice of sources is large, we are starting to see the development of an evidence base around factors which should influence delivery and exploitation of sources. Informed by a knowledge of the sources that users want, what they cover and how they are likely to be used, the health information professional can not only ensure the availability of those resources but also that they actually will be well used by their users.

Key points

- The information protocol can be valuable in formulating explicit searching strategies and in developing clear end-user instruction programmes.
- The medical profession's information needs have been well researched but other professions have received comparatively little attention.

- Textbooks, journals and colleagues seem to be the preferred sources of information, but each of these has limitations.
- Users' preferences for information sources depend upon factors such as familiarity and availability as well as more objective characteristics such as study design and sample size.
- Profound differences in information patterns exist even between the literature of closely associated specialties and librarians must develop a knowledge of the characteristics of those subject fields that they are most likely to encounter.

17
Searching the databases

Louise Falzon

Introduction

Health information professionals have long been the acknowledged experts in the field of literature searching. When online databases and CD-ROMs first became available the cost of searching online and the inexperience of end-users required information professionals to carry out searches on their behalf. Now databases are widely available both in libraries, and in clinical settings on people's desktops, but are often underexploited by health professionals because they lack basic skills in how to search them. The current climate in which evidence based practice (EBP) requires researchers and practitioners to find evidence in the medical literature to support their decision-making, means that database searching is a requirement rather than an option. Moreover the emergence of systematic reviews to aid the EBP process demands greater sophistication in search methods to ensure retrieval of high-quality, relevant studies. The availability of medical databases such as MEDLINE across the Internet means that more and more people have access, but the variety and complexity of interfaces means that there is a lack of understanding of how to search them effectively.

This chapter begins by examining the search methods and techniques of database searching. It discusses the different ways of accessing the main biomedical database, MEDLINE, reviews how users search for information, and looks at the new developments in technology which are helping searchers navigate the plethora of information now available.

Subject searching approaches

Approaches to subject searching can be broadly divided into free-text and subject heading techniques. Each has its own merits and disadvantages and an optimal search strategy will, in practice, utilize both approaches. These approaches are considered below.

Free-text

Free-text searching allows for maximum retrieval of hits, as it will look for the given keywords in any part of the record: author field, title field, abstract or subject headings. This method will, however, give more irrelevant hits than a thesaurus or index based search which will only retrieve references with the word occurring in the subject heading field. Free text is, however, an easy means of searching in that the user can input their own terms without first having to find the appropriate subject heading. It is also flexible because the searcher can use techniques such as truncation to search on the stem of a word and pick up any variants. For example using the truncation symbol on MEDLINE ($ or alternatively *), inputting 'diseas$' would retrieve disease, diseases and diseased.

Other techniques possible in free-text searching are proximity searching where the searcher specifies that two terms must be within a certain number of terms of each other, eg 'heart adj disease' would find any references with the words heart and disease next to each other, whereas 'heart adj2 disease' would retrieve references where heart and disease are within two words of each other in either order.

Sometimes free-text searching is the only means available because a subject is too new to have been assigned a subject heading, eg 'clinical governance'. Another instance would be where a searcher only wanted articles in which their specific terms appeared, eg NHS where a searcher wants articles about the British National Health Service whereas the equivalent thesaurus term would include the health systems in other countries.

Thesaurus based

A thesaurus based search will give fewer, but more specific results. In this type of search you only retrieve records which have been assigned a specific subject heading. The example from MEDLINE in Figure 17.1 shows a record with several subject headings; these have been chosen from the list of MeSH (Medical Subject Headings).

Authors : Khunti K. Sorrie R. Jennings S. Farooqi A.
Title : Improving aspirin prophylaxis after myocardial infarction in primary care: collaboration in multipractice audit between primary care audit group and health authority.
Source : BMJ. 319(7205):297, 1999 Jul 31.
MeSH Subject Headings
   *Aspirin / tu [Therapeutic Use]
   Family Practice
   Female
   Human
   Male
   Medical Audit
   *Myocardial Infarction / pc [Prevention & Control]
   *Platelet Aggregation Inhibitors / tu [Therapeutic Use]
   Retrospective Studies
   Support, Non-U.S. Gov't

Fig.17.1   *A record with several subject headings*

Indexers at the National Library of Medicine (NLM) in America are responsible for devising and maintaining the list of MeSH headings which represent concepts in biomedical literature. Lowe and Barnett (1994) describe the process whereby each citation added is assigned the appropriate headings (usually ten to 12) to describe as accurately as possible the content of the article. MeSH headings may also be preceded by an asterisk to indicate the major focus of the article; headings without an asterisk represent a concept which is present, but which has less importance.

The degree to which subject headings are structured varies from one database to another. Some databases such as the Science Citation Index, despite assigning subject headings to its articles, do not have an index field from which to search. ASSIA (Applied Social Science Index and Abstracts) has an index of subject headings arranged alphabetically. More sophisticated databases such as MEDLINE and CINAHL have thesauri which group subject headings into a hierarchical tree of related terms, the most general term being at the top graduating to the most specific at the bottom. The thesaurus display will show the searcher broader, narrower and related terms to aid searching. For example:

Diseases
    Cardiovascular diseases
        Heart diseases
            Myocardial Ischemia
                Myocardial infarction

Sophisticated thesauri may also contain subheadings to make searches more specific. For example, searching for myocardial infarction as a MeSH heading on MEDLINE will offer a range of subheadings which could be applied, such as diagnosis, drug therapy, prevention and control and surgery.

Subject heading systems

Databases have different subject heading systems which make up either a straightforward alphabetical index or a more complex thesaurus. One of the most common systems used in biomedical databases is that of Medical Subject Headings (MeSH headings) as described above. MeSH headings are used by MEDLINE, HealthSTAR and the Cochrane Library to form their thesauri, as well as by some of the newer evidence based databases such as DARE (Database of Abstracts of Reviews of Effectiveness). Other databases employ their own subject headings systems. CINAHL, for example, is based on MeSH headings and employs the MeSH tree structure, but adds a specific nursing vocabulary, while EMBASE employs the EMTREE vocabulary, which like MeSH is arranged hierarchically, but reflects the strong pharmaceutical coverage of the database. EMBASE has two types of descriptor: the DE field contains all non-drug terms and the DR field contains 'terms specific to the Chemicals and Drugs facet of EMTREE' (from EMBASE help screen). Other controlled vocabularies such as SNOMED (Systematized Nomenclature of Medicine) and ICD (International Classification of Diseases) have been devised to provide consistent indexing of non-bibliographic databases, such as medical record systems.

Field searching

Field searching allows for records to be retrieved where the given keyword is located in a particular field, such as the title or the author. This may be used when trying to locate articles written by a particular author, or where the title of a paper is known, or the searcher wants their keywords to be found in the title of an article, making a search more specific than either a free-text or thesaurus search. Field searching can also be used to narrow down an initially broad search, eg searching the publication year or language of publication fields.

Citation searching

Databases which provide a list of references referred to in the original article (citations) enable the searcher to extend their search. Citations from a number of key articles can be followed up to yield a further set of articles and references. The Science Citation Index and Social Science Citation Index are both databases which allow searching in the citation field by author and name of journal.

Lateral searching

Lateral searching is a variant of citation searching. Beginning with one key article the searcher can follow the references from that article both backwards, ie the references which have been cited in the main article, and forwards, ie articles which cite the main one. This method enables the searcher to follow a given thread from its conception to conclusion.

These search methods all have their own strengths and weaknesses. Free text, as we have seen, is a flexible and comprehensive means of searching, but gives a higher proportion of irrelevant results. Using a thesaurus is a more precise means of searching and gathers together word variants and synonyms, but gives fewer results and can be inappropriate in some instances. Citation and lateral searching are both useful models for following a particular debate or specific theme, but would exclude relevant articles in the subject area which did not appear in any of the references cited. A school of argument could therefore possess its own corpus of literature, but fail to acknowledge its critics or opposing schools. Similarly field searching is strong when looking for very specific articles such as those written by the key authors in a particular area, or where terms appear only in the title of an article, but may miss many more relevant articles in which the terms appear in the abstract or subject heading.

Boolean operators and other means of combining searches

The three Boolean operators AND, OR and NOT enable the searcher to manipulate their search terms in order to produce the most relevant set of references possible.

The 'AND' operator combines two terms together and so locates any article which contains both terms within the same record. The more terms grouped together with the AND operator, the more specific the results.

Example: heart attack AND aspirin

The 'OR' operator retrieves any article which has either one term or the other in the record. This broadens out a search and is used when a term can be described in more than one way.

Example: myocardial infarction OR heart attack

It can also be used when the searcher wants to look for two separate terms.

Example: diet OR aspirin

The 'NOT' operator will exclude any record which contains an unwanted term. This will narrow down a search.

Example: myocardial infarction NOT beta-blockers

Boolean operators can be combined in very sophisticated formulae to retrieve a specific set of records.

Example: (myocardial infarction OR heart attack) AND (prevention NOT aspirin).

Some systems use methods other than Boolean logic to retrieve relevant documents. Relevance ranking is a means whereby the number of occurrences of the given terms in a document are counted. Results are then displayed with documents with the largest number of occurrences at the top and progressively less relevant as the count decreases. Fuzzy logic is also becoming more popular with the trend towards natural language searching; both of these concepts are described in more detail at the end of this chapter. Boolean was originally designed as a tool for librarians at a time when end-users had little or no database access, but as this situation changed the trend moved towards more user-friendly search methods, such as relevance ranking. The arrival of evidence based practice, however, has meant that searchers need to employ exacting methods of searching to find high-quality, highly relevant studies in order to answer focused clinical questions. Boolean has therefore been given a new lease of life, as it is currently the only means of manipulating search terms to the degree required.

Sensitive, specific and precise searches

Sensitive searches aim to retrieve the maximum number of citations from a database. This will usually be achieved using both free-text and subject searching and will capture every instance of the specified terms. This is alternatively referred to as recall. A sensitive search would be executed when there is likely to be a low number of relevant records on the database. In this case the searcher would want to find any records with the specified terms to ensure that all available records have been retrieved. It would also be appropriate when the subject itself is quite obscure and there has been little published on it, or when the concept is a new one and not yet indexed as a subject heading, eg clinical governance.

Specific searches aim to retrieve the most relevant citations. This would probably be achieved using a subject heading search so that only articles with specific subject headings assigned to them would be found. Alternatively the use of a named drug or product would also give specific results. A specific search would be carried out when there is a wealth of references on the subject and a sensitive search would give an unwieldy number of hits.

The objective for search relevance is precision, which McKibbon and Walker-Dilks (1995) have defined as 'the proportion of citations in a search that are relevant to the search question'.

Principles of designing a search strategy
Choice of appropriate database

An important part of the search strategy is deciding which databases to search, as this will ensure time is used effectively. If a searcher is unsure of which databases are the most relevant, advice should be sought from an expert familiar with the coverage of databases in the area under investigation. Knowing a little about the databases to be used will determine the terms and type of searches to be carried out. For example does the database have a thesaurus, or index of subject headings?

Careful planning of search terms including synonyms, alternative spellings and plurals

Once you have selected your databases, you will need to consider which terms to use and how best to retrieve relevant records. It is advisable to work out terms first together with any synonyms, alternative spellings and plurals so that they can be incorporated into search statements. If you are using a database with a thesaurus or index of subject headings, it is advisable to check either online or in the printed version the most relevant terms available along with any preferred or related terms.

Deciding scope

It is advisable before you begin searching to decide what your specific aims are. Is it important, for example, to have only very recent material? Is the type of study important? How many references do you aim to retrieve? These factors will all have a bearing on which databases you search and how you search them. If you have a specific requirement for publication year you can use the limit option to automatically retrieve only the relevant years. In the case of publication type many databases will have a limit option which will allow for this, or you could investigate filters (see Chapter 19). The number of records to be retrieved will influence your limits and scope and the way you search the database; a high number of records would be best served by a sensitive search, a low number by a specific search.

Strategies for dealing with too few or too many records

Even a well-planned search may not yield the number of references you intend. In many cases you will either retrieve too few or too many records and it is important to decide at the beginning what to do in either of these scenarios. In the case of too few records you will need strategies to broaden your search. For example if you have carried out a thesaurus search, you would probably change to free text to pick up more records. You may introduce new terms or remove any scoping limits you may have applied at the beginning of the search. If your search retrieves 0 hits the first thing is to check spellings and the logic of the search strategy. If this still retrieves 0 you may wish to drop one particular concept at a time to see where the over-restriction lies. The Centre for Evidence Based Medicine has an excellent website for finding evidence in the research literature, including a page on

how to broaden and narrow searches
http://cebm.jr2.ox.ac.uk/docs/searching.html#senspec.

Too many records can be dealt with by applying limits if none have been specified at the start. Using the thesaurus if you have not already done so, focusing rather than exploding, or applying subheadings will also reduce the number of hits.

Keeping record of searches

Whether searching one or more databases it is important to keep a record of the search strategies used. You may want to run the same search in more than one database, or you may want to amend a search. Furthermore there may be instances in which you need to demonstrate how you obtained your results, eg searching in support of a systematic review.

Allow plenty of time for both searching and obtaining information

Searching requires careful planning to retrieve the most relevant results, but even a well-planned search may give unexpected results. Where too few or too many records are retrieved the search will need to be amended. Sometimes this will be a cyclical process of searching, evaluating results, amending the search and beginning again. So plenty of time must be set aside in order to ensure the best results are obtained.

Furthermore, databases contain records from a great number of journals, usually from across the globe. Only a small proportion of records retrieved will be available locally. Searchers inevitably find that a proportion of the articles required will need to be ordered from another library, which can be a time-consuming task in itself.

Searching methods employed by practitioners, researchers and information workers in healthcare

As the number of health professionals using databases increases, interest has grown in the methods of searching they employ and how effective they are. A study by Sewell and Bevan (1976) found that the most common errors in searching were misspelled words and the misuse of the controlled vocabulary.

Walker et al (1991) examined 'unproductive searches' using Internet Grateful Med and found that the searchers had not constructed appropriate search strategies and had not used the search features effectively. More recently Wildemuth and Moore (1995) identified a number of 'missed opportunities' by a group of end-users, such as infrequent use of the limit function, rare use of 'or' and 'not' as Boolean operators, lack of manipulation of Boolean operators and failure to use the online thesaurus. However, 'the most common missed opportunity by far was the failure to exploit the controlled vocabulary, such as by substituting Medical Subject Headings (MeSH) terms for free-text terms or by exploding a MeSH term'. These findings illustrate the need for end-users to be educated in the principles of literature searching. This is supported by Rosenberg et al's study which compared the search results of two groups of students, one of which had had training and one which had not (Rosenberg et al, 1998). The trained group performed significantly better than the non-trained group.

In addition to education, the sophistication of searching systems offered by information resource units should not be ignored. Health professionals, however capable at searching, should not neglect the expertise offered by specialist information units. A review of studies on search behaviour (Hersh and Hickam, 1998) pointed to a number that revealed that, while end-users were satisfied with their results, information professionals identified flaws in their approach which resulted in lower recall and precision. Information professionals have a grounding in the construction of databases and an implicit understanding of retrieval methods, which enable them to achieve high levels of sophistication when searching. They also have knowledge of subject coverage and availability of a whole range of systems, and the experience of the different search techniques needed to exploit them, including skills in formulating the most pertinent search strategy for any given question. Indeed as a profession they are responsible for continually updating and developing knowledge in this area. Last, but not least, information resource units can advise on how to obtain the required material from a list of references.

MEDLINE

MEDLINE is the most comprehensive biomedical database, with records going back to 1966. It indexes approximately 3800 biomedical journals and currently holds about 9 million records. It is produced by the National Library of Medicine in the USA and its records are sold to numerous commercial vendors, of which Ovid and SilverPlatter are the most well known. The coverage includes medicine, nursing, dentistry, veterinary medicine and the pre-clinical sciences. Citations are produced by the NLM and International MEDLARS (Medical Literature Analysis and Retrieval System) partners and other cooperating professional bodies.

Individuals and organizations can subscribe to MEDLINE on CD-ROM or access it via the Internet. The software of both main providers (Ovid and SilverPlatter) allows for a highly sophisticated level of searching, employing features such as the thesaurus from which terms can be focused or exploded, wild-card and proximity searching, and limit facilities. The Internet version of each has links to full-text journal articles where available.

In 1997 the NLM launched a service giving free searching of MEDLINE via two Internet sites, Internet Grateful Med and PubMed. The US government's commitment to both freedom of information and providing health information to the public were the driving forces behind this initiative. A range of other sites also give access to parts of the MEDLINE database. Search functionality, charging policy and the number of records available vary between sites. Many also offer online document delivery services such as Lonesome Doc, where the user either has an account or can pay by credit card to have the document sent or faxed to them. Some of these services are briefly described below.

- PubMed gives free access to all of the MEDLINE database, plus PRE-MEDLINE which adds new records not yet assigned MeSH headings on a daily basis. It has been developed by the National Center for Biotechnology Information at the NLM and is part of the Entrez information retrieval system.
- Internet Grateful Med is also produced by the NLM and has free access to MEDLINE, but also to other databases such as AIDSLINE, AIDS-DRUGS, HealthSTAR, OLDMEDLINE (citations from 1960 to 1965) and TOXLINE.
- HealthGate has a similar range of databases to Grateful Med, but also gives access to CINAHL, for which registration is required; searching is free, but users are charged for records displayed in full.
- Avicenna is a commercial host and requires registration, but it is free and immediate. It provides free access to MEDLINE from 1990 onwards, as well as several other resources such as Outlines in Clinical Medicine (summaries of medical topics) and links to clinical trials.

- BioMedNet provides evaluation of selected MEDLINE records; articles are reviewed by experts and are tagged 'of special interest' or 'of outstanding interest'. Document delivery is provided via the British Library.

Hansen (1998) illustrates the differences between these and other free MEDLINE sites and discusses the varying levels of sophistication they allow in searching and how their search engines work, which may not be apparent to the novice user. There is also the highly regarded Dr Felix website which gives access to, and an evaluation of, the main providers. It is available at **http://www.docnet.org.uk/drfelix/**.

Ongoing advances and future directions in information retrieval in healthcare

As database features become more sophisticated, and with more people using them, *natural language* searching has emerged and is increasingly being investigated. This is particularly important given the growing number of full-text databases. Also as Pritchard-Schoch (1993) states, this is because of 'the dramatic drop in the cost of hardware, including the cost of memory. At the same time, the processing of speed of computers has accelerated exponentially.' Natural language involves asking the database a question as you would express it to another person, eg 'Can you find the link between aspirin and the risk of a second stroke?' Systems which use natural language searching are indexed in a different way to the standard bibliographic databases. Quint (1994) describes natural language as 'a complex series of algorithms to analyze statistical counts of terms (the number of terms in each document, frequency of terms in the document compared to frequency of terms in the database etc.). The more often a concept appears in a document, the greater weight it is given.' As Tomaiuolo and Packer (1998) have stated, 'Natural language searching is good for vague or broad questions. The searcher must be willing to tolerate less relevant and even unrelated material in the retrieved set.' Natural language systems are also easier for end-users, especially if they are not experienced searchers and have no skills in formulating search strategies. Another advantage which Tomaiuolo and Packer (1998) point out is that 'while Boolean searches are precise, natural language searches are comprehensive'.

Pritchard-Schoch (1993) expands on this by explaining that Boolean is an exact model of retrieval because retrieved items are ones which have complied with defined criteria; 'in general, the exact model works well for known-item searching and for bibliographic and field searching.'

Fuzzy logic was developed by Lotfi Zadeh of the University of California, Berkeley and is a system which aims to overcome the problem of answering questions which do not have a straightforward yes or no answer. In fuzzy logic truth values are given somewhere between 'completely true' and 'completely false'. In the theoretical definition of fuzzy logic, elements of a fuzzy set are given a value based on a scale of 0 to 1 to represent how true they are. In the example given by Korfhage (1997, 70) a set of tall people in an ordinary set might be defined as people being at least 6 feet tall, so anyone under this height would be excluded. In a fuzzy set each person would have a grade or 'degree of tallness'. For example a person who was 4ft 5in would have a grade close to 0.0 whereas someone who was 6ft 10in would have a grade close to 1.0. In terms of information retrieval, documents will be retrieved on the strength of the number of occurrences of the given terms and their variants.

As Korfhage (1997, 70) points out, the argument for fuzzy information retrieval is that 'the system (and often the user) can't accurately tell whether a given document will meet the information need. This uncertainty is modelled in a "fuzzy" evaluation of the document with respect to the query.'

The need for consistency across all health and biomedical databases has been recognized for some time. As Wright et al (1999) say, 'Biomedical information is scattered among many information sources, each of which has to be searched separately, often using different search techniques. Furthermore, these sources are organized and indexed differently, and often use widely divergent medical vocabularies.' The *Unified Medical Language System* (UMLS) has been developed by the National Library of Medicine to address this issue.

The aim of the project is 'to aid the development of systems that help health professionals and researchers retrieve and integrate electronic biomedical information from a variety of sources and make it easy for users to link disparate information systems, including computer-based patient records, bibliographic databases, factual databases and expert systems' (National Library of Medicine, 1999).

UMLS is made up of three Knowledge Sources: the Metathesaurus, the Specialist Lexicon and the Semantic Network. The Metathesaurus pulls together biomedical terms from about 50 different controlled language vocabularies and provides a way of linking terms to each other. The Specialist Lexicon provides information about words and phrases. The lexicon entry for each word, term or phrase includes syntactic category, and inflectional variation (singular and plural for nouns, conjugations of verbs and comparative and superlative for adjectives and adverbs). The current version of the lexicon contains 108,000 lexical records. The Semantic Network, according to McCray and Nelson (1995), 'provides a structure that encompasses and unifies all of these vocabularies (in the Metathesaurus) by virtue of its high level categories to which every Metathesaurus term is mapped.'

Conclusion

It can be seen from the above that health professionals find themselves at the crossroads of an information rich world. A large number of databases cover different aspects of healthcare and, as this chapter has demonstrated, many are available in different versions, exemplified by MEDLINE. There are a variety of approaches to searching, with different databases offering an array of search techniques from the very simple to the highly sophisticated. Database producers are employing new techniques such as fuzzy logic and natural language, making searching easier for lay users but increasing the complexity of their choice.

At the same time, access to information is being increasingly widened, due in large part to the Internet. Muir Gray and de Lusignan (1999) see the world wide web as something which has 'blown away the walls and doors of medical libraries, which once shielded medical knowledge from the public gaze' and which now permits access on a level previously available to information specialists only.

Health professionals may thus find themselves faced with the dilemma of having some basic search skills, and access to a bewildering array of databases to search, but the insecurity of not knowing which to choose and how best to search them. As we have also seen, some databases employ techniques of retrieving information which are not obvious to the inexperienced searcher. Information professionals have as great a role to play in advising on databases now as they have ever done because they understand the mechanisms of searching. Wildemuth and Moore (1995) stress that interfaces for novice and intermittent users should be different from those used by experienced searchers, but are often identical. Further research is required into search behaviour so manufacturers can continue to improve the design of end-user interfaces. Meanwhile health professionals should continue to draw upon the expertise of their information colleagues to fully exploit the knowledge available to support their practice. While the information revolution has provided, and will continue to provide, health workers with the knowledge base they need they can be reassured that they do not have to manage it alone.

Key points

- Evidence based practice means that searching is now a requirement, not an option.
- It is important that searchers become familiar with the underlying principles of literature searching, and the techniques required to effectively exploit databases.
- The expertise offered by information professionals should be used to complement, and not replace, user education in search skills.
- The availability of MEDLINE free on the Internet has opened up a whole new area of access to medical information.
- New developments in information retrieval such as fuzzy logic, natural language and the Unified Medical Language System make it easier for non-expert searchers to access health information.
- Further research is needed into search behaviour so that databases can develop in a manner appropriate to trends towards end-user searching.

18
Searching the Internet

Andrew Booth

Introduction

The 1990s were characterized by the appearance of thousands of networked information resources available to individuals and institutions with access to the Internet. Kassirer (1995) describes this phenomenon as the 'next transformation in the delivery of health care'. Initially improved access to healthcare information was heralded with great enthusiasm, but recent years have seen the injection of a more appropriate note of caution (Obst, 1998) – caveat surfer! (Silberg, Lundberg and Musacchio, 1997; Booth, 1998). Attempts now concentrate not simply on making information available via the world wide web but also in providing the tools and skills to evaluate and appraise materials (Jenkins, Grey-Lloyd and Hancock, 1998).

This chapter discusses approaches to systematic searching of the Internet. The concepts of free-text and index based Internet search engines are introduced and major examples of each discussed. Guidance will be provided on methods of effective searching of the Internet sources. The chapter will conclude with a discussion of how websites might be evaluated and the potential role for the health information professional in exploiting the Internet.

The role of the Internet

Simmons (1997) succinctly summarizes the limitations of the Internet thus:

*   its sheer size
*   the difficulty of finding exactly what you need on an ever-growing number of web pages
*   the sheer amount of information, mesmerizing new users who are

tempted to spend a disproportionate time looking
- the lack of quality information
- difficulties in identifying authors' identities.

Notwithstanding this cautionary note, there are three very good reasons to include the Internet in the knowledge base of healthcare. First, the Internet as a *delivery mechanism* provides access to a range of full-text and summary documents otherwise difficult or impractical to acquire. An example is the area of health technology assessment where evaluations of new or high-cost technologies conducted in Australia, North America or the countries of Europe and previously published as grey literature, are now available to healthcare organizations world-wide. Secondly, the Internet as a *source of intelligence* acts either as an 'early warning system' or, alternatively, as a source of valuable supplementary data. Again, new drugs or biotechnology products can now be identified far in advance of their appearance in the international marketplace. Finally, and most importantly, the Internet as a *source of value-added information* assists in identification, critical appraisal and synthesis of disparate, and even conflicting, research evidence.

Getting started

With an estimated 100,000 Internet sites dealing with health (Eysenbach, Ryoung Sa and Diepgen, 1999) it is clear that a systematic approach will need to be adopted. A number of authors attempt to systematize the process. Potter (1995) outlines a five-step approach to answering reference questions over the Internet: gather information and tools, learn the terminology, assemble a manual, write a strategy, and make bookmarks. Such an approach is rooted in mainstream reference work. MacCall (1997) describes a 'metastrategy for World-Wide Web information retrieval', analogous to the information protocol of Chapter 16, which makes distinctions between the context of the information need (anticipated versus unanticipated clinical information needs) and also between the available tools (WWW catalogs for retrieving websites and WWW databases for retrieving web pages). Littleton (1998) reviews several strategies for finding health information via the Internet. However, there are very few authors who actually try to describe both content *and* the sequence of a process to find information. Put very simply, an information-seeking process for locating information might use one or all of the following stages:

- use of medicine-specific search engines, eg OMNI, MedicalWorld Search
- use of general search engines or meta-search engines, eg Alta Vista, Hotbot, Lycos or Google, Inference Find, Copernic 2000
- use of databases or library catalogues, eg PubMed, Medical SUM search, Uncover, BMA Catalogue, BL OPAC
- use of resource lists, eg Netting the Evidence, Cambridge Public Health, Nursing and Healthcare
- use of discussion lists and archives, eg Mailbase, Liszt.

There are a number of reasons for using resources in the order listed above. First the search would start with specific, and usually evaluated, sources within the field of medicine. These would offer the prospect of a full-text 'answer' to the query in hand. General search engines too may supply a full-text solution but their yield, while being more sensitive (ie less likely to miss something relevant) is usually unevaluated. Meta-search engines broaden the coverage, but may lack the sophisticated search facilities of the individual search engine. Databases and library catalogues, particularly those of a subject-specific collection, may help in the identification of useful materials but will not necessarily help with regard to access. Resource lists, again those of a subject-specific nature, may potentially cover a topic of interest, but will require a large number of hypertext links to be followed. Finally discussion lists and their archives may yield highly relevant materials but their validity is subject to doubt. Notwithstanding this, their interactive function can be incredibly powerful.

Search engines

Medicine-specific search engines

In this chapter a distinction is made between resources offering direct access to clinical information (eg web pages), designated 'search engines' and usually indexed automatically using free-text terms, and those that offer pointers to information (eg books, publications, journal articles etc), designated 'databases and catalogues' and typically indexed using a recognized system of subject headings. In practice this distinction is arbitrary, as regards information content (an increasing number of databases offer a hybrid product such as appraised abstracts), resource content (a number of resources search both references and full-text products, eg the Cochrane Library) and indexing (some medical search engines use Medical Subject Headings).

The attraction of Internet resources that provide ready information in health-related topics is self-evident and both public sector and commercial Internet providers have made a foray into this market. OMNI is a UK based gateway to Internet resources in medicine, biomedicine, allied health, health management and related topics. It aims to provide comprehensive coverage of the UK resources in this area and access to the best resources worldwide (Welsh, 1997). The main catalogue, indexed using Medical Subject Headings (MeSH), contains over 4000 records describing quality biomedical Internet based resources. A review of OMNI and other discipline-specific gateways identified a need for a broader subject based approach and in spring 2000, a new gateway BIOME will build on the experiences, skills and content of the OMNI service while expanding coverage to all areas within the health and life sciences.

Medical World Search (Suarez, Hao and Chang, 1997) is a search engine for medical information on the Internet that uses the National Library of Medicine's Unified Medical Language System and a carefully selected but large database of medical sites. Other examples include Cliniweb International, which uses the hierarchical structure of MESH allied to the powerful retrieval capability of the Unified Medical Language System, to allow both search and browse functions.

All the above sites share a number of features: they apply quality and/or relevance criteria, they classify materials according to an established medical terminology, either MeSH or UMLS, and, in contrast to the broad coverage of the web as a whole, their coverage is limited and uneven. This is true too of the otherwise valuable evidence based medicine tools such as Turning Research Into Practice (TRIP) and Medical SUMSearch.

Use of general search engines or meta-search engines

A powerful facility of the Internet is in delivery of full-text reports or other documents. UK healthcare managers can sit at their desks and interrogate the Department of Health's Circulars on the Internet (COIN) database. Having identified a Health Service Guideline, with the aid of free downloaded software, they can then print out its digital image in portable document format (pdf). The document can be stored on their hard disk for retrieval at a later date or, as some health organizations do, the file can be placed on a hospital intranet (Simmons, 1997). However this is a 'known item search', deceptive in its ease, and analogous to going to a library to pick up a book known to be on the shelves. A far greater challenge is retrieval of an item answering a specific question or clinical information need. That is analogous to a user identifying books on a broad subject and then scanning through them, or perhaps even checking their index, for the information required. A study looking at advice offered to patients with urinary incontinence found that, although information provided was mostly correct, the most informative site was found only with general search engines, not medical index sites (Sandvik, 1999).

Booth and O'Rourke (1999) identify three information retrieval principles that translate from traditional sources to general search engines: focusing the question (see Chapter 15), constructing the search strategy (see Chapter 17) and filtering the results (Chapter 19). These techniques are specifically appropriate to retrieval of full-text documents although they may also identify other significant items.

Case study

An Alta Vista search

A drug rep has been aggressively marketing his lipid-lowering agent, Atorvastatin, stating that it is better for coronary heart disease than all others. Your postgraduate tutor, a general physician, wishes to assess the evidence so that his junior doctors get an objective picture of treatment options. He prepares a drug seminar on the topic, enlisting your help to find relevant literature.

Clearly a single term search on Alta Vista for 'Atorvastatin' will not be effective, yielding 1,296 hits. Using a focused question (condition and intervention), Boolean logic and truncation the query 'Atorvastatin AND coronary heart disease*' yields a more manageable 342 hits. Combining 'Atorvastatin AND coronary heart disease*' with a filter (eg controlled trial* or clinical trial*) yields 231 hits. Finally two separate searches combining the focused question with either 'systematic review*' (12 hits) or 'randomi* controlled trial*' (23 hits) variously yield very useful materials including a drug monograph on Atorvastatin (**http://www.rxlist.com/cgi/generic/atorvastatin.htm**) and an evidence based article entitled 'Atorvastatin – Another HMG-CoA Reductase Inhibitor?' from the free Medscape service. Other restrictions might include limiting to UK materials by combining with 'AND host:uk'.

Comparing search engine performance

It is a very small shift for the health information professional to move from evaluation of traditional bibliographic databases to assessing coverage and quality of Internet search engines. Informal surveys conducted via discussion lists have revealed very little consensus in the general search engines that librarians choose to use. Librarians will have competing priorities that will govern selection; for example, subject coverage may determine Northern Lights, presentation may determine Yahoo, while Alta Vista may be chosen because of its advanced Boolean functions. Search engines use different methods, for example, Google interprets a link from page A to page B as a vote, by page A, for page B and thus assesses a page's importance by the votes it receives. The specific context in which the engine will be used will also be important. Wu and Li (1999), for example, have conducted an evaluation of seven search engines using representative consumer health topics, assessing them for content relevancy, system features and attributes.

Individual evaluations are not necessarily going to be reproducible across other topics and a librarian will need to keep informed and up to date on the features of all the major search engines. Heidenreich (1997) provides a set of nine questions to assist in comparing search engines.

Meta-search engines

It is increasingly recognized that single search engines are not sufficient for comprehensive coverage of the web. In fact it was calculated that even the most comprehensive search engine (HotBot) covers no more than about 34% of the then estimated 320 million pages of the 'publicly indexable Web' (Lawrence and Giles, 1998). The same authors have subsequently revised their estimate to around 800 million pages on 3 million servers (Lawrence and Giles, 1999). It is thus necessary to use meta-search engines to maximize potential retrieval. A number of meta-search engines exist, eg Metacrawler, Inference Find and Dogpile, to search several search engines simultaneously. Products such as Copernic 2000, with its facility to conduct Boolean searches across numerous engines and then store the results locally, are likely to increase the range of client server options.

Databases and library catalogues

The lead in offering databases free of charge via the web was set by the National Library of Medicine who made MEDLINE, along with other databases such as HealthSTAR and Cancerlit, available via the Internet Grateful Med service with MEDLINE also offered via PubMed (Wilson, 1997; Vine, 1997). A number of sites offer free databases in the UK with the English National Board for Nursing, Midwifery and Health Visiting, the NHS Centre for Reviews and Dissemination, York and the Health Education Board for Scotland being amongst the pioneers for noticeably different types of information (Kiley, 1997b, c).

Increasingly, the development of Z39.50 compatible library catalogues offers improved access via the web. Major institutions that do this include the National Library of Medicine, British Medical Association, the Health Education Authority, the Royal Society of Medicine, the British Library and the Health Service Management Centre in Birmingham. Union catalogues are a particularly attractive proposition for the web. Library networks that offer their union catalogues include those in North Thames, South Thames and Oxford. Consortia of academic libraries doing the same include CARL (in the USA) and the powerful COPAC resource (UK academic libraries). *Trawling the Net,* a listing of free access databases and catalogues of interest to those working in the NHS, is maintained at **http://www.shef.ac.uk/~scharr/ir/trawling.html**.

Resource lists

The resource list is analogous to the arrangement of a physical library; entries are usually classified in a subject order or arranged alphabetically. The least helpful are those where the author compiles them in the order in which they were identified! A resource list can relate to a condition, eg CancerWeb; a broad specialty, eg nursing; a particular group of users, eg the Cambridge Public Health pages; or merely the idiosyncratic interests of its creator. Resource lists usually betray their simple origins by lacking either a search engine or specific inclusion criteria. Specific resources can be found only by typing a text word into the Find window and searching for its occurrences. Extended resource lists need shortcut links to specific sections of the page for speedier navigation.

Case study

Netting the Evidence: a ScHARR introduction to Evidence Based Practice on the Internet includes items on the methodology of evidence based health care and resources that use these techniques. An alphabetical listing contains over 140 annotated entries; each is linked to the relevant page, with each URL clearly displayed for future reference. The resource list started in 1995 as an in-house resource to answer reference enquiries about EBHC but has since grown to be the resource list used in the Cochrane Library, available in virtually every medical library in the country and in a large number of institutions world-wide.

A number of methods keep it up to date:

- A web-monitor site, The Informant, provides weekly updates.
- A meta-search engine, Copernic2000, is used to search regularly and results are stored for review.
- The page is run against a URL-checker to identify invalid links.
- Other EBHC link pages are reviewed regularly.

About one afternoon a month is spent on revising the resource list. Its shortcomings include not having a search engine nor explicit inclusion criteria for entries. As a recent reviewer wrote:

> It reminds me of a bookstore – it assembles a wide variety of resources in one place, and you can visit it to choose a few for your regular use. However it also has a bookstore's drawbacks – you can't be sure that it contains everything you might need, it takes time to find what suits you, and you might have to order some items and pay for them (Lipman, 2000).

Discussion lists and archives

Discussion lists (mailing lists) use an automated server to distribute a single e-mail message to all subscribers to a list. Discussion lists usually have a set purpose or objective and require the list to be used only for these purposes. They have three main functions:

- as an interactive medium by which other subscribers can be asked for information, advice or opinion (eg Does anyone use the Bookdata system and if so what are its strengths and weaknesses?)
- as a publishing medium for details of conferences, new publications, reports etc

- as an archive of recent debates or postings (eg you could search for the keywords 'access policies' to see if anyone has discussed or provided examples of internet access policies, typically over the last two years).

The most relevant discussion lists are:

- lis-medical – for medical librarians
- lis-nursing – for nursing librarians
- evidence-based-libraries – covering the research base in librarianship
- evidence-based-health – covering all issues of evidence based healthcare.

In addition, there are regional network discussion lists and subject-specific lists identifiable via the Liszt service.

File transfer

File transfer, using the comparatively dated ftp (file transfer protocol) facility, is a means of downloading documents, often quite lengthy in nature, from remote sites. In the past it was used as a separate function using purpose-designed software. More recently it can be activated from within a web browser without the user being aware of it. For example, the British Medical Association website has a number of professional statements and reports that can be downloaded in this manner. Most typically a user will only encounter ftp if uploading documents or web pages onto a website.

Evaluating web resources

An interesting phenomenon has been that nearly as many pages have been devoted to the quality of health information in the mainstream medical press as in the information literature. This is undoubtedly because, as Eysenbach and Diepgen (1998a) point out, 'misinformation could be a matter of life or death'. Studies investigating the quality of health information have looked at a number of Internet contexts including websites (Impicciatore et al, 1997), mailing lists and newsgroups (Culver, Gerr and Frumkin, 1997; Hernandez-Borges, Pareras and Jimenez, 1997) and e-mail communication between patients and doctors. Impicciatore et al (1997) found in a study of the advice given on the web for management of feverish children that, of 41 web pages retrieved, only four web pages adhered closely to recommendations of published guidelines. A case report of acute renal failure as a result of one source of web based information illustrates the dangers (Weisbord, Soule and Kimmel, 1997).

Issues around evaluating websites are not clearcut. For example, which instrument should be used? A systematic review examining 47 rating instruments concluded that 'many incompletely developed instruments to evaluate health information exist on the internet. It is unclear, however, whether they should exist in the first place, whether they measure what they claim to measure, or whether they lead to more good than harm' (Jadad and Gagliardi, 1998). Kim et al (1999) reviewed 29 sources of published criteria to identify areas of consensus. Most frequently cited criteria dealt with content, design and aesthetics of site, disclosure of authors, sponsors or developers, currency of information (including frequency of update, freshness, maintenance of site), authority of source, ease of use, and accessibility and availability. They concluded that there was good agreement on key criteria and a need to identify a clear, simple set of consensus criteria that the general public could use. Then there is the issue around 'who should do the quality assessment?' Silberg, Lundberg and Musacchio (1997) dismiss the option of quality control at the time of production as neither possible nor desirable. This leaves what Eysenbach and Diepgen (1998a) distinguish as 'downstream filtering' (by consumers) and 'upstream filtering' (by an intermediary, eg a third-party rating service). Given the number of sites and, indeed, the different contexts in which the information might be used, it seems that downstream filtering is the more promising. Blumberg and Sparks (1999) describe how public health graduate students developed the capacity to evaluate resources over a six-month period with reliability and objectivity of the source evolving as the most used criterion.

The role of the librarian

The Internet has tremendous potential to affect the work of the information professional (Bates, 1997). This includes extending their domain from published materials to 'intelligence', including news and 'grey' literature resources. Discussion lists and newsgroups enable librarians to expand their resources beyond their collections and selective dissemination of information can also be done via the Internet. Librarians must develop skills in appraising and evaluating Internet sources for their end-users.

Another important role is in setting up a library bookmarks page documenting sites of local interest and relevance (Carr and Stibravy, 1999). As bookmarks are stored by the Netscape browser as an html file, it is a non-technical process to organize these into folders and then upload the librarian's bookmarks on to a local intranet.

Their role in providing training and advice is likely to extend to instructing users in the use of basic network tools such as file transfer, remote log-in, and electronic mail and answering questions concerning network access and information system design (Warling and Stave, 1995). Librarians have always demonstrated an ability to survive and thrive despite increasing disintermediation and changes in information technologies.

A hint of a potential role for the health information provider of the future is provided by the Sheffield-based WISDOM project, a virtual learning community (O'Rourke et al, 1999). Here a qualified information professional has a role in developing a web library, in producing web based and e-mail delivered informatics seminars and in managing and contributing to a discussion list.

It is essential that the health LIS professional maintains good current awareness with regard to Internet developments, new sites and related issues. Two primary sources are the journals *Medicine on the Net* and *He@lth on the Internet* while a steady stream of articles can be found in the general medical press. Of course the Internet is itself a valuable source of current awareness for information professionals (McNab and Winship, 1996).

There is little consensus on how best to train librarians in the skills used to exploit the Internet successfully. Isolated examples exist in the literature – the article by Mikita and Drusedum (1993), for example, is now quite dated. It seems likely, therefore, that the main lessons to be learned are from academic sector initiatives such as the NetLinkS project (Levy, 1999). In this way, the Internet can be both a medium for continuing professional development and the subject of it.

Montague and Tomlin (1999) focus instead on the end-user and describe the syllabus for training primary healthcare professionals as part of the Primary Care Sharing the Evidence (PRISE) project to bring high-quality information to primary care teams. The potential for major library input into networked information development at a regional level is signalled by Project Connect operating out of North Thames (Rees, 1998).

Conclusion

During the last decade, the Internet has moved from being a specialist channel used by technicians to a mainstream source of information for both health professionals and the public. The healthcare librarian must draw a careful balance between uncritical acceptance of its use, a complete anathema to evidence based practice, and overprescriptive health warnings designed to deter. The way forward is in bringing to bear the same skills and techniques used in a more conventional setting – definition of the question, design of search strategies, and use of filtering mechanisms – together with general principles regarding evaluation and appraisal of resources and the information contained therein. The future of the knowledge base may well be 'digital', but traditional skills developed over the past century will be the key to its successful management.

Key points

- Although the Internet is sprawling, chaotic and anarchic, it is useful as a delivery medium, a source of intelligence and a source of value-added information.
- To exploit the Internet successfully, a structured approach will be required; this will include selection of resources and focusing of the question to be investigated.
- Medical search engines will usually be the first port of call followed by general search engines; pointers to information such as catalogues will come next before, finally, resource lists and discussion lists.
- Quality of information on the Internet is a major issue that has led to the generation of numerous scales and evaluation tools.
- The librarian will continue to play a major part in exploitation of the world wide web: in identifying and signposting resources, in providing end-user training and in cataloguing and classifying resources of potential use to their customers.

Relevant websites

General

Alta Vista **http://altavista.digital.com/**
> Extensive web and Usenet index (index to electronic bulletin boards with messages linked by threads) with good advanced searching options.

DejaNews **http://www.dejanews.com/**
> Searches Usenet newsgroup postings.

Excite **http://www.excite.com/**
> Searches web pages and the most recent two weeks of Usenet news.

Google **http://www.google.com**
> A search engine that works by ranking pages according to numbers of relevant links.

Liszt **http://www.liszt.com/**
> Directory of e-mail discussion groups.

Lycos **http://www.lycos.com/**
> Subject guides plus a search tool.

Inference Find **http://www.infind.com/**
> A powerful meta-search engine that allows time-limited searching.

MetaCrawler **http://metacrawler.cs.washington.edu/**
> Simultaneous searches of several search engines.

WebCrawler **http://webcrawler.com/**
> General search tool.

Yahoo **http://www.yahoo.com**
> Good searchable index, directory classification and people-searching capabilities.

Medical specific

Cliniweb International **http://www.ohsu.edu/cliniweb/**
Medical SUMSearch
> **http://SUMSearch.UTHSCSA.edu/cgi-bin/SUMSearch. exe**

MedicalWorld Search **http://www.mwsearch.poly.edu**
OMNI **http://www.omni.ac.uk**
> A subject-classified search engine using MeSH headings.

Turning Research Into Practice (TRIP) **http://www.ceres.uwcm.ac.uk/**

Resource lists

Cambridge Public Health **http://www.medschl.cam.ac.uk/phealth/phweb.html**
CancerWeb **http://www.graylab.ac.uk/cancerweb.html**
> A directory listing of sites related to cancer.

Netting the Evidence **http://www.shef.ac.uk/~scharr/ir/netting.html**
    A comprehensive list of sources for evidence based healthcare.
Nursing and Health Care Resources on the Net **http://www.shef.ac.uk/~nhcon/**
Trawling the Net **http://www.shef.ac.uk/~scharr/ir/trawling.html**
    A list of free databases of interest to NHS staff.

Other tools

Copernic2000 **http://www.copernic.com**
    Downloadable software allowing multiple search engine searching, stored
    results and Boolean logic.
Informant **http://informant.dartmouth.edu/**
    A free web-monitoring service allowing specification of keywords or sites.

19
Filtering and evaluating the knowledge base

Suzy Paisley

Introduction

The very nature of literature searching implies a process of filtering and evaluating. A reference interview is undertaken to establish what is and what is not relevant to the enquirer. Keywords and subject headings are evaluated in terms of relevance to the enquiry. Strategies are developed to filter from the mass of information contained in a database only those references relevant to the enquiry. The skills and the tools available allow enquirers' needs to be assessed and also establish the importance or relevance of unfamiliar clinical terms. Information can be managed in a way which allows access to the few key references from the many available.

This chapter considers the tools and resources available to filter and evaluate the knowledge base. This includes tools that help interrogate familiar traditional sources (eg MEDLINE) and the newer resources designed to provide quick access to the knowledge base. It begins by considering how the process of evidence based practice can inform the way we filter and evaluate information and how familiarity with the methods of critical appraisal can make the concept of 'high-quality evidence' as manageable as the unfamiliar clinical terms we encounter from day to day.

Importance of relevance

Consider for a moment this concept, 'relevance'. It is comfortable for LIS professionals who deal with the process of establishing the subject relevance of an enquiry. There are few problems meeting an enquirer's need for 'something recent' or 'some kind of review covering the major points'. It is not so simple assisting the enquirer for 'some good evidence on . . .' or 'some high-quality studies on . . .'. As evidence based practice (EBP) continues to make itself known, there is increasing pressure on the LIS professional to develop knowledge, skills and resources to accommodate this additional dimension to our enquirers' needs.

The process of evidence based practice, as defined by Sackett et al (1997), requires the practitioner to track down 'the best evidence'. The process also specifies that the practitioner should track down the evidence 'with maximum efficiency'. From the literature on evidence based practice there are three elements which constitute effective searching to support EBP. These are:

- Identification of the best quality evidence (as demonstrated above).
- Control over the volume of available literature (to meet the current awareness needs of the evidence based practitioner). This corresponds to the requirement to read 19 articles per day in order to keep up to date (Haynes, 1993).
- Quick access to the literature (to support 'real-time' problem-solving and decision-making). *Best Evidence*, the electronic version of the *ACP Journal Club* and *Evidence Based Medicine* journals, measures its value, in part, by number of seconds and number of keystrokes required to retrieve relevant citations (McKibbon, 1998).

Haynes refers to a '4S taxonomy of information packaging and delivery' to support EBP (Jaeschke et al, 1999). That is, there are four levels of evidence based information resources aimed at meeting the requirements of the *efficient best evidence seeker*. The 4Ss are:

- Original Studies
- Syntheses of studies, in the form of systematic reviews
- Synopses (for example in the form of structured abstracts)
- Systems in which the studies, syntheses and synopses are organized (ranging from databases such as MEDLINE to clinical decision-making tools).

Evidence based process

Tracking down the best evidence forms one part of the evidence-seeking process (Figure 19.1). Other parts of the process, namely defining the answerable ques-

1	Convert information needs into answerable questions.
2	Track down, with maximum efficiency, the best evidence with which to answer them.
3	Critically appraise that evidence for its validity (closeness to the truth) and usefulness (clinical applicability).
4	Apply the results of appraisal to practice.
5	Evaluate performance.

Fig. 19.1   *Sackett's 5 step evidence based process (1997)*

tion and critically appraising the evidence, help in refining search results to retrieve higher quality and more relevant references.

Answerable questions

By first identifying or classifying the type of question being asked, critical appraisal skills can be applied to identify the appropriate type of research or study design to answer that question. Five enquiries on breast cancer will be considered to identify different types of clinical question.

Is paclitaxel, used in combination therapy, effective in reducing the development of breast cancer tumours?
This is a treatment, or therapy, question. It looks at an intervention, given to the patient, aimed at curing or improving the condition of the patient.

Does structured information or education provided to breast cancer patients increase patient participation in the treatment decision-making process?
This can also be classified as a therapy question even though it does not deal with a clinical treatment. It looks at an intervention aimed at improving the condition of the patient.

Fine needle tests are less invasive and therefore more acceptable to the patient than open surgical biopsy. But are they as effective in the detection of breast tumours?
This is a diagnosis question. The intervention is aimed at detecting the presence of disease in patients presenting with symptoms.

Are women who take hormone replacement therapy (HRT) more likely to develop breast cancer?

This is an aetiology, or 'cause' question. It considers the risk of developing a particular condition and aims to establish an association between the exposure (in this example HRT) and the disease.

Does psychological or emotional stress increase the rate of progression of disease in women with breast cancer?
This is a prognosis, or natural history question. It looks at the course or rate at which the disease progresses once it has been diagnosed.

The classification of different types of question does not in itself help to identify higher quality studies. MEDLINE indexing has subheadings for most of the questions we have defined (drug therapy, therapeutic use, diagnosis, aetiology), but it has been argued that these have been applied too liberally to be useful in identifying clinically applicable studies (Sievert et al, 1996). In order to do that we need to consider the critical appraisal step in the evidence based process.

Critical appraisal

Critical appraisal is probably the stage in the process most inextricably associated with evidence based practice. In a series of *British Medical Journal* articles on 'How to read a paper', later published in book form, Greenhalgh (1997) refers to critical appraisal as not just reading papers but reading the 'right papers'. Sackett et al (1997) describe it as a process of weighing up the evidence 'to assess its validity (closeness to the truth) and usefulness (clinical applicability)'.

To set the application of critical appraisal skills to searching for evidence into context we will consider two 'devices': the hierarchy of evidence and the checklist. Many proponents of evidence based practice have developed variations on these devices. For illustrative purposes the *Levels of evidence and grades of recommendation* developed by the Centre for Evidence Based Medicine (CEBM) at Oxford University (Ball et al, 1999–) and the *Users' guides to the medical literature* (EBMWG 1993–) published in the *Journal of the American Medical Association* and developed by the Evidence Based Medicine Working Group will be used.

Hierarchies of evidence

The hierarchy of evidence is another means of 'classifying' the evidence. Unlike the types of question identified earlier, which classified questions according to aspects of the condition or disease, the hierarchy of evidence seeks to label research studies according to their quality and the appropriateness of their design. As the term suggests, the hierarchy indicates what is considered strong evidence (Level 1 on the hierarchy) and what is considered weak evidence (Level 5). It can act as a guide to decision-making with Level 1 evidence being used as a basis for a Grade A recommendation for practice (although only when that evidence has undergone a thorough appraisal).

Different types of clinical question require different research methods and therefore different study designs. Systematic reviews (secondary research, comprising a comprehensive and systematic evaluation of existing research on a given question – more on these later in the chapter) are 'labelled' as Level 1a evidence for all types of question on the CEBM hierarchy. However, much progress is needed before we reach the situation where there is a systematic review available for every clinical question. For the majority of enquiries primary research (ie research done with patients as opposed to evaluations of existing research) supplies the best available evidence (the **S** studies in Haynes' 4S taxonomy) (Jaeschke et al, 1999). In the absence of a systematic review, the 'best' or most appropriate study designs associated with the different types of clinical question as they appear in the CEBM hierarchy are outlined in Table 19.1.

Table 19.1 *'Best' quality study designs for primary research*

Type of question	Study design
Therapy	Randomized controlled trial (RCT)
Diagnosis	Independent blind comparison of patients undergoing both diagnostic test and 'gold' standard test
Aetiology	Randomized controlled trial (seldom feasible) or cohort study (McKibbon, 1999)
Prognosis	Inception cohort study

Critical appraisal checklists

The hierarchy of evidence cannot be used to judge the quality of individual studies. The randomized controlled trial may be the gold standard for therapy questions, but there are good RCTs and there are weak RCTs. Critical appraisal checklists have been developed to evaluate systematically the characteristics of individual studies. Below is a brief summary of the Evidence Based Medicine Working Group's checklists or *Users' guides* (EBMWG) for the four types of clinical question.

Therapy questions (Guyatt, Sackett and Cook, 1993):

- Method of randomization
- Completeness of follow up
- Blinding
- Similarity of baseline characteristics of study and control groups
- Significant effect size of the intervention being tested.

Diagnosis questions (Jaeschke, Guyatt and Sackett, 1994):

- Blinded assessment of test results
- Representative patient group covering all stages of disease
- Comparison with an existing 'gold standard' test
- All tests under evaluation received by each participant
- Outcomes include tests of sensitivity and specificity, predictive value and false positives and false negatives.

Aetiology questions (Levine et al, 1994):

- Comparison groups similar except for the exposure or risk under investigation
- Comparison groups assessed in same way
- Sufficient time lapse before follow-up
- Strength of association between risk and outcome
- Precision of estimate of risk.

Prognosis questions (Laupacis et al, 1994):

- Participants at similar stage in progression of disease
- Sufficient time-lapse and completeness of follow-up
- Objective outcomes criteria
- Adjustment for prognostic factors.

This chapter does not aim to give a comprehensive overview of the whys and wherefores, methodologies and skills, tools and resources associated with critical appraisal. Other resources concentrate on these aspects in much greater detail. (CASP; CEBM; Greenhalgh, 1997; McKibbon, 1999; Sackett et al, 1997). It is worth reinforcing the fact that LIS professionals do not necessarily have to be expert appraisers of evidence to be effective searchers of higher quality evidence. As previously mentioned, familiarity with the terms surrounding critical appraisal and EBP makes searching on these concepts achievable for health LIS professionals

Methodological search filters

Dickersin, Scherer and Lefebvre (1994) have observed that until fairly recently there has been an emphasis on developing MeSH terms for subject matter rather than methodology. The problems associated with the retrieval of references based on search terms relating to study design and research methods are well documented (Johnson, McKinin and Sievert, 1992; Sievert et al, 1996; McKibbon, 1999). They range from a lack of indexing vocabulary, inconsistent or incorrect indexing to poor reporting of methods in abstracts. Yet retrieval based on methodology is a chief requirement in the filtering of higher quality studies from search results. Developments in bibliographic databases are, to a certain degree, improving the situation. The introduction of publication types relating to study design, the retrospective tagging of RCTs in MEDLINE and the introduction by some journals of structured abstracts (Booth and O'Rourke, 1997) all suggest a greater awareness of the value of documenting these terms to improve retrieval.

Other tools available to us are search 'hedges' containing combinations of textwords and indexing terms relating to the types of clinical question and their associated study designs and methodological terminology. These hedges, more commonly known as methodological or quality filters, are an important tool in the retrieval of references which constitute the 'best evidence'. A study by Haynes et al (1994) established that the retrieval of clinically relevant topics could be substantially enhanced by combinations of selected terms. The study tests the sensitivity and specificity of over 100,000 unique combinations of search terms. An outcome of the study was the development of a set of filters to be used in the retrieval of clinical studies on treatment, prevention, diagnosis, aetiology and prognosis. Variant filters for each type of question have been developed to achieve maximum sensitivity, maximum specificity or optimal sensitivity and specificity in retrieval. The filters have been adapted for use with both OVID and SilverPlatter search software and can be found on the website of the Institute for Health Sciences, University of Oxford (IHS Library Filters). Table 19.2 lists the optimally sensitive filters together with 'best one-line filters' applied to example searches based on the clinical questions from earlier in the chapter. The examples use OVID search language.

Applying the filters

The methodological filters in Table 19.2 have been developed to aid the process of clinical decision-making. A series of articles published in *ACP Journal Club* uses clinical scenarios to demonstrate the application of the filters in 'real-time' situations (McKibbon and Walker-Dilks, 1994a; McKibbon and Walker-Dilks, 1994b; Walker-Dilks, McKibbon and Haynes, 1994; McKibbon et al, 1995). The National Library of Medicine's free MEDLINE service, PubMed, and the Internet gateway SUMSearch, based at the University of Texas, have incorporated the filters into their search software. Subject queries can be focused to retrieve articles relating to a specific type of clinical question. The systems search first on the subject keywords, then limit the results using the specified filter.

McKibbon (1999) acknowledges that the effectiveness of methodological filters is limited by the original context of their developmental research. Due to be updated in 1999, the measures of sensitivity and specificity for filters relating to therapy, diagnosis, aetiology and prognosis are based on the retrieval of studies published in 1986 and 1991 only (Haynes et al, 1994). In their current format the filters are designed for use with MEDLINE and HealthSTAR. Similar filters for sources such as EMBASE have not yet been devised and evaluated. In anticipation of further developmental work, the text by McKibbon (1999) provides a comprehensive overview of the indexing vocabulary and practices relating to clinical research methodology in MEDLINE, CINAHL, PsycINFO and EMBASE.

The concept of methodological or 'quality' filters is not new. Sievert et al (1996) point out that 'the call for filters in information systems was first sounded in 1971'. However, the development and application of filters throughout the 1990s owe much to the demands placed on information systems by evidence based practice. In addition to filters designed for clinical questions, other filters include guidelines, systematic reviews, treatment outcome and evidence based healthcare methodology. These filters are also listed at the IHS website (IHS Library Filters, 1998–).

Table 19.2 *Methodological filters with search examples*

Therapy

Filter for optimal sensitivity and specificity	Best one-line filter	Search examples (MEDLINE 1991–9)	
1 randomized controlled trial.pt.	1 clinical trial.pt.	1 exp Breast neoplasms/	40926
2 exp drug therapy/		2 Paclitaxel/	3330
3 tu.xs.		3 Cisplatin/	10003
4 random$.tw.		4 Antineoplastic agents, combined	22761
5 or/1-4		5 2 and 3 and 4	329
		6 1 and 5	33
		7 limit 6 to clinical trial	18
		1 exp Breast neoplasms/	40926
		2 Patient education/	13356
		3 Patient participation/	3003
		4 1 and 2 and 3	31
		5 limit 4 to clinical trial	3

Diagnosis

Filter for optimal sensitivity and specificity	Best one-line filter	Search example (MEDLINE 1991–9)	
1 exp "sensitivity and specificity"/	1 sensitivity.tw.	1 exp Breast neoplasms/	40926
2 sensitivity.tw.		2 Biopsy, needle/	10364
3 exp diagnosis/		3 surgical biopsy.tw.	603
4 exp pathology/		4 surgical excision.tw.	2667
5 specificity.tw.		5 3 or 4	3256

Table 19.2   *continued*

Aetiology

Filter for optimal sensitivity and specificity	Best one-line filter	Search example (MEDLINE 1991–9)	
1 exp cohort studies/	1 risk.tw	1 exp Breast neoplasms/	40926
2 exp risk/		2 Estrogen replacement therapy/	4654
3 (odds and ratio$).tw.		3 1 and 2	613
4 (relative and risk).tw.		4 risk.tw.	177304
5 (case and control).tw.		5 3 and 4	291
6 or/1-5		6 1 and 2 and 5	167
		7 sensitivity.tw.	92008
		8 6 and 8	31

Prognosis

Filter for optimal sensitivity and specificity	Best one-line filter	Search examples (MEDLINE 1991–9)	
1 incidence/	1 exp cohort studies/	1 exp Breast neoplasms/	40926
2 exp mortality/		2 Stress, psychological/	11972
3 follow-up studies/		3 1 and 2	157
4 prognos$.tw.		4 exp cohort studies/	196726
5 predict$.tw.		5 3 and 4	20
6 course.tw.			
7 or/1-6			

Greenhalgh (1997) differentiates between 'quality filters for everyday use' (ie the filters developed by Haynes et al (1994)) and 'quality filters for research'. The latter is a reference to optimally sensitive filters to identify RCTS (developed by the Cochrane Collaboration (Dickersin, Scherer and Lefebvre, 1994; Mulrow and Oxman, 1997) and systematic reviews (developed by the NHS Centre for Reviews and Dissemination (NHS CRD, 1996)). These lengthy, highly sensitive filters are used by those undertaking secondary research, such as systematic reviews, and in the development of databases to support evidence based practice (the **S**yntheses and **S**ystems in Haynes' 4S taxonomy (Jaeschke et al, 1999)).

Sources to support evidence based practice

This chapter has concentrated so far on original, 'primary' studies and on methods to filter the higher quality original studies from traditional sources such as MEDLINE. Newer sources, designed specifically to provide evaluative and easy access to the evidence base, are becoming available. That is, sources in the form of **S**yntheses, **S**ynopses and **S**ystems (Jaeschke et al, 1999), which aim to incorporate the concepts of 'maximum efficiency' and 'best evidence' (Sackett et al, 1997) into the literature-searching process.

Systematic reviews

One motivation behind the evidence based practice movement is the persistence of clinical practice which is not based on research. Another is that proportion of available research evidence which cannot easily be accessed. As a consequence of the latter, the same research question may be tested repeatedly despite there already being a solution in the evidence base. An example of this is the effect on mortality of intravenous streptokinase for acute myocardial infarction (Lau et al, 1992). A synthesis of existing trials would have established the effectiveness of this intervention in 1971, nearly 20 years before it was finally established by a single large trial reported in 1988. Archie Cochrane, a British epidemiologist, whose philosophy on the delivery of healthcare (Cochrane, 1972) formed the basis for the development of the Cochrane Collaboration, made this comment:

> It is surely a great criticism of our profession that we have not organised a critical summary, by specialty or subspecialty, adapted periodically, of all randomised controlled trials (Cochrane, 1979).

Systematic reviews, a form of secondary or integrative study, have developed in response to this criticism. Systematic reviews, or overviews, aim to provide a comprehensive identification, appraisal and synthesis of all studies on a specified question (Cook et al, 1997). Their purpose is to provide a basis for clinical decision-making. A rigorous systematic review can be more useful than individual primary studies for several reasons. First, the review assembles information on all relevant individual studies and so provides control over the volume of available literature. Secondly, through the synthesis of results of smaller studies (using a technique called meta-analysis) reviews can provide information of greater statistical significance. Lastly, systematic reviews can explain, or at least alert attention to, differences between results of individual studies on the same topic.

The usefulness of systematic reviews in supporting evidence based practice has led to a steep increase in their availability. The number published annually has increased at least 500-fold in the past decade (Cook et al, 1997). In addition, there has been an increased interest in the development of systematic review methodology. As the role of the review as a decision-making tool increased in importance, concern was expressed over the scientific rigour of the traditional or 'narrative' review (Mulrow, 1987). The international Cochrane Collaboration, set up to 'prepare, maintain and promote the accessibility of systematic reviews of the effects of healthcare interventions' (Cochrane Collaboration, 1999) and its sibling organization, the NHS Centre for Reviews and Dissemination (1996) play a major role in the development of methodologies to support high-quality systematic reviews. Systematic reviews are described as 'scientific investigations in themselves' (Cook at al, 1997). The expectations placed on primary research in terms of scientific rigour, minimizing bias and the explicit reporting of methods as well as of results are equally applicable to the evaluation of systematic reviews. As for the appraisal of primary research studies, the Evidence Based Medicine Working Group has identified a checklist, or *User guide* (EBMWG) for the appraisal of systematic reviews.

Systematic reviews (Oxman et al, 1994) require:

- Clearly focused question
- Explicit criteria for the inclusion of studies
- Comprehensive literature search
- Appraisal of validity of included studies
- Reproducible assessment of included studies
- Similar results from study to study.

The problems associated with the retrieval of studies based on methodological keywords are particularly apparent in the retrieval of systematic reviews from traditional sources such as MEDLINE. The science of systematic reviews is relatively young and as yet there is little standardization of methodological terms. It has always been possible to limit MEDLINE searches by 'review' as a publication type but this is not particularly helpful. There is a huge gap between a traditional, narrative review and a scientifically rigorous systematic review, yet very little to differentiate the two in terms of search terminology. As part of a series on systematic reviews in the *Annals of Internal Medicine*, later published in book form (Hunt and McKibbon, 1997; Mulrow and Cook, 1998) Hunt and McKibbon developed two search strategies for the retrieval of systematic reviews. The 'simple' strategy is given in Figure 19.2.

An alternative or additional approach to locating systematic reviews is to consult a specially collated listing or collection. Several sources of high-quality systematic reviews, aimed specifically at improving access to good evidence, have been developed.

Cochrane Library

The Cochrane Library contains the outputs of the Cochrane Collaboration and is available from Update Software by CD-ROM or Internet subscription. The Library contains a number of databases including the Cochrane Database of Systematic Reviews (CDSR), which provides full-text access to completed and in progress reviews undertaken by the Cochrane Collaborative Review Groups (CRGs).

Database of Abstracts of Reviews of Effectiveness (DARE)

DARE is produced by NHS CRD and is available as part of the Cochrane

1	meta-analysis.pt.
2	meta-anal$.tw.
3	review.pt and medline.tw.
4	1 or 2 or 3

Fig. 19.2   *'Simple' strategy for the retrieval of systematic reviews (Hunt, 1997)*

Library and via the NHS CRD web page. The database aims to provide access to details of good quality, 'non-Cochrane' systematic reviews. Reviews are identified via regular searches of traditional sources such as MEDLINE. DARE structured abstracts provide detailed information on the question, methods and results of reviews and include an evaluative commentary by a CRD reviewer.

NHS HTA (Health Technology Assessment) programme

A source of systematic reviews of particular importance to the UK National Health Service is the NHS HTA programme. One of the aims of the programme, set up as part of the NHS R&D strategy, is to identify areas of uncertainty and undertake systematic reviews to establish what is and isn't known with a view to informing future research priorities. Reports of systematic reviews are available as full-text documents at the National Co-ordinating Centre for Health Technology Assessment website (NCCHTA).

Effective Healthcare Bulletins (EHCB)

EHCBs, produced by NHS CRD, are concise summaries of the clinical and cost effectiveness of healthcare interventions, based on systematic reviews. They are distributed widely amongst NHS practitioners and use devices such as summary points and structured reporting to facilitate access to the evidence. The bulletins are bi-monthly and are available by subscription from the Royal Society of Medicine or from the NHS CRD website.

Best Evidence

Best Evidence, a CD-ROM resource produced by the American College of Physicians (ACP) and available from BMJ Publishing, is the electronic version of the paper based journals *ACP Journal Club* and *Evidence Based Medicine*. These, together with other similar journals (*Evidence based Nursing, Evidence based Mental Health* and *Evidence Based Healthcare*), do not publish original papers but rather provide structured, evaluative summaries, similar to the abstracts found in DARE, of scientifically rigorous studies thought to be of particular applicability or relevance to clinical practice.

Clinical guidelines

Clinical guidelines or practice guidelines are, like systematic reviews, a form of integrative or secondary publication. They are described as 'statements intended to assist practitioners and patients with decisions about appropriate healthcare' (Cook et al, 1997). As such, they take the use of research evidence in clinical decision-making one stage further than systematic reviews in that they attempt to give an indication of how information on effectiveness can be implemented in practice. As with reviews, there is an enormous variation in the quality of available guidelines. A 'good' evidence based guideline should be based on a rigorous systematic review of evidence. The Healthcare Evaluation Unit (HCEU) at St George's Hospital Medical School has produced an appraisal instrument for use with clinical guidelines (Cluzeau et al, 1997). Due to the increasing importance of clinical guidelines in evidence based practice and the variation in quality and disparate nature of sources of guidelines, it is worth listing, briefly, some useful locations. These can be found at the end of the chapter.

Conclusion

The protagonists of evidence based practice warn that 'not all that glitters is gold' and provide us with critical appraisal tools with which to dig out the valuable nuggets. This chapter has demonstrated the applicability of critical appraisal skills in finding the evidence, but what about the validity of such skills? Evidence based practice is certainly not without its opponents. In response to criticisms of authoritarianism Sackett modified his definition of evidence based medicine to place greater emphasis on the value of clinical expertise (Sackett et al, 1996). A whole issue of the *Journal of Evaluation in Clinical Practice* is devoted to the limits of evidence based medicine (3 (2), 1997). Critics state that there is nothing new in the 'new paradigm' called evidence based medicine and that the concept of a hierarchy of evidence has little logical meaning (Shahar, 1997). Others argue that evidence based practice doesn't go far enough. That, for example, whilst methods for the appraisal and systematic review of RCTS are well established, methods for all types of relevant research are required if practitioners are to be truly evidence based in all areas of healthcare. As locators of research evidence, can health LIS professionals be sure that they are not missing valuable references when they limit search results with methodological filters? How useful are the new, focused sources of evidence when compared with the volume of information and breadth of coverage of MEDLINE and its equivalents?

In response to these doubts it could be argued that the destination has not been reached, but the journey is going in the right direction. Evidence based practice is a young science, but it is developing very quickly. The scope of the Cochrane Collaboration is expanding exponentially in terms of volume of output, range of clinical specialty and profession and methods of review. Developments in information retrieval have resulted in huge progress in terms of the volume of information available to us and the speed with which we can access it. However, the same developments have made little progress in improving the effectiveness of retrieval in terms of relevance (McKibbon, 1999). The study by Sievert et al (1996) sets out to establish which factors influence a clinician's decision to choose to read one paper over another. The study, which does not contain the phrases 'evidence based' or 'critical appraisal', cites 'methodological rigor' as the most important measure of relevance after subject content. The investigative work undertaken by Haynes and his associates (Haynes et al, 1994), the steady improvement in methodological reporting in abstracts, improvements in indexing terms and practice, the development of systems to provide access to higher quality, evaluated research evidence and a basic knowledge of the concepts of critical appraisal, whilst not solving all the problems, can progress some way towards meeting the enquirers' definition of relevant information.

Key points

- Evidence based practice (EBP) defines the relevance of research evidence in terms of subject and methodological rigour.
- A basic understanding of the terms and concepts of critical appraisal is helpful in the retrieval of high-quality evidence.
- There exist four levels of information resources to support EBP: studies, syntheses, synopses and systems.
- Quality filters, comprising methodological keywords and indexing terms, can substantially improve the retrieval of clinically relevant references from MEDLINE.
- Syntheses of evidence and new critically appraised information resources provide evaluative control over the volume of available literature.

Useful web addresses for guidelines

Alberta Medical Association **http://www.amda.ab.ca/cpg/index.html**
CPG Infobase (Canadian Medical Association) **http://www.cma.ca/cpgs/**
HSTAT **http://text.nlm.nih.gov/ftrs/gateway**
> HTA gateway to the Agency for Healthcare Research and Quality
> (AHRQ) supported guidelines and U.S. National Institutes for Health
> (NIH) consensus statements.

NICE (National Institute for Clinical Excellence) **http://www.nice.org.uk/**
North of England Evidence Based Guidelines project
> **http://www.ncl.ac.uk/chsr/publicn/tools/tools.htm**

SIGN (Scottish Intercollegiate Guidelines Network)
> **http://pc47.cee.hw.ac.uk/sign/home.htm**

U.S. National Guideline Clearing House **http://www.guidelines.gov/index.asp**

20
Organizing a personal knowledge base

Andrew Booth

Introduction

The exponential growth of the evidence base, and the volume of literature required for systematic review activities in particular, make it desirable, if not essential, to use software to manage paper based collections and associated bibliographic references. There are two main options: using a generic database package such as Access (Microsoft relational database software) or Idealist (a text retrieval package), or alternatively purchasing specific reference management software (R G Jones, 1993). Advantages of the former are that software may be available locally, that it can store and organize data additional to the brief bibliographic record and that there will often be internal expertise for such packages. Conversely data can generally only be manipulated in the form in which it was originally imported and designing import filters for numerous database sources is time-consuming and technically complex. The arrival of personal bibliographic management software (PBMS) has revolutionized acquisition of research references. PBMS benefits from bespoke input and output facilities for source databases and target journals and utilities for commonly performed functions. However, the PBMS is more limited if being used for purposes other than those for which it was originally designed.

This chapter discusses how the searcher can organize information retrieved to ensure effective access to, and use of, search results. Structured abstracts, evidence digests and critically appraised topics (CATS) are described as valuable approaches to summarizing information. Methods of referencing print and electronic information are outlined. The uses of reference management software are considered.

The LIS professional's role in reference management

For over ten years librarians have been encouraged to extend their information management skills to PBMS (Strube et al, 1989). It need not be seen as a revolutionary step to extend such skills from the library to the clinician's office, but rather as a natural extension of the advice traditionally given to health professionals wishing to organize personal reference collections. Knowledge of automated alternatives to overgrown manual reprint files can be a considerable asset to the population that the health LIS professional serves. The challenge is, though, to a greater extent similar to that posed by any constantly developing category of software, namely the need to be aware of new features of successive versions as they appear. As Matthews (1999) states:

> Reviewing software products is similar to shooting at a moving target. Announcements of new product versions for a variety of platforms seem to appear almost overnight. In addition, news that one company has acquired another and absorbed its product line seems ubiquitous in the software industry.

In fact this recent article by Matthews, a collaborative review by six librarians published in *Nature*, is an exception to a general pattern that sees PBMS reviews scattered across library and information management journals. This situation has been alleviated, at least to a certain extent, via three routes – the development of Internet sites that review all PBMS currently available (eg Evaluation of Reference Management Software which compares Papyrus with ProCite, Reference Manager, Idealist, Endnote, GetARef and Citation 7 (Shapland, 1999)), the availability of showcase workshops and events that allow cross-ways comparisons, and the appearance of websites for all the major PBMS producers (see below).

Many LIS professionals find themselves spending an ever-increasing amount of time not simply in teaching users how to search databases but in helping end-users to manage their search results with PBMS. Several library instruction programmes respond to this need by including the use of PBMS applications within instruction in information management. Owen (1997) describes how a class centred on PBMS software was used to introduce users to broader issues of personal information management skills.

What is a reference management package?

PBMS are designed to handle a wide range of reference types, including not only the more traditional types such as books, articles, journals, book chapters, etc, but also less common types such as music scores and maps, in the same database. For example Reference Manager has over 30 different formats. Each reference type has record definitions that include only those fields appropriate to that type. This contrasts with database systems that either force sub-optimal use of field contents or an unwieldy record based on a lowest common denominator. PBMS software typically employs a variable-length record structure and permits repeating values, eg multiple authors. The structure of the database is often predefined, unlike general text retrieval packages and database packages.

Kelly (1994) identifies three critical tasks involved in the process of downloading of references from online or CD-ROM databases: building the database of references to periodical articles, books or similar materials; searching the database created; and generating a list of selected items from the database. To this must be added the recently added facility to communicate with Internet databases. The four corresponding components of reference management software are as follows:

- the 'capture' utility
- the search engine
- the report utility
- the communications utility.

Increasingly, the four components are bundled together, but in the past direct comparisons were complicated because of differing licence and pricing arrangements. For example, the standard database package for Reference Manager allowed manual data input, but users wishing to capture references from existing databases had to purchase an additional capture module.

The capture utility

The capture utility is used to import references from source databases such as MEDLINE. References are often batch loaded from external databases so a 'library' of import formats is required, not only according to database, but also according to specific vendor or provider (eg different import formats for Silver-Platter, Ovid and PubMed MEDLINE versions). With the speed of appearance of new data sources, together with the regularity of modified versions of existing databases, the user needs to be able to create new formats and to modify existing ones.

The search engine

The search engine is used to locate references once added to a database. PBMS systems usually compromise between comprehensiveness of indexing and size of database. If every word were indexed large texts could be searched rapidly for particular strings, but the database would consume a correspondingly large amount of space. The search engines differentiate key index fields such as author and journal from textual fields such as title and abstract. Searches on the former are very speedy, while those on the latter may take some time. Search facilities typically include:

- phrase searching
- truncation
- authority lists of terms used
- Boolean queries
- progressive refinement of search queries in the light of retrieval results.

The report utility

The report utility is used to export references in various formats, both print-based and electronic. Journal publishers have differing requirements for the presentation of references. Even if two journals use the same basic format (eg Harvard or Vancouver style) they may have different requirements in terms of typography (bold, italic or normal) or punctuation. The PBMS requires a 'library' of bibliographic formats with the facility to create a new format if required. In practice, standardization within publishing houses means that a sibling journal from the same stable can be used as a template for the journal of interest. Other facilities should include specification of fonts and selection from a wide range of printer drivers.

Where PBMS software comes into its own, however, is with the creation of bibliographies automatically from embedded codes within a master document. So, for example, the Reference Manager package requires that unique identifying numbers for each reference are coded within curly brackets (eg {520}). A final manuscript is produced automatically by running a program that replaces the embedded codes with the required reference in text format and transfers the corresponding bibliography into a word-processor. The real asset of such systems is their interaction with standard word-processing packages, usually being accessible via a toolbar from within the WP package. Bibliographies can also be generated from a marked list independently of a manuscript.

The communications utility

A comparatively new feature of reference management software is its facility to interface with online databases or Z39.50 compatible library collections via the Internet. For example, Reference Manager allows connection with the MEDLINE PubMed database or with Z39.50 library databases. A comparable initiative in 1996 was when Sea Change Corporation and Personal Bibliographic Software Inc (PBS), the former developers of ProCite, collaborated to link Sea Change's Book Where? Internet search and retrieval product with PBS's ProCite PBMS. This too enables users to search hundreds of Z39.50 compatible library collections via the Internet, retrieving and storing references in a ProCite database for later processing (Combs, 1996a). Similarly, EndNote has a communications facility called EndLink (Bjorner, 1995a, b) allowing connection to online databases.

Evaluating reference management software

An authoritative evaluation checklist was produced in the early 1990s (Moore, 1991) and still provides a useful starting point. It has to be acknowledged that technology has moved on considerably since then and features such as interfaces with Internet data sources have been added. Software producers are also responding to the web publishing revolution, providing the capability to export citations in HTML format and thus enabling users to either generate web outputs or to mount a searchable database on the web. Such a facility should be added to optimal criteria (Delfino, 1996; Gauvin, 1998). The criteria identified by Moore (1991) fall under the following domains: the software, general features and the supplier. The reader is referred to this article for the more detailed questions that fall under each domain.

There are four leading PBMS packages – EndNote, Papyrus, ProCite and Reference Manager – all with enthusiastic advocates. In a very competitive software market with features continually being added, the LIS professional should keep an eye on the current state of each package. The picture is more complicated with ProCite having been acquired by Research Information Systems, the developers of Reference Manager, who then announced the acquisition of Niles Software, Inc., which develops EndNote software. Niles Software and Research Information Systems have subsequently now merged to form ResearchSoft (**http://www.researchsoft.com**). The Institute of Scientific Information is now the parent company of EndNote, ProCite and Reference Manager. Initially, ResearchSoft plans to continue to develop all three. Brief details on each of the main packages are given below.

EndNote

Marketed by Niles Software Inc, this package is currently available as EndNote 3.0.1. A free trial version and up-to-date product information can be found at: **http://www.niles.com/**

Papyrus

Papyrus is marketed by Research Software Design, 2718 SW Kelly Street, Suite 181, Portland OR 97201, USA. This package is currently available as Papyrus 7.0 for DOS/Windows and Version 8.0 for the Macintosh. It is available only in MS-DOS and Macintosh versions (the release of a new full Windows version of Papyrus, based on the Macintosh version, is expected in 1999). Up-to-date details can be requested from info@rsd.com or found at: **http://www.teleport.com/~rsd/**

ProCite

ProCite originated within the library and information sector, but has gained wide acceptance amongst other disciplines. Currently available as ProCite 4.03 for Windows 98/95/NT4 and Macintosh, up-to-date details and a demonstration copy can be found at: **http://www.risinc.com/**

This site includes a head-to-head comparison between ProCite and its stablemate, Reference Manager.

Reference Manager

Developed within the life sciences community, Reference Manager is currently available as Reference Manager 9.0 (beta) for Microsoft Windows 98/95/NT4 and as Version 7 for Windows 3.1. A recent addition is a web interface called Reference Web Poster. Reference Manager is marketed by Reference Information Systems and details can be found at: **http://www.risinc.com/**

A booklet, entitled 'How to Select Bibliographic Management Software' is available at no charge from Reference Information Systems Inc, Camino Corporate Center, 2355 Camino Vida Roble, Carlsbad CA 92009, USA.

Other packages

Other packages available as Windows versions include Bibliographica 6.5, Bookwhere? 2000 3.0 (beta), Citation 7.0, GetaRef and Library Master. Bookends Plus is available for Macintosh only, by download from the web.

Methods of referencing print and electronic information

A traditional role for librarians is to provide advice concerning the layout and formatting of references. The world wide web has greatly assisted this support function. A number of the more popular style guides are available on the web and, in addition, many journal publishers have made their instructions to authors accessible from journal home pages. The primary sources for referencing styles are:

*   Vancouver style (Uniform Requirements for Manuscripts Submitted to Biomedical Journals):
    http://www.acponline.org/journals/resource/unifreqr.htm
*   the very useful Writer's Toolkit from the Health Science Library, University of Washington, covering a range of other common styles:
    http://www.hslib.washington.edu/toolkits/writer.html
*   the Medical College of Ohio has probably the largest collection of Instructions for Authors covering the principal biomedical journals:
    http://www.mco.edu/lib/instr/libinsta.html

In the past much time would be taken photocopying the relevant pages for instructions to authors or in compiling an index to issues containing the most recent version of these instructions. Now, thanks to the distributed power of the world wide web, such information is now within the reach of even the smallest biomedical collection.

Organizing bookmarks

Another skill of information organization and retrieval of more recent onset is compiling Internet bookmarks (or favourites, as they are called in Internet Explorer). Although an average Internet user might collect no more than 50 to 100 bookmarks in the course of their everyday work, a health library, with its variety of clients and the types of enquiries they generate, is soon able to amass over 200 key sites.

A preliminary step is to organize these into subject folders; either by specialty (eg cardiology or dermatology) or by purpose (eg directories, search engines, quick reference etc) or by a mixture of both. Additional refinements rely on the fact that bookmarks in Netscape are actually stored as HTML files of links and therefore can be copied and edited as required. For example, if a number of staff compile their own lists of bookmarks it is often good to merge these various bookmark pages into a single file using an ordinary text editor. The resultant page can then be saved on a server as a permanent web page. The staff, and users who are particularly interested, can then link to this bookmark page rather than having an endlessly accumulating list.

Another useful hint is to reconcile bookmarks between browsers using shareware software available on the web. So, for example, using Internet Explorer at home and Netscape Navigator at work you could use the *SAB Bookmark Converter* to convert Internet Explorer favourites to Netscape bookmarks or vice versa.

Other knowledge bases

All the above focus on the organization of materials without any implicit requirement for quality control. However, the advent of Evidence Based Healthcare has introduced a need to organize materials of high quality in an attempt to answer clinically meaningful questions. There are three information management techniques that can be used to improve retrieval and utilization of information identified for this purpose. These are structured abstracts, evidence digests and critically appraised topics.

Structured abstracts

Structured abstracts were proposed in the early 1980s as a means of organizing journal abstracts so as to yield valuable information, particularly on study design and methodology, speedily and efficiently. Structured abstracts are used by many of the major biomedical journals (eg the *British Medical Journal*, the *Journal of the American Medical Association*, etc) as well as by many evidence based databases (DARE, NEED, the Cochrane Library and Best Evidence). Work in the social sciences has shown that such abstracts are easier to read and elicit greater detail, while work in clinical medicine has shown that they can be used for more specific retrieval of articles answering clinical questions. The MEDLINE database contains a number of structured abstracts, but fails to capitalize on their improved retrieval potential because it places all the structured components in a single abstract field. It is clear, even at this early stage, that structuring abstracts in retrieval systems is a relatively easy and low-cost method of improving the organization of personal knowledge bases (McKibbon and Walker-Dilks, 1995).

Evidence digests

Another information management technique of increased popularity is the evidence based digest. Digests have been in the armoury of the business librarian for many years. In recent years they have come to be appreciated as a means of summarizing the main points of otherwise lengthy research articles and then providing a brief and easily read means of dissemination. There are two main types of evidence based digest: topic based and article based.

Topic based digests are usually stimulated by clinical or purchasing questions and provide brief summaries of the body of literature on a particular topic. They are designed as a launch pad to original source materials that provide more detailed coverage of a topic. Such digests are found in the *Journal of Clinical Excellence* as well as being produced by the Primary Care Information Service at South Humber Health Authority (*Evidence Matters*). They usually contain basic information in support of the epidemiology and the importance of a particular topic followed by evidence on clinical effectiveness (usually graded according to source). An example of the use of evidence based digests is in Barnsley Health Authority where evidence supporting bids for development monies was presented as one-page summaries for the public health doctors (Dixon, Booth and Perrett, 1997).

Article based digests take their lead from the single-page articles included in the journals *Evidence Based Medicine, Evidence Based Healthcare, Evidence Based Nursing* and *ACP Journal Club*. The stimulus for production is the appearance of new research likely to provide an answer to a clinically important question. The distinction between these and the topic based digests lies in the fact that they are driven by the availability of relevant literature. They are selected according to methodological rigour and the appropriateness of the study design to the question under consideration. An example of these in a practical setting is the *Verdict* bulletin produced by North Cumbria Health Authority which covers findings from articles of local relevance.

Digests, whether topic based or article based, have an important part to play in the management of the volume and the quality of healthcare information. To this end training in the production of critically appraised digests has been delivered to librarians in Trent Region, South Thames Region and those working in the Department of Health Library.

Critically appraised topics (CATS)

A form of digest that requires separate mention, both for its immediacy to clinical decisions and its potential for developing personal knowledge bases, is the critically appraised topic (CAT) (Sauve et al, 1995; Wyer, 1997; Sackett and Straus, 1998). Using a format developed by the pioneers of evidence based medicine and then popularized through the development of CAT-Maker demonstration software, these digests are instigated as a result of a clinical problem presenting to an individual clinician. The clinician will conduct a specific search on the problem and then appraise the evidence in a brief digest. These CATS can then be stored in the purpose-made software and shared with other colleagues. Examples of these are found on the web at: **http://cebm.jr2.ox.ac.uk/docs/catbank.html**

Trial software called CAT-Nipper, so called because the user is given 'nine lives' or digests, is available for downloading from the Centre for Evidence Based Medicine website. The *British Medical Journal* has published a number of evidence based case reports (eg May 30 1998, July 25 1998, February 6 1999, March 20 1999, April 17 1999, July 17 1999, July 31 1999, January 8 2000 and January 15 2000) that illustrate the process behind the creation of CATS and related products (Glasziou, 1998; Mulrow, 1998; Dawes et al, 1999; Hicks et al, 1999; Graham and Fahey, 1999; Samanta and Beardsley, 1999; Vause and Macintosh, 1999; Parker, 2000; Del Mar, 2000).

Conclusion

Effective information management is no longer the sole province of the library or information resource centre. The increasing availability of reasonably inexpensive software to assist in the management of references or the results of research, coupled with increasing enthusiasm and proficiency in their use, has opened up a new role for librarians as consumer adviser, consultant and trainer. The increasing demand for Personal Bibliographical Management Software increases the opportunities for librarians to deliver integrated training from retrieval through to management and report production. It has never been easier for an individual to manage their own knowledge base – the challenge for health information workers is how they may improve individual knowledge management while continuing to operate within a more hands-off and arms-length distributed information culture.

Key points

- The exponential growth of the literature and interest in evidence based healthcare has placed a premium on reference management skills and the software to facilitate them.
- Many personal bibliographic management packages share common features including data capture, a search facility, a report utility and, optionally, a communications facility.
- Criteria for evaluating personal bibliographic management software will include the software, general features and the supplier.
- Traditional skills in organizing and managing bibliographic references now need to be augmented by the ability to organize Internet bookmarks and to handle evidence based products in a variety of formats.

21
Keeping up to date with the knowledge base

Andrew Booth

Introduction

Healthcare organizations are being required to develop knowledge management to enable clinicians to retrieve information at the point of need, as well as to facilitate tailored periodic update. The imperative for clinical governance, a recent feature of the British National Health Service, requires targeting of clinical effectiveness information. As Richardson (1999) states: 'Widespread awareness of research evidence is central to improving clinical effectiveness. But if information is not disseminated, the process breaks down.'

This chapter provides guidance on how to monitor the knowledge base and keep up to date with advances in research and practice. Methods of setting up selective dissemination of information (SDI) services, and using contents page delivery services, are described. Use of the Internet will be discussed, including various current awareness systems and intelligent agents. The aim of this chapter is to equip readers with the information and skills required to keep their knowledge base refreshed with relevant, timely and accurate information.

Current awareness services

The architect of the National electronic Library for Health, Muir Gray (1998), states that there are two major challenges to keeping up to date with the knowledge base:

> Firstly, the probability that a disseminated document will arrive on someone's desk the moment it is needed is infinitesimally small. Secondly, the probability that the same document will be found three months later, when it is needed, is even smaller.

Such a situation is by no means a new one. What *is* new is accountability within an organization for the adoption and monitoring of information on clinical effectiveness. It is to this that Muir Gray alludes when he continues:

> Just who is responsible in an organization for looking at the new Cochrane reviews each quarter and drawing the board's attention to the action that is required? Who is responsible for ensuring that the people who are buying equipment – ripple mattresses, for example – are receiving a knowledge service from the librarian?

LIS professionals have many decades of experience in information retrieval and current awareness, particularly SDI, services. A current awareness service (CAS) is 'a service which provides the recipient with information on the latest developments within the subject areas in which he or she has a specific interest or need to know' (Hamilton, 1995). In short, a good CAS is based on four main factors (Hamilton, 1995):

- knowing what topics to cover
- knowing who wants what
- knowing the sources for obtaining the latest information
- supplying that information regularly and reliably, year in and year out.

Bate (1995) identified eight important principles that should determine the local configuration of a CAS: types of user, coverage, timeliness, relevance, content, ease of use, cost and feedback.

The detail of how to set up a CAS is well covered by Cox and Hanson (1992), still one of the best introductions to the issues involved. It covers such obvious considerations as local needs of users and local requirements of software and sources of data. It also covers less obvious issues such as staffing, charging for the service, promotion, creation of search profiles, mailing of results, record-keeping, document supply, effects on periodicals subscriptions and impact on users, the issues that continue to impact most on the organization and delivery of a CAS.

The concept of a CAS is very alluring to health professionals. A survey of nursing staff in Plymouth (Crane and Urquhart, 1994) found 92% would use a specialized CAS were it available. Such services require intensive investment of the time and knowledge of LIS staff, careful strategic planning and a robust business case (Harris and Marshall, 1996). On the one hand a tailored CAS provides a wonderful marketing opportunity to raise the profile of the information service; on the other hand opportunity costs may lie in cataloguing backlogs and lengthening turnaround for enquiries. Crane and Urquhart (1994) found that subjects chosen for an SDI service were general and multidisciplinary in nature, requiring searching through a wide range of journals. They point out that users often use 'current awareness' services as a check that they have read the relevant literature, rather than for current awareness *per se*. They suggest that more emphasis be placed on educating users in skills for lifelong updating rather than on a library-centred SDI service. Certainly the philosophy that users take responsibility for their ongoing education is in tune with evidence based practice and lifelong learning.

Recent years have seen improvements in technology, the free availability of bibliographic databases via the Internet (such as the impressive UnCover service (Galpern and Albert, 1997)) and the increasing view among journal publishers, subscription agents and database vendors that current awareness information is an essential value-added service. These factors have combined to reduce the marginality of the decision as to whether or not a local service should provide current awareness services. The potential for the LIS professional to act more as guide than gatekeeper, accompanied by a corresponding popularity for end-user retrospective services, presages a role that may optimize skills and resources.

Bibliographic based services

The SDI service has been a regular feature of online services for many years. The service provider or host provides the facility to set up and save search strategies to be run on a regular basis (Trench, 1997). In the past a monthly printout would be sent to the requesting library which would record details on cost and number of references before delivering it through the internal mail (Watson, Christopher and Wood, 1997). Profiles would often be prepared offline and loaded to the host machine as a batch file.

Increasingly, the electronic CAS is not regarded as an additional cost item over and above the database subscription (for example, the Ovid Biomed service allows each user to store a number of profiles to be run on a periodic basis), and delivery is via e-mail to the user's own mailbox. Presentation of results in electronic form allows uploading of results to a personal reference management system (see Chapter 20) where users can mark relevant items and generate photocopy requests. Databases such as MEDLINE and the Cochrane Library increasingly have the tailored facility to search for items added since the last update.

A related facility, offered by the National Library of Medicine's Internet Grateful Med interface, allows a LIS to embed Hypertext Markup Language (HTML) into a library web page, creating a button by which a user can activate a specific search against the database. As Internet Grateful Med includes PRE-MEDLINE, which prioritizes bibliographic details from core journals for rapid processing, the user has, in effect, a subject index to current articles on their library shelves.

Journal based services

The niche marketing of specialty journals has ensured that contents pages play an important part in alerting services. Photocopying contents pages, an alternative to the slow circulation of a key journal around an organization, was the precursor to services such as the Institute for Scientific Information's Current Contents services. With the development of electronic publishing, reproduction of contents pages is no longer only for the specialist service. Most journals provide contents pages of their most recent issue as part of their web presence. However, readers are expected to visit the site on a periodic basis or may they receive a direct e-mail containing the contents pages? Publishers very often want to attract the reader to their site for advertising purposes, yet the reader does not want to check sites fruitlessly. A compromise is found in hybrid systems where the reader is perhaps sent an alert with titles only and then visits the site to view abstracts or selective full text. Excerpta Medica has created e-mail distribution lists for many of its journals as an alerting service to subscribing institutions. The UK academic BUBL service also combines the table of contents and abstracts of some 200 largely library and information science-oriented journals with an e-mail alerting service (Kibbee, 1994; McMahon, 1995).

Journal subscription agents also recognize the added value of current awareness facilities alongside their traditional journal supply. An example is EBSCO which offers a CAS (EBSCO Alert) alongside the EBSCOHost world wide web (WWW), based online, and the EBSCO Online electronic periodicals service system. Another example comes from the Information Services Group of the Dawson corporation. Their online web based research tool, Information Quest

(IQ), includes current awareness (IQ Alerts) alongside document delivery, pay-per-view and journal management. The *British Medical Journal* provides an update facility as part of its free electronic BMJ (eBMJ) Internet service. The reader registers an author name or keyword with the eBMJ's server, thereby generating an automatic e-mail alert whenever that search term is found in the latest journal issue.

Internet based services

Several authors draw parallels between the new generation of publish and subscribe (push) technologies available via the Internet and the traditional special libraries' SDI function (eg Anderson, 1998; Brenner, 1997). Push technology is designed to publish information across the Internet and world wide web on an individual basis, based on predefined interests, direct to users' hard drives (Collins, 1997). Andrews (1997) has produced a state of the art review. The Internet also has considerable impact as a delivery mechanism for the more traditional CAS (Kiley, 1997a).

Intelligent agents

An intelligent agent is 'a piece of software which learns from your responses, and is able to search the Web while you are not there, looking for more information which can then be presented to you when you log on next time' (Bradley, 1999). Intelligent agents may be hosted on a website or downloaded as client software on your own PC. An example of the former is Informant, where the user registers a profile in terms of keywords and/or sites of interest and then receives an e-mail informing them of new sites or amendments. The user then logs in to their personal space to view results and follow any identified links of interest. A drawback of such a site is the opaqueness of the identification process. Sites that have been in existence for some time can be flagged up as 'new' and minor textual changes can register as 'updated'. Nevertheless, the value of such sites, particularly in a tightly defined topic area, should not be underestimated.

An example of the client software approach is the Agentware Suite produced by Autonomy. In this case one 'trains' an agent, either by entering keywords or by indicating the relevance of particular sites. Then the agent is unleashed on the web to retrieve similar items for review. Despite the novelty value of some of its features – the agent is represented as a dog – this software has tremendous potential for a CAS. As Bradley (1999) concludes:

> If you are running a Current awareness service an intelligent agent may well be the best approach to take by presenting you with a variety of results. You can then just pick the best, saving you the time and energy it would otherwise have taken to run the search once a month or even once a day.

A variation on the intelligent agent is the customized newspage. This can be a unique view of articles from a single newspaper arranged according to your specified interest (as being investigated by *The Times*) or a compilation of news items from a number of sources brought together in a single web page. Each time you visit your newspaper it is updated with information from preselected subject categories. The migration of this technology from popular press to professional journals, allowing clinicians to design their personalized professional update, is surely just around the corner. An example of such a personalized newspaper is Crayon (**http://www.crayon.net**). Within the field of library and information science the NewsAgent for Libraries project (Tedd and Yeates, 1998; Secker, Stoker and Tedd, 1997; Stoker and Secker, 1997), funded by the Electronic Libraries (eLib) Programme in the UK (**http://www.sbu.ac.uk/litc/newsagent/**) aims to create a user-configurable electronic news and current awareness service for library and information professionals.

A less sophisticated use of the Internet is the e-mail newsletter. The reader registers for a free subscription and then periodically (typically weekly) receives a newsletter containing snippets of news together with hypertext links to fuller articles. An example of this is Pharmaceutical Online Newsletter which monitors business news and product developments in the pharmaceutical industry (**http://www.pharmaceuticalonline.com**). Although such services have impressive currency, they are increasingly populated with commercial advertising at the expense of information richness. The Internet has extended the concept of current awareness beyond printed sources, for example with the facility to search newsgroups (Notess, 1998).

In-house systems

Although technological advances have improved the feasibility of CAS and have transferred the onus from intermediary to end-user, it is wrong to assume that there is no place for small-scale paper based systems. As the eBMJ web author and editor of the BMJ (Delamothe and Smith, 1998) remind us, 'the 2% of the world's population who are online may be suffering from an information glut, but what of the 75% who have yet to hear a telephone dial tone, let alone get online?' In the developing world, where Internet access can neither be guaranteed nor taken for granted (Smith, 1998), services based on the regular receipt of CD-ROM updates still persist (Herala, Ravi and Rajashekar, 1995). As Delamothe and Smith report:

> Poor connections mean that even those with internet access 'must spend hours downloading material that would take only minutes for those in the developed world with the best access'.

However, Delamothe and Smith qualify their argument by stating that:

> Medical libraries in these countries seem far more likely to acquire computers with internet access than they do to fill their shelves with a critical mass of current information.

Even in the developed world, many libraries still perform a valuable alerting function simply by displaying new accessions and distributing accession lists or by circulating journals or photocopying contents pages. However, where the medium acts not simply as an alerting function but is also an integral part of the service (eg where the reader can respond by reserving or requesting a book title), it is less likely that it will be perceived as a mere marketing ploy. It is the LIS manager's task to balance demands for such services with available resources. It is important, too, to record those success stories where timely information delivered in a current awareness context leads to greater efficiency or effectiveness within the organization. Intranet technologies also expand opportunities for cross-organization networking, e-mail and the creation of bulletin boards (Shipman, 1994).

A current awareness function that continues to demonstrate its usefulness is the press cuttings service. Traditionally performed either in-house or through daily receipt from an agency of clippings that match a library's profile, the increasing availability of free online quality newspapers (*The Times* and *Daily Telegraph*) and of online news services (Reuters or the BBC) makes such activities increasingly feasible. Distribution can be via the WWW (as with the King's

Fund service), via an intranet, via e-mail or as paper via internal mail or the traditional press cuttings board.

Case study

Keeping a ScHARR-P eye on the news

The School of Health and Related Research (ScHARR), University of Sheffield, uses a number of methods for current awareness. Each morning an information assistant interrogates web versions of *The Times* and *Daily Telegraph* and prints out articles retrieved against a number of keywords. These include 'health technology assessment', 'health services research', 'National Institute for Clinical Excellence', the name and acronym of the school and the names of the various health ministers. This is followed by a quick browse of the Department of Health's website for new press releases. Although e-mail distribution is being considered, it is felt that the positioning of a press cuttings board outside the Dean's Office in close proximity to the staffroom gives the facility high profile and acceptability.

Information on research funding is identified from e-mails, websites and preferential paper based mailings and distributed via an internal e-mail discussion list. Hypertext links to relevant application forms or further details of funding calls are included in the e-mail and occasionally electronic versions of the forms are placed on the school's intranet. A final current awareness function relates to the Higher Education Funding Council for England's Research Assessment Exercise (RAE) and funding opportunities from major bodies such as the Medical Research Council. URLs for relevant web pages are registered with the Informant intelligent agent and the information assistant informed of changes by a weekly e-mail.

Evaluation of CAS

A danger for the CAS is that, without good evaluation and feedback mechanisms, it may gain a life of its own. Readers can tolerate regular delivery of a redundant current awareness listing for a considerable time before alerting the library of its obsolescence. Bate (1995) suggests that a brief evaluation form should accompany the SDI listing at regular, possibly quarterly or six-monthly, intervals. She goes on to say that 'at its worst the service will do little more than add to information overload leading to a devaluing of the service'. Significantly, an otherwise good book outlining the practice of current awareness (Hamilton, 1995) makes little mention of review and evaluation.

A recent study comparing the features and performance of four CAS pre-eminent in the medical information field (Bandemer and Tannery, 1998) identifies three factors of importance: ease of use, health sciences coverage, and journal currency. Davies, Boyle and Osborne (1998) conducted a series of surveys at the Imperial Cancer Research Fund, UK, over a four-year period. By 1997, for over 50% of a sample of titles, the shelf issue was more current, or as current, as the alerting services. They conclude that the performance of current awareness services combined with individual article supply (CASIAS) services needs to be monitored for the foreseeable future. The British Library Research and Innovation Centre has funded an examination of CASIAS in the academic research community, exploring issues relating to users' views and implications for libraries and service providers (Brunskill, 1996; Brunskill, 1997a, b).

Evaluation of CAS is not only an opportunity for monitoring, but provides an 'excuse' for regular contact with potentially heavy users of other library services. It can help identify new staff members or subject areas and provide valuable intelligence on the business activities of the organization. This in turn can yield considerable benefits for processes such as enquiries or book and journal selection.

Conclusion

It is difficult to predict with any great accuracy the future direction of CAS due simply to the tremendous pace of development. Services are likely to get more personalized and more integrated with other unrelated everyday activities. Technology *has* made it easier to transfer information faster, but the answer to the longstanding issues of delivery of CAS lies in the intelligence being brought to the search engines. The trend for the article rather than the journal to be the unit of customization will likely continue. The textual emphasis that still predominates is likely, with increasing bandwidth, to be overtaken by audio and audiovisual media such as news broadcasts and digital pictures. The means for access will probably migrate from keyboard based systems to those using touch screens or, more likely, voice recognition. The context for information will probably change too with the separation between the work environment and the home environment becoming increasingly indistinct. Notwithstanding the above, the future of an 'intelligent agent' (Zick, 1999) that will mediate the information profile of its users from appropriate sources and optimize retrieval at the point of need (aka the health information worker) looks assured for considerable time to come!

Key points

- A good CAS is based on knowing what topics to cover, knowing who wants what, knowing the sources for obtaining the latest information and supplying that information regularly and reliably.
- Some commentators believe that training end-users to find information for themselves should command more attention than provision of CAS.
- An increasing number of market sectors, including journal publishers, subscription agents and database vendors, provide current awareness facilities.
- 'Intelligent agents' and 'push technologies' hold out the prospect of personalized information services, supplied direct to the user.
- CAS require a great deal of effort and thus should be monitored and evaluated on a regular basis to ensure they remain in line with users' objectives.

22
Some concluding trends and themes

Andrew Booth and Graham Walton

Introduction

The composite picture painted by the contributors to this book has sought to harmonize individual interpretations with recurring trends and themes. The foreground of our 'scope of practice' is becoming ever more complex and continues to be offset against the backdrop of an operating environment that is subject to constant change and revision. Information scientists may be equipped to scan the horizon, but they possess silicon chips, not crystal balls, and should heed the cautionary lessons afforded by eminent commentators who have gone before:

> There is not the slightest indication that [nuclear energy] will ever be obtainable. It would mean that the atom would have to be shattered at will. (Albert Einstein, 1932)

> [Television] won't be able to hold on to any market it captures after the first six months. People will soon get tired of staring at a plywood box every night. (Darryl F. Zanuck, head of Twentieth Century Fox, 1946)

The purpose of this epilogue is to accentuate some of the trends already highlighted by contributors that will impact on health library and information service providers.

Health services

Health services have continued to be a microcosm for prevailing trends from society as a whole, for example the self governance of education and the accountability of social services. Primary care is increasingly becoming the focus for the delivery of healthcare and this has seen increased interest in cooperative arrangements for information collection and provision. Primary care groups or trusts potentially offer the same stimulus for information service delivery as the purchasing intelligence movement of the 1990s provided for health authorities (see Chapters 3 and 4). Two essential differences exist, however. First, the technology now exists to make such visions of integrated corporate information systems a reality (eg intranet technologies). Secondly, the operating environment is likely to embrace several competing, or even conflicting, practice cultures instead of the relative uniformity of a single health authority.

Debates continue to rage around issues of quasi-rationing – the conflict for resources between low-volume, high-cost technologies (exemplified by beta interferon, donepezil, riluzole, etc) and less spectacular but more routine healthcare interventions (compression stockings for leg ulcers) continues to occupy the domain of the commissioners of health services (see Chapter 1). The creation of the National Institute for Clinical Excellence in the UK is likely to yield further impetus to the so-called 'guidelines movement'. Such a trend towards centralist control is ironic, running counter to the decision of the US government that halted guideline production at the Agency for Healthcare Policy Research in favour of the production of evidence reviews. The managerial versus clinical battle for power, neatly side-stepped over a decade ago by making clinical audit a peer-reviewed activity, is now likely to be enacted under the standard of 'clinical governance' (see Chapter 2) . Whether this will see the end of medical autonomy and the 'tyranny' of the clinician remains to be seen. Will the health information provider become the supplier of the 'clinical effectiveness stick' by which the manager beats the clinician? Or the bulwark against which clinicians build their risk minimization defence? The jury is still out.

The very concept of 'health services' is itself being challenged by the growth in 'self care". The realization that an individual is a being more than the sum of his/her physical and psychological parts is reflected by the growth in complementary therapies and renewed interest in coping strategies and empowerment (see Chapters 1 and 5). Such a development is intriguing given the potential for the increasing mechanization, and corresponding dehumanization, offered by high-tech healthcare.

Technology

Interest in the technology of healthcare tends to concentrate on 'Tomorrow's World' scenarios of highly expensive equipment and increasingly specialist staff. In practice it is the potential of existing consumer technologies as they migrate to the healthcare domain that is more revolutionary. An obvious example is the smart card – now universal in the sphere of banking – which has the potential to store health data as a patient-held clinical record. Spin-off possibilities for information are not so far-fetched as to be the domain of science fiction. The prospect of being presented with supporting evidence linked to the clinical record or of printing off patient-tailored information on a condition or its treat-ment is more likely to be impeded by procedural and medico-legal considerations than technical ones. Similarly the application of telemedicine (see Chapter 1), already evidenced in the telemonitoring of foetal heartbeats or the digitization and transmission of medical images, is being broadened through developments in satellite or fibreoptic communications. The 'plywood box' mentioned above, ironically, might become an umbilical cord for commu-nication between householder and primary care gatekeeper.

The end-user

The end-user phenomenon is mentioned several times throughout this book (see Chapters 2 and 11), and health LIS providers, in common with many other information professionals, are facing difficult decisions relating to the appropri-ate balance between time spent on direct service provision and user training (see Chapter 14). A disturbing fact is that human–computer interfaces are not devel-oping at a pace that is commensurate with the explosion of information resources. Information providers therefore find that they are spending a fixed amount of time spread more thinly across an increasing number of tools and interfaces. Given that discussions about proprietal versus generic interfaces have commanded the attention of the CD-ROM industry for over 15 years with lit-tle apparent progress, there are few reasons for optimism in the even more complex world of the Web.

More and more frequently, users are likely to explore an increasing range of routes for obtaining customized information (see Chapter 21) and the informa-tion provider will therefore be required to operate in something of a 'free market' (see Chapter 12). This will require that they emphasize the value-added nature of their services including an increasing role as 'web navigator' (see Chapter 18) and the evaluator and appraiser of resources (see Chapter 9) .

Location of resources

The emphasis of this book has not been on any physical location or resource, but rather on the management of knowledge and the skills required to enable this. Critics of this approach might feel that the balance has swung too far – cataloguing and classification of knowledge now command barely a page of text. Nevertheless trends in information provision have not only seen the renaissance of peripatetic roles such as the clinical medical librarian and the emergence of roles in the community or in general practice, but even the stereotypical location-bound hospital librarian being offered an ancillary 'virtual' location via the hospital intranet. Increasingly, the prospect of users receiving a comprehensive package of information services without having to set foot in a location that is labelled 'the library' is proffered by networking technologies.

A logical extension of the 'library without walls' is referred to by several of the contributors in the form of the National electronic Library for Health (NeLH) (eg Chapter 11). Significantly the source material for envisaging what this much-heralded resource might look like is, at present, both scarce and sketchy. It will only be once the *Information for health* strategy starts realizing its deliverables that health information providers will fully appreciate the impact that the NeLH may have on local information provision. The lack of a National Library of Medicine in the UK had been bemoaned for a long time prior to the Cumberlege seminars that appraised the state of the knowledge base of healthcare (see Chapter 3). It is likely that the NeLH may yield the clearest picture yet of what such a deficiency means in practice. It is also imperative that those driving the NeLH draw on the very relevant knowledge base, mentioned several times within this book, derived from the experience of the academic eLib projects.

Role of health LIS providers

The array of skills that makes up the role of the health LIS provider continues to grow at a bewildering rate (see Chapter 4). The solution to such demands continues to lie, not just in the professional development of the individual, but also in improved patterns of networking and collaborative working, perhaps no longer constrained by geographical proximity. Virtual networks of professionals working in a particular speciality, for example orthopaedics librarians, can comprise an impressive knowledge base – one whose potential is already hinted at by the increasing number of success stories arising from use of general purpose discussion lists.

Health LIS units derive much of their rationale and many of their tenets of professional practice from the fact that they are, in the main, special libraries that focus on health. This is being evidenced ever more clearly in the health information specialist being required to work on the interpretation and evaluation of materials and not just their identification. Critical appraisal skills and the accompanying requirement to digest and synthesize information (see Chapter 19), rather than solely locate it (see Chapters 17 and 18), move the librarian closer to the clinician and bring in new considerations around liability and risk management. Rather than seeing such a transition as a threat, the entrepreneurial health LIS manager will seek to construct the principles and procedures that serve to ensure safe and competent practice. A parallel movement in those health libraries with more of an academic base is seen in the development of a problem based learning paradigm where the subject specialist is required to equip the users with skills rather than merely exploit resources (see Chapter 2). One way or another, the health LIS specialist appears destined to become more accountable and this places an imperative on their own skills for lifelong learning. Professional networks are correspondingly beginning to evolve from information 'swap-shops' to ever more important channels for expertise and repositories for knowledge.

Accumulated expertise and a shared knowledge base are characteristics of another trend that may contribute to an increasing profile for the healthcare information providers – an emphasis on evidence based librarianship. Library and information science, ironically for a profession responsible for information acquisition and transfer, is not renowned for its utilization of research findings. Health information professionals are in a uniquely advantageous position to apply the methodologies of systematic review and critical appraisal to information science. The challenge is for researchers to tackle the questions, and indeed to design the 'right type' of studies, to contribute to a poorly served knowledge base for our professional practice.

Consumer health information

Any classification of the health information domain, prerequisite as it may be to the structure of a book such as this, is likely to have both strengths and deficiencies. A regrettable consequence of the way we have structured the book is that, notwithstanding excellent treatment in the chapter on consumer health information (see Chapter 5), coverage of the interests of consumers may appear somewhat tokenistic. Of course nothing could be further from the truth. NHS Direct Online experienced over 1.5 million hits within its first 48 hours and its impact will continue to escalate. Information providers who serve the professional community will be required to counterbalance the free flow of consumer health information with comparably reliable, timely and up-to-date information to the constituencies that they serve. Those who directly deliver information to the consumer will have to build in checks and quality assurance procedures to safeguard both their own interests and those of an ever more demanding clientele. The consumer health information sector could well drive an agenda that other health LIS units will seek to follow.

Conclusion

With health services, technology, users, location, roles and the interests of consumers all witnessing such sustained development, the health LIS manager risks concluding 'The only constant is change'. This book belies such an impression. The skills required in managing knowledge in health services will continue to be the most valuable asset the health LIS professional can supply. These include the skills needed to evaluate, and respond to, the external environment (Part 1; Chapters 1–5), the skills required to develop and sustain a health information service (Part 2; Chapters 6–14) and the technical skills required, by LIS professionals and users alike, to exploit information resources (Part 3; Chapters 15–21). These skills are a greater legacy than cumulated lists of resources or directories of contact details. We, the editors, commend these skills to the health LIS professionals of today and tomorrow, speaking not as the exponents of such skills, but merely as those who have been privileged both to observe and to record them.

References

Abbott, C M (1998) Personal career development in converged services, *Librarian Career Development*, **16** (3), 107.

Adams, V M and Plosker, G R (1997) Concepts in end-user training: how to convert end users into effective searchers, *Searcher*, **5** (5), 8–20.

Adcock, D et al (1995) *Marketing principles and practice*, 3rd edn, Pitman Publishing.

Alexander, L D (1989) Successfully implementing strategic decisions. In Asch, D and Bowman, C (eds) *Readings in strategic management*, Macmillan, 388–97.

Allen, Bryce L (1996) *Information tasks. Towards a user-centered approach to information systems*, Academic Press.

Anderson, C R (1998) Proactive reference, *Reference and User Services Quarterly*, **38** (2), 139–40.

Andrews, W (1997) Planning for the push, *Internet World,* **8** (5), 44–52.

Anon (1999) On the critical list, *The Economist* (13 February), 89–90.

Ansoff, H (1986) *Corporate strategy*, Penguin.

Antman, E M, Lau, J, Kupelnick, B, Mosteller, F and Chalmers, T C (1992) A comparison of results of meta-analyses of randomized control trials and recommendations of clinical experts. Treatments for myocardial infarction, *Journal of the American Medical Association*, **268** (2), 240–8.

Appleby, J (1998) Population projections, *Health Service Journal* (7 May), 38–9.

Asch, D (1989) Strategic control: an overview of the issues. In Asch, D and Bowman, C (eds) *Readings in strategic management*, Macmillan, 398–408.

Ash, J S (1999) Factors affecting the diffusion of online end user literature searching, *Bulletin of the Medical Library Association*, **87** (1), 58–66.

Audit Commission (1995) *For your information: a study of information management and systems in acute hospitals*, HMSO.

Auster, E (1983) User satisfaction with the online negotiation interview: contemporary concern in traditional perspective, *RQ*, **23** (1), 47–59.

Ball, C et al (1999–) *Levels of evidence and grades of recommendation*. Centre for Evidence-Based Medicine, available at:
http://cebm.jr2.ox.ac.uk/docs/levels.html

Bandemer, J and Tannery, N H (1998) A comparison of four current awareness services, *Medical Reference Services Quarterly*, **17** (2), 29–36.

Banwell, L et al (1994) Northumbria University at Newcastle, *R & D information in the NHS: information needs assessment phase 2 in the Northern and Yorkshire Region,* NHS Executive (N & Y) Research and Development.

Banwell, L, Day, J and Ray K (1999) *Managing organisational change in the hybrid library*, UKOLN.

Barden, P (1997) Training and development for library and information workers for the future: a manifesto, *Librarian Career Development*, **5** (1), 1–4.

Barker, J (1999) *NICE Project (new information for clinical effectiveness): Project closure report,* Clinical Effectiveness Support Unit, for Welsh Office.

Barlow, J and Harrison, K (1996) Focusing on empowerment: facilitating self-help in young people with arthritis through disability organisations, *Disability and Society,* **11** (4), 539–51.

Barnes, E (1961) *People in hospital*, Macmillan.

Barnes, J (1998) Complementary medicine: homeopathy, *Pharmaceutical Journal*, **260**, 492–7.

Barraclough, C (1993) Planning an automated library, *Cape Librarian,* **37** (10), 6–8.

Barrie, A R and Ward, A M (1997) Questioning behaviour in general practice: a pragmatic study, *British Medical Journal*, **315**, 1512–15.

Barry, C A (1997) Information skills for an electronic world: training doctoral research students, *Journal of Information Science*, **23** (3), 225–38.

Barton, J and Blagden, J (1998) *Academic library effectiveness: a comparative approach*, Research and Innovation Report 120, British Library.

Basker, J (1997) Resourcing the information centre. In Scammel, A (ed) *Handbook of special librarianship and information work*, 7th edn, Aslib.

Batchelor, B (1997) Marketing the Information Service. In Scammell, A (ed) *Handbook of special librarianship and information work*, 7th edn, Aslib.

Bate, L (1995) Current awareness services. In Carmel, M (ed) *Health care librarianship and information work*, 2nd edn, Library Association Publishing.

Bates, M E (1997) The Internet: threat or asset? *Information Outlook,* **1** (1), 20–3.

Bawden, D and Robinson, K (1994) *Information systems for nursing specialities*, BLRD Report, British Library Research and Development Department.

Baymann, A (1992) Planning a microlaboratory: ergonomic factors, *Health Libraries Review*, **9** (1), 38–40.

Beatty, A (1996) *The integration of text-based information into management information strategies in health care: developing a framework for the effective delivery of text information services to managers and policy makers to support the implementation of the Irish national health strategy*, MSc dissertation, University of Wales Aberystwyth.

Belbin, M (1981) *Management teams: why do they succeed or fail*, Heinemann.

Bell, J (1998) The new genetics of clinical care, *British Medical Journal*, **316** (7131), 618–20.

Bennett, P (1997) Editorial, *Health Libraries Review*, **14**, 199–200.

Berger, A and Smith, P (1999) New technologies in medicine and medical journals, *British Medical Journal*, **319**, (7220), 0, available at: **http://www.bmj.com/cgi/content/full/319/7220/0**

Biggs, D R (1995) *ProCite in libraries: applications in bibliographic database management*, Information Today, Inc.

Bisnath, V and Bolam, T (1999) *Mental health care: a core collection including further reading: The Derwen List*, Tomlinsons.

Bjorner, S (1995a) Bibliography formatting software for managing search results: EndNote Plus and EndLink, *Online*, **19** (5), 38–43.

Bjorner, S (1995b) Moving online search results into EndNote, *Online*, **19** (6), 62–7.

Blansit, B D and Connor, E (1999) Making sense of the electronic resource marketplace: trends in health-related electronic resources, *Bulletin of the Medical Library Association*, **87** (3), 243–50.

Blumberg, P and Sparks, J (1999) Tracing the evolution of critical evaluation skills in students' use of the Internet, *Bulletin of the Medical Library Association*, **87** (2), 200–5.

Blumenthal, D (1999) Health care reform at the close of the 20th century, *New England Journal of Medicine*, **340** (24), 1916–20.

Bonnett, P (1992) The development of interlending through the BMA's institutional membership scheme, *Assistant Librarian*, **85** (12), 179–82.

Bonnett, P (1997) Editorial, *Health Libraries Review*, **14** (4), 1999, 200.

Booth, A (1995) Teaching evidence-based medicine – lessons for information professionals, *IFMH Inform*, **6** (2), 5–6.

Booth, A (1996) In search of the evidence: informing effective practice, *Journal of Clinical Effectiveness*, **1** (1), 25–9.

Booth, A (1998) The Internet: quantity not quality, *Student British Medical Journal*, **6**, 49.

Booth, A and Haines, M (1993) Information audit: whose line is it anyway? *Health Libraries Review*, **10** (4), 224–32.

Booth, A and Madge, B (1998) Finding the evidence. In Bury, T J and Mead, J M, *Evidence-based healthcare: a practical guide for therapists*, Butterworth Heinemann.

Booth, A and O'Rourke, A J (1997) The value of structured abstracts in information retrieval from Medline, *Health Libraries Review*, **14** (3), 157–66.

Booth, A and O'Rourke, A J (1999) Searching for evidence: principles and practice, *Evidence-Based Medicine*, **4** (5), 133–6.

Borger, R and Seaborne, A E M (1982) *The psychology of learning*, Penguin.

Boshuizen, H P A and Schmidt, H G (1992) On the role of biomedical knowledge in clinical reasoning by experts, intermediates and novices, *Cognitive Science*, **16**, 153–84.

Boud, D, Keogh, R and Walker, D (1985) *Reflection: turning experience into learning*, Kogan Page.

Bradley, P (1998) *Web/CD-ROM hybrids*, available at:
http://www.philb.com/webcd.htm

Bradley, P (1999) Intelligent agents on the Web, *Managing Information*, **6** (1), 35–41.

Braude, R M (1989) Role of libraries in medical education, *Bulletin of the New York Academy of Medicine,* **65** (6), 704–27.

Breeding, M (1999) Does the web spell doom for CD and DVD? *Computers in Libraries*, **19** (10), 70–5.

Brember, V L and Leggate, P (1985) Linking a medical user survey to management for library effectiveness: I The user survey, *Journal of Documentation* **41** (1), 1–14.

Brenner, E (1997) A 'push' by any other name, *Information Today*, **14** (3), 11.

British Library (1992) *Health care information in the UK: report of a seminar held on 1st July 1992 at the King's Fund Centre, London chaired by Baroness Cumberlege*, British Library R&D Report 6089, British Library.

British Library (1993) *Managing the knowledge base of healthcare: report of a seminar held on 22nd October 1993 at the King's Fund Centre, London chaired by Baroness Cumberlege*, British Library R&D Report 6133, British Library.

British Library (1994) *Managing the knowledge base of healthcare: follow up survey by Alan Beevers*, British Library R&D Report 6182, British Library.

British Library (1997) *Guide to libraries and information sources in medicine and health care. Second edition edited by Peter Dale*, British Library (new edition in preparation).

Brittain, J M (1985) *Consensus and penalties for ignorance in the medical sciences: implications for information transfer*, Taylor Graham.

Brittain, J M and MacDougall, J (1993) New opportunities for NHS librarians and information scientists, *Health Libraries Review*, **10** (1), 10–19.

Brittain, M and Maggs, J (1993) Ships in the night, *British Journal of Healthcare Computing and Information Management*, **19** (7), 20–2.

Broadway, T (1995) The role of the media in the provision of health care, *Bibliotheca Medica Canadiana*, **17** (1), 4–8.

Brogan, L L and Lipscomb, C E (1982) Moving the collections of an academic health sciences library, *Bulletin of the Medical Library Association,* **70** (4), 374–9.

Brooker, R J (1999) *Genetics: analysis and principles*, Addison Wesley Longman Inc.

Brown, C (1995) Interiors and furniture: questions and answers, *Community and Junior College Libraries*, **8** (1), 19–25.

Brown, C C (1994) Creating automated bibliographies using Internet-accessible online library catalogs, *Database,* **17** (1), 67–71.

Brown, H and Dickinson, D (1999) Netlines. *British Medical Journal*, **319** (18 September), 790.

Brunskill, K (1996) CASIAS services: a critical evaluation of the functionality, costs, impact and value, *British Library Research and Innovation Report*, **4**, 1996, 1–129.

Brunskill, K (1997a) The issues surrounding the provision of CASIAS services in libraries, *Interlending and Document Supply*, **25** (2), 57–63.

Brunskill, K (1997b) Measuring researchers' preferences for CASIAS, *New Review of Information Networking*, **3**, 1997, 93–102.

Bryant, S L (1997) Practice libraries: managing printed information and meeting the information needs of staff in general practice, *Health Libraries Review*, **14** (1), 9–21.

Bryant, S L (1999) Information services for primary care: the organizational culture of general practice and the information needs of partnerships and Primary Care Groups, *Health Libraries Review*, **16** (3), 157–65.

Buckland, S (1994) Unmet needs for health information: a literature review, *Health Libraries Review*, **11** (1994), 82–95.

Bunyan, L E and Lutz, E M (1991) Marketing the hospital library to nurses, *Bulletin of the Medical Library Association*, **79** (2), 223–5.

Burdick, A J, Butler, A and Sullivan, M G (1993) Citations patterns in the health sciences: implications for serials/monographic fund allocation, *Bulletin of the Medical Library Association*, **81** (1), 44–7.

Burnes, B (1996) No such thing as . . . a 'one best way' to manage such organizational change, *Management Decision*, **34** (10), 11–18.

Burns, F (1998) *Information for health: an information strategy for the modern NHS 1998–2005: a national strategy for local implementation*, NHS Executive.

Burrows, S C and Tylman, V (1999) Evaluating medical student searches of MEDLINE for evidence-based information: process and application of results, *Bulletin of the Medical Library Association*, **87** (4), 471–6.

Burton, J E (1995) The impact of medical libraries and literature on patient care in New Zealand, *Bulletin of the Medical Library Association*, **83** (4), 425–30.

Butler, R N (1997) Population ageing and health, *British Medical Journal*, **315** (7115), 1082–4.

Calvert, P (1999) A report on preliminary investigations of attitudes to integrated performance measures among New Zealand university library staff. In *Proceedings of the third Northumbria International Conference on Performance Measurement in Libraries and Information Services, 27–31 August*, Department of Information and Library Management, University of Northumbria at Newcastle.

Canning, C, Edwards, A and Meadows, S (1995) Using focus groups to evaluate library services in a problem-based learning curriculum, *Medical Reference Services Quarterly,* **14** (3), 75–81.

Capel, S (1997) Library and information services for the nursing professional: methods of funding and delivery. A summary of the LINC Health Panel Research Project, *Health Libraries Review,* **14** (2), 122–4.

Capel, S, Banwell, L and Walton, G (1997) *Provision of future library and information services to community-based practitioners in Newcastle and North Tyneside: information needs assessment*, Department of Information and Library Management, University of Northumbria at Newcastle.

Capel, S, Banwell, L and Walton, G (1998) *Provision of future library and information service to community-based practitioners in Newcastle and North Tyneside. Information needs assessment. Final report,* Department of Information and Library Management, University of Northumbria at Newcastle.

Carmel, M (1991) Management by agreement: contracting for library services in South West Thames, *Health Libraries Review*, **8**, 63–80.

Carmel, M (ed) (1995) *Health care librarianship and information work*, 2nd edn, Library Association Publishing.

Carmel, M (1998) Regional library and information services in the NHS – why, where, what and whither?, *Health Libraries Review*, **15** (4), 225–30.

Carpenter, J (1999) *What makes a digital librarian? A critical analysis of the management culture needed for effective digital library development*, British Library Research and Innovation Report 174, The British Library Board.

Carr, A F and Stibravy, R (1999) Designing a Web bookmarks page for reference desk use, *Bulletin of the Medical Library Association*, **87** (1), 80–2.

Carrigan, D P (1995) From Just-in-Case to Just-in-Time – Limits to the alternative library-service model, *Journal of Scholarly Publishing*, **26** (3), 173–82.

CASP (Critical Appraisal Skills Programme), available at:
http://www.phru.org/casp/

CEBM (Centre for Evidence-Based Medicine), available at:
http://cebm.jr2.ox.ac.uk/

Central Statistics Office (1999) *Social Trends*, available at:
http://www.statistics.gov.uk/statbase/xsdataset.asp [accessed 29/11/99)

Chambliss, M L and Conley, J (1996) Answering clinical questions, *Journal of Family Practice*, **43**, 140–4.

Chapman, J (1999) NHS Direct, *CHIC Update*, **13**, 4–5.

Charles, C, Whelan, T and Gafni, A (1999) What do we mean by partnership in making decisions about treatment?, *British Medical Journal*, **319** (7212), 780–2.

Childs, S M (1994) A survey of nursing libraries in the Northern Region, *Health Libraries Review*, **11** (1), 3–28.

Christakis, N A (1995) The similarity and frequency of proposals to reform US medical education, *Journal of the American Medical Association*, **274** (9), 706–11.

Chu, L F and Chan, B K (1998) Evolution of web site design: implications for medical education on the Internet, *Computers in Biology and Medicine,* **28** (5), 459–72.

Cibbarelli, P (1995) Cibbarelli's surveys: user ratings of bibliographic citation management software, *Computers in Libraries,* **15** (4), 25–40.

Cimino, J J, Aguirre, A, Johnson, S B and Peng, P (1993) Generic queries for meeting clinical information needs, *Bulletin of the Medical Library Association,* **81** (2), 195–206.

Cimpl, K (1985) Clinical medical librarianship: a review of the literature, *Bulletin of the Medical Library Association,* **73** (1), 21–8.

Claridge, J (1989) Selecting a subscription agent: a West Midlands view, *Serials,* **2** (2), 43–5.

Clark, J R (1997) The research process: a beginner's guide, *Health Libraries Review,* **14** (3), 145–56.

Clark, M J (1999) Changing landscape for the information professional, *Serials,* **12** (2), 95–101.

Clarke, J M (1989) Planning the accessible hospital library for patients, *Health Libraries Review,* **6** (2), 111–3.

Clarke, Z (1999) EQUINOX: the development of performance indicators for the electronic library. In *Proceedings of the third Northumbria International Conference on Performance Measurement in Libraries and Information Services, 27–31 August,* available at:
http://equinox.dcu.ie/reports/pilist.html

Clay, S T, Harlan, S and Swanson, J (1999) *The universe at your fingertips: continuing web education,* University of California, Santa Barbara, available at:
http://www.library.ucsb.edu/universe/clay.html [accessed 25/11/99]

Cluzeau, F et al (1997) *Appraisal instrument for clinical guidelines,* available at:
http://www.sghms.ac.uk/phs/hceu/form.htm

Cochrane, A L (1972) *Effectiveness and efficiency: random reflections on health services,* Nuffield Provincial Hospitals Trust.

Cochrane, A L (1979) 1931–1971: a critical review, with particular reference to the medical profession. In *Medicines for the year 2000,* Office of Health Economics.

Cochrane Collaboration (1999) *Cochrane Collaboration brochure,* available at:
http://hiru.mcmaster.ca/cochrane/cochrane/cc-broch.htm

Cogdill, K W and Moore, M E (1997) First-year medical students' information needs and resource selection: Responses to a clinical scenario, *Bulletin of the Medical Library Association,* **85** (1), 51–4.

Cohen, E (1989) Talking to the architects, *American Libraries,* **20** (4), 299.

Cohen, E (1994) The architectural and interior design planning process, *Library Trends,* **42** (3), 547–63.

Cohn, J S (1995) Planning a new library facility: lessons learned at the UMDNJ-Health Sciences Library at Stratford, *New Jersey Libraries,* **28** (1), 6–10.

Collins, A M K (1995) Planning and presenting the library. In Carmel, M (ed) *Health care librarianship and information work,* 2nd edn, Library Association Publishing.

Collins, S (1997) Push, Push, Puuusssshhh!, *net,* **32,** (May), 66–7, 69, 17–2l.

Collins, T (1996) EBSCO's plans for handling electronic journals and document delivery, *Collection Management,* **20** (3/4), 15–18.

Colyer, H and Kamath, P (1999) Evidence-based practice: a philosophical and political analysis: some matters for consideration by professional practitioners, *Journal of Advanced Nursing,* **29** (1), 188–93.

Combs, J (1996a) BookWhere? Pro for Windows, version 2: a Z39.50 search and retrieval client from Sea Change Corporation, *Library Software Review,* **15** (3), 176–88.

Combs, J (1996b) ProCite 3.1 for Windows: professional and personal bibliographic reference management from Personal Bibliographic, Inc, *Library Software Review,* **15** (2), 119–31.

Combs, J (1998) Reference Manager for Windows 95/NT from Research Information Systems, *Library Software Review,* **17** (3), 219–27.

Compton-Ellis, J (1988) Planning and executing a major bookshift/move using an electronic spreadsheet, *College and Research Libraries News,* **49** (5) 282–7 .

Connor, J J (1989) Medical library history: a survey of the literature in Great Britain and North America, *Libraries and Culture,* **24** (4), 460–74.

Cook, D J et al (1997) Systematic reviews: synthesis of best evidence for clinical decisions, *Annals of Internal Medicine,* **125** (5), 376–80.

Cooke, A (1999) *A guide to finding quality information on the Internet: selection and evaluation strategies,* Library Association Publishing.

Cooper, E R (1991) Marketing the hospital library to physicians: one approach, *Bulletin of the Medical Library Association,* **79** (1), 86–7.

Cooper, L (1997) How much should it cost? An introduction to management use of costing information, *Health Libraries Review,* **14** (4), 209–17.

Cooper, W (1994) Integrating information technologies for the library environment, *Library Administration and Management,* **8** (3), 131–4.

Coote, H (1997) *How to market your library service effectively*, 2nd edn, Aslib.

Cornwall and South Devon Education Purchasing Consortium, Library Project Steering Group (1999) *Health libraries for a new millennium: a strategy for Cornwall and South Devon. Report to the NHS Executive South West*, NHS Executive South West.

Corrall, S (1998) Assistants as change agents, *Library Association Record*, **100** (1), 583–4.

Corrall, S and Brewerton, A (1999) *The new professional's handbook: your guide to information services management*, Library Association Publishing.

Coult, G (1999) Intelligent agents, *Managing Information*, **6** (1), 33–4.

Coulter, A (1999) Paternalism or partnership? *British Medical Journal*, **319** (7212), 719–20.

Covell, D G, Uman, G C and Manning, P R (1985) Information needs in office practice: are they being met? *Annals of Internal Medicine*, **103** (4), 596–9.

Cox, A (1997) Using the World Wide Web for library user education: a review article, *Journal of Librarianship and Information Science*, **29** (1), 39–43.

Cox, A, Godwin, P and Yeates, R (1999) Towards a checklist for choosing electronic journal aggregation services, *VINE*, **110**, 38–41.

Cox, J (1995) Rolling your own: publishing databases on the Internet, *Managing Information,* **2** (4), 30–2.

Cox, J and Hanson, T (1992) Setting up an electronic current awareness service, *Online,* **16** (4), 34–43.

Cox, R P (1997) Family health care delivery for the 21st century, *Journal of Obstetric and Gynecological Neonatal Nursing*, **26** (1), 109–18.

Cox, R W (1996) End Note Plus 2 and End Note Link 2: database reference management packages, *Managing Information,* **3** (5), 58–9.

Crabtree, A B and Crawford, J H (1997) Assessing and addressing the library needs of health care personnel in a large regional hospital, *Bulletin of the Medical Library Association*, **85** (2), 167–75.

Crane, S and Urquhart, C (1994) Preparing for PREP: the impact of changes in continuing education for nurses on library provision of journals and current-awareness services: a case study, *Health Libraries Review*, **11** (1), 29–38.

Craven, D, Griffin, E and Sinclair, D (1998) *Continuing medical education 'on the line': the Surf Doctors project,* University of Dundee Tayside Centre for General Practice.

Crawford, G A (1999) Issues for the digital library, *Computers in Libraries* (May), 62–4.

Creaser, C and Spiller, D (1997) *TFPL survey of UK special library statistics*, LISU Occasional Paper 15, Loughborough University, Library and Information Statistics Unit (LISU).

Critical Appraisal Skills Programme and Health Care Libraries Unit (1999) *The evidence-based health care workbook including the evidence-based health care CD-ROM*, CASP and HCLU.

Crockford, N (1993) A plain guide to space planning, *Aslib Information*, **21** (1), 24–5.

Cullen, R (1997) The medical specialist: information gateway or gatekeeper for the family practitioner, *Bulletin of the Medical Library Association*, **85** (4), 348–55.

Culver, J D, Gerr, F and Frumkin, H (1997) Medical information on the internet: a study of an electronic bulletin board, *Journal of General Internal Medicine*, **12**, 466–70.

Cumbers, B J and Donald, A (1998) Using biomedical databases in everyday clinical practice, *Health Libraries Review*, **15** (1), 255–65.

D'Alessandro, M P et al (1998a) Peer reviewing and curating the health care information infrastructure: experiences and recommendations. In *Proceedings AMIA Annual Symposium,* 643–7.

D'Alessandro, M P et al (1998b) The Virtual Hospital: experiences in creating and sustaining a digital library, *Bulletin of the Medical Library Association*, **86** (4), 553–63.

D'Alessandro, M P, Nguyen, B C and D'Alessandro, D (1999) Information needs and information-seeking behaviors of on-call radiology residents, *Academic Radiology*, **6** (1), 16–21.

Davidoff, F et al (1995) Evidence based medicine, *British Medical Journal*, **310** (6987), 1085–6.

Davies, C (1990) *The collapse of the conventional career*, ENB Project Paper 1, English National Board for Nursing, Midwifery and Health Visiting.

Davies, M, Boyle, F and Osborne, S (1998) CAS-IAS services: where are we now?, *Electronic Library,* **16** (1), 37–48.

Davies, R et al (1997) *Establishing the value of information to nursing continuing education: report of the EVINCE project*, British Library RIC Report 44, British Library (available from the Document Supply Centre).

Davis, E and Stone, J (1998) From A to Z: automated catalogue to Web OPAC and Z39.50, *Health Libraries Review,* **15** (2), 128–32.

Dawes, M et al (1999) Evidence based case report: treatment for head lice, *British Medical Journal*, (6 February), **318** (7180), 385–6.

Dawson, A (1999) Inferring user behaviour from journal access figures, *Serials Librarian*, **35** (3), 31–41.

Dawson, S et al (1995) *Managing in the NHS. A study of senior executives,* HMSO.

Dee, C and Blazek, R (1993) Information needs of the rural physician: a descriptive study, *Bulletin of the Medical Library Association*, **81** (3), 259–64.

Delamothe, T (1999) NIH's plans for online publishing could threaten journals, *British Medical Journal*, **318** (7186), 754.

Delamothe, T and Smith, R (1998) The *BMJ*'s website scales up, *British Medical Journal*, **316** (7138), 1109–10.

Delamothe, T and Smith, R (1999) The joy of being electronic, *British Medical Journal*, **319** (7208), 465–6.

Delamothe, T et al (1999) Netprints: the next phase in the evolution of biomedical publishing, *British Medical Journal*, **319** (7224), 1515–6.

Delfino, E (1996) 'Automatic' HTML Part 2: creating HTML from a database program, *Online*, **20** (6), 96–8.

Del Mar, C (2000) Evidence based case report. Asymptomatic haematuria . . . in the doctor, *British Medical Journal*, (15 January), **320** (7228), 165–6.

Denny, E (1999) The politics of health. In Masterson, A and Maslin-Protheroe, S (eds) *Nursing and politics: power through practice*, Churchill Livingstone.

Department of Health (1989) *Working for patients. Presented to Parliament by the Secretaries of State for Health, Wales, Northern Ireland and Scotland by command of Her Majesty,* HMSO.

Department of Health (1992a) *The health of the nation: a strategy for health in England. Presented to Parliament by the Secretary of State for Health by command of Her Majesty July 1992,* HMSO.

Department of Health (1992b) *Implementation of the health information services*, HSG (92) 21, Department of Health, NHS Management Executive.

Department of Health (1995) *Provision of the national free phone health information service*, HSG **95** (44), Department of Health.

Department of Health (1996a) *The National Health Service: a service with ambitions*, Cm 3425, The Stationery Office.

Department of Health (1996b) *Primary care: delivering the future,* The Stationery Office.

Department of Health (1997a), *Health Service guidelines: library and information services*, Department of Health.

Department of Health (1997b) *The new NHS: modern, dependable. Presented to Parliament by the Secretary of State for Health by command of Her Majesty – December 1997,* The Stationery Office.

Department of Health (1998a) *A first class service: quality in the new NHS. A consultation document issued under cover of HSC 1998/113,* Department of Health.

Department of Health (1998b), *Information for health*, Department of Health.

Department of Health (1998c) *Information for health: an information strategy for the modern NHS 1998–2005, a national strategy for local implementation,* The Stationery Office.

Department of Health (1998d) *Partnership in action: new opportunities for joint working between health and social services*, Department of Health.

Department of Health (1998e) *Working together: securing a quality workforce for the NHS,* The Stationery Office.

Department of Health (1999a) *Agenda for change: modernising the NHS pay system,* The Stationery Office.

Department of Health (1999b) *Continuing professional development: quality in the new NHS*, HSC 1999/154, Department of Health.

Department of Health (1999c) *Hospital, public health medicine and community health services. Medical and dental staff in England: 1998–1999*, available at: **http://www.doh.gov.uk/public/sb9915.htm** [accessed 29/11/99]

Department of Health (1999d) *NHS hospital and community health services: statistics*, available at: **http://www/doh.gov.uk/HPSS/TBL_D.HTM** [accessed 29/11/99]

Department of Health (1999e) *Patient and public involvement in the new NHS,* Department of Health.

Department of Health (1999f) *Saving lives : our healthier nation. Presented to Parliament by the Secretary of State for Health by command of Her Majesty – July 1999,* The Stationery Office.

Department of Health and NHS Management Executive (1992) *Implementation of the health information services,* HSG (92)21, Department of Health, NHS Management Executive.

Department of Health and NHS Executive (1995) *Provision of the national freephone health information service,* HSG (95)44, Department of Health, NHS Executive.

Department of Health and Social Security (1970) *Library services in hospitals,* HM (70)23, DHSS.

Dibb, S and Simkin, L (1994) *The marketing casebook,* Routledge.

Dickersin, K, Min, Y I and Meinert, C L (1992) Factors influencing publication of research results, *Journal of the American Medical Association,* **267,** 374–8.

Dickersin, K, Scherer, R and Lefebvre, C (1994) Identifying relevant studies for systematic reviews, *British Medical Journal,* **309** (6964), 1286–91.

Dixon, S, Booth, A and Perrett, K (1997) The application of evidence-based priority setting in a District Health Authority, *Journal of Public Health Medicine* **19** (3), 307–12.

Donaldson, K and MacKay, D (1997) HEBSWeb: creating a World Wide Web health information service, *Health Libraries Review,* **14** (3), 173–80.

Doney, E (1998) Developing opinions of the attitudes of ILS staff to continuing professional development, *Library Management,* **19** (8), 1–9.

Donnugh, A et al (1998) *Books for primary health care: a core guide to collection development,* Tomlinsons.

Doran, B M (1989) Planning a new medical library: a personal perspective and review of the literature, *Health Libraries Review,* **6** (2), 63–75.

Dorsch, J L and Landwirth, T K (1994) Document needs in a rural GRATEFUL MED outreach project, *Bulletin of the Medical Library Association,* **82** (4), 357–62.

Doughty, K (1998) Telemedicine, *Family Medicine,* (November), 36–7.

Drucker, P F (1991) The discipline of innovation. In Henry, J and Walker, D (eds) *Managing innovation,* Sage, 9–17.

Dunckel, J and Parnham, E (1984) *The Business Guide to Effective Speaking,* Kogan Page.

Durand-Zaleski, I, Colin, C and Blum-Boisgard, C (1997) An attempt to save money using mandatory practice guidelines in France, *British Medical Journal,* **315** (113), 943–6.

Dwyer, M (1999) A Delphi survey of research priorities and identified areas for collaborative research in health sector library and information services UK, *Health Libraries Review,* **16,** 174–91.

Dyer, H and Buckle, P (1995) Who's been using my CD-ROM? Results of a study on the value of CD-ROM searching to users in a teaching hospital library, *Health Libraries Review*, **12** (1), 39–52.

Dyer, H, and Rolinson, J (1995) In the right vein? How adequately are departments of information and library studies educating for health care information management and library services in a changing world?, *Health Libraries Review*, **12** (1), 29–37.

Earl, M F and Neutens, J A (1999) Evidence-based medicine training for residents and students at a teaching hospital: the library's role in turning evidence into action, *Bulletin of the Medical Library Association*, **87** (2), 211–14.

East, L (1999) The role of local government. In Masterson, A and Maslin-Protheroe, S (eds) *Nursing and politics: power through practice*, Churchill Livingstone.

EBMWG (Evidence-Based Medicine Working Group) (1993–) *Users' guides to the medical literature*, available at:
http://www.cche.net/principles/content_all.asp

Ebrahim, S (1997) Public health implications of ageing, *Journal of Epidemiology and Community Health*, **51** (5), 469–72.

Edward, E M and Prior, P (1998) West Midlands Health Libraries Network, *Health Libraries Review*, **15** (4), 233–7.

EHCB (Effective Health Care Bulletins), available at:
http://www.york.ac.uk/inst/crd/ehcb.htm

Eldredge, J (1999) Characteristics of peer reviewed clinical medicine journals, *Medical Reference Services Quarterly*, **18** (2), 13–26.

Eldredge, J D et al (1998) The roles of library liaisons in a problem-based learning (PBL) medical school curriculum: a case study from University of New Mexico, *Health Libraries Review*, **15**, (3), 185–94.

Ely, J W et al (1999) Analysis of questions asked by family doctors regarding patient care, *British Medical Journal*, **319** (7206), 358–61.

Eng, T R et al (1998) Access to health information and support: a public highway or a private road?, *Journal of the American Medical Association*, **280** (15), 1371–5.

Entwistle, V A et al (1996a) *Information about health care effectiveness. An introduction for consumer health providers,* The King's Fund.

Entwistle, V A et al (1996b) Supporting consumer involvement in decision making: what constitutes quality in consumer health information?, *International Journal for Quality in Health care*, **8** (5), 425–37.

EQUINOX: Library Performance Measurement and Quality Management System, available at:
http://equinox.dcu.ie

Evans, G E (1976) *Management techniques for librarians*, Academic Press.

Evidence Based Medicine Working Group (1992) Evidence Based Medicine: a new approach to teaching the practice of medicine, *Journal of the American Medical Association*, **268** (17), 2420–5.

Eysenbach, G and Diepgen, T L (1998a) Responses to unsolicited patient e-mail requests for medical advice on the world wide web, *Journal of the American Medical Association*, **280** (15), 1333–5.

Eysenbach, G and Diepgen, T L (1998b) Towards quality management of medical information on the internet: evaluation, labelling, and filtering of information, *British Medical Journal*, **317** (7171), 1496–1502.

Eysenbach, G, Ryoung Sa, E and Diepgen, T L (1999) Shopping around the internet today and tomorrow: towards the millennium of cybermedicine, *British Medical Journal*, **319**, 1294.

Farley, T, Broady-Preston, J and Hayward, T (1998) Academic libraries, people and change: a case study for the 1990s, *OCLC Systems and Services*, **14** (4), 1–17.

Farmer, J and Campbell, F (1997) Information professionals, CPD and transferable skills, *Library Management*, **18** (3), 1–9.

Farmer, J and Campbell, F (1998) *Continuing professional development and career success: is there a causal relationship?*, British Library Research and Innovation Report 112, BL Research and Innovation Centre.

Farmer, J and Peffer, M (1995) Matching resources to needs: drug information for rheumatology patients, British Library R&D Report 6227, British Library.

Farmer, J and Peffer, M (1996) Comparing needs with available resources: a study of the use of drug information by rheumatology patients, *Journal of Librarianship and Information Studies*, **28** (4), 227–39.

Farmer, J and Richardson, A (1997a) Information for trained nurses in remote areas: do electronically networked resources provide an answer?, *Health Libraries Review*, **14** (2), 97–103.

Farmer, J and Richardson, A (1997b) *Attitudes to librarianship and information science education and academic-practitioner liaison: report of a survey conducted for the Library Association Health Libraries Group*, Robert Gordon University, School of Information and Media. Also in *Health Libraries Review*, **15** (2), 97–109.

Farrow, J (1997) Management of change: technological developments and human resource issues in the information sector, *Journal of Managerial Psychology*, **12** (5), 1–6.

Fenn, T, Weatherby, N L and Pasquariella, S K (1990) Guidelines for establishing automated libraries in developing countries, *Computers in Libraries,* **10** (2), 21–8.

Fishman, D L and DelBaglivo, M (1998) Rich in resources/deficient in dollars! Which titles do reference departments really need?, *Bulletin of the Medical Library Association*, **86** (4), 545–50.

Fitzgerald, D (1996) Problem-based learning and libraries: the Canadian experience, *Health Libraries Review*, **13** (1), 13–32.

Flanagan, J C (1954) The critical incident technique, *Psychological Bulletin*, **51** (4), 327–58.

Flemming, K (1998) Asking answerable questions, *Evidence-Based Nursing*, **1** (2), 36–7.

Florance, V (1992) Medical knowledge for clinical problem solving: a structural analysis of clinical questions, *Bulletin of the Medical Library Association*, **80** (2), 140–9.

Foote, S M (1995) An architect's perspective on contemporary academic library design, *Bulletin of the Medical Library Association*, **83** (3), 351–6.

Forrest, M and Cawasjee, A (1997) Costing the library services. Cairns Library: a case study, *Health Libraries Review,* **14**, 219–32.

Forsythe, D E (1998) Using ethnography to investigate life scientists' information needs, *Bulletin of the Medical Library Association*, **86** (3), 402–9.

Forsythe, D E et al (1992) Expanding the concept of medical information: an observational study of physicians' information needs, *Computers and Biomedical Research*, **25**, 181–200.

Fowler, C (1998) Accreditation for health care libraries in the United Kingdom, *Health Libraries Review*, **15** (4), 295–9.

Fox, L M, Richter, J M and White, N E (1996) A multidimensional evaluation of a nursing information-literacy program, *Bulletin of the Medical Library Association*, **84** (2), 182–90.

Francis, B W and Kelly, J A (1997) Active learning: its role in health sciences libraries, *Medical Reference Services Quarterly*, **16** (1), 25–37.

Fraser, V (1998) Editorial of the NHS 50 issue of *Health Libraries Review*, **15** (4).

Fraser, V (1999a) Continuing professional development in the NHS – what is to be done?, *Health Libraries Review*, **16** (4), 268–70.

Fraser, V (1999b) The New NHS: developing the National Electronic Library for Health, *Managing Information,* **6** (6), 36–7, 55.

Fuller, S S et al (1999) Integrating knowledge sources at the point of care: opportunities for librarians, *Bulletin of the Medical Libraries Association*, **87** (4) 393–403.

Gallagher, D M (1999) Era of managed care: struggle of cost containment and compassionate effective care of persons with HIV/AIDS, *Nursing Clinics of North America*, **34** (1), 227–35.

Galpern, N F and Albert, K M (1997) UnCover on the Web: search hints and applications in library environments, *Medical Reference Services Quarterly*, **16** (3), 1–18.

Gann, R (1987) The people their own physicians: 2000 years of patient information, *Health Libraries Review*, **4**, 151–5.

Gann, R (1991) Consumer health information: the growth of an information specialism, *Journal of Documentation*, **47** (3), 284–308.

Gann, R (1995) Making decisions in the year 2000: realising the potential of Consumer Health Information Services. In McSean, T et al (eds) *Health information – new possibilities*, Kluwer Academic Publishers.

Garland, K J, Anderson, S J and Noyes, J M (1999) The Intranet as a learning tool: a preliminary study, *Information Research*, **4** (1), available at: **http://www.shef.ac.uk/~is/publications/infres/paper51.html** [accessed 25/11/99]

Garrod, P (1997) New skills for information professionals, *Information UK Outlooks*, **22**.

Garvin, D A (1988) *Managing quality: the strategic and competitive edge*, Free Press.

Gauvin, J F (1998) Posting your references on the web, *Database*, **21** (6), 41–7.

Geddes, J (1999) Asking structured and focused clinical questions: essential first steps of evidence based practice, *Evidence Based Mental Health*, **2** (2), 35–6.

Gilbert, R and Logan, S (1996) Future prospects for evidence based child health, *Archives of Diseases in Childhood*, **74** (6), 465–73.

Ginzberg, E (1998) US health system reform in the early 21st century, *Journal of the American Medical Association*, **280** (17), 1539.

Glasziou, P (1998) Twenty year cough in a non-smoker, *British Medical Journal*, (30 May), **316** (7145), 1660–1.

Glitz, B (1997) The focus group technique in library research: an introduction, *Bulletin of the Medical Library Association*, **85** (4), 385–90.

Godbolt, S (1995) Books in the health sciences. In Carmel, M (ed) *Health care librarianship and information work*, 2nd edn, Library Association Publishing.

Godbolt, S and Hewlett, J (1992) The funding of postgraduate medical education in NHS libraries: is a formula workable? A case study from the North East and North West Thames Regions, *Health Libraries Review*, **9** (2), 77–81.

Godbolt, S, Williamson, J and Wilson, A (1997) From vision to reality – managing change in the provision of library and information services to nurses, midwives, health visitors and PAMs: a case study of the North Thames experience with the Inner London Consortium, *Health Libraries Review*, **14** (2), 73–96.

Goncalves, S et al (1999) Integration of all information sources in a clinical environment. In *SHIMR99 The fourth international symposium on health information management research, University of Sheffield 14–15 June*, 35–48, Centre for Health Information Management Research, University of Sheffield.

Goodman, M (1998) Ethical issues in health care rationing, *Nursing Management*, **5** (4), 29–33.

Goodman, N W (1999) Who will challenge evidence based medicine?, *Journal of the Royal College of Physicians of London*, **33** (3), 245–51.

Gorman, G E and Clayton, P (1997) *Qualitative research for the information professional: a practical handbook*, Library Association Publishing.

Gorman, G E and Howes, B R (1989) Form and content of collection development policies. In Gorman, G E and Howes, B R, *Collection development for libraries*, Bowker-Saur.

Gorman, P, Ash, J and Wykoff, L (1994) Can primary care physicians' questions be answered using the medical journal literature?, *Bulletin of the Medical Library Association*, **82** (2), 140–6.

Gorman, P N and Helfand, M (1995) Information seeking in primary care: how physicians choose which clinical questions to pursue and which to leave unanswered, *Medical Decision Making*, **15**, 113–9.

Goulding, A and Kerslake, E (1996) Flexible working in libraries, *Library Management*, **17** (2), 1–12.

Gove, S (1992) Formula funding in a multi-disciplinary medical library: a case study at St. George's Hospital Medical School, University of London, *Health Libraries Review*, **9** (2), 81–2.

Graham, A and Fahey, T (1999) Evidence based case report. Sore throat: diagnostic and therapeutic dilemmas, *British Medical Journal*, (17 July), **319** (7203), 173–4.

Green, J (1998) Grounded theory and the constant comparative method. Commentary, *British Medical Journal*, **316** (7137), 1064–5.

Green, L (1998) Using evidence-based medicine in clinical practice, *Primary Care*, **25** (2), 391–400.

Greenhalgh, T (1997) *How to read a paper: the basics of evidence-based medicine,* BMJ Publishing.

Grefsheim, S, Franklin, J and Cunningham, D (1991) Biotechnology awareness study, part 1: where scientists get their information, *Bulletin of the Medical Library Association*, **79** (1), 36–44.

Grieves, M (1998) The impact of information use on decision making: studies in five sectors – introduction, summary and conclusions, *Library Management*, **19** (2), 78–85.

Grover, R and Carabell, J (1995) Toward better information service: diagnosing information needs, *Special Libraries*, **86** (1), 1–10.

Guyatt, G H, Sackett, D L and Cook, D J (1993) Users' guides to the medical literature. II. How to use an article about therapy or prevention. A. Are the results of the study valid?, *Journal of the American Medical Association*, **270**, 2598–601.

Hague, H (1997) *Core collection of medical books and journals*, Medical Information Working Party.

Haines, M (1995) Health library provision in the UK. In Carmel, M (ed) *Health care librarianship and information work*, 2nd edn, Library Association Publishing, 270–87.

Haines, M (1996) The role of the NHS Library Adviser in developing NHS Library and Information Services, *Inform (Newsletter of IFM Healthcare)*, **7** (3), 11–13.

Hall, J (1999) Training in teamwork in British university libraries, *Library Management*, **20** (30), 1–12.

Halub, L P (1999) The value of Web-based library services at Cedars-Sinai Health System, *Bulletin of the Medical Library Association*, **87** (3), 256–60.

Hamilton, F (1995) *Current awareness, current techniques,* Gower.

Handy, C (1995) *Beyond certainty: the changing worlds of organisations,* Hutchinson.

Hannabuss, S (1995) Approaches to research, *Aslib Proceedings*, **47** (1), 3–11.

Hansen, M A (1998) Free online access to medical information: MEDLINE web interfaces, *Health Care on the Internet*, **2** (4), 29–43.

Hanson, T (1995) *Bibliographic software and the electronic library,* University of Hertfordshire Press.

Hanson, T and Day, J (eds) (1998) *Managing the electronic library: a practical guide for information professionals*, Bowker-Saur.

Harbourt, A M, Knecht, L S and Humphreys, B L (1995) Structured abstracts in MEDLINE, 1989–1991, *Bulletin of the Medical Library Association*, **83** (2), 190–5.

Harris, G and Marshall, J G (1996), Building a model business case: current awareness service in a special library, *Special Libraries,* **87** (3), 181–94.

Harvey, T (1998) Untangling the intricacies of the world wide web: site design part 1, *British Journal of Health Care Management*, **4** (10), 507–9.

Haug, J D (1997) Physicians' preferences for information sources: a meta-analytic study, *Bulletin of the Medical Library Association*, **85** (3), 223–32.

Hay, R J (1995) Sick library syndrome, *Lancet*, **346**, 1573–4.

Haynes, R B (1987) A proposal for more informative abstracts of clinical articles, *Annals of Internal Medicine*, **106**, 598–604.

Haynes, R B (1990) Loose connections between peer-reviewed clinical journals and clinical practice, *Annals of Internal Medicine*, **113** (9), 724–8.

Haynes, R B (1993) Where's the meat in clinical journals?, *ACP Journal Club*, (November–December), A22–3.

Haynes, R B et al (1990) Online access to Medline in clinical settings: a study of use and usefulness, *Annals of Internal Medicine*, **112**, 78–84.

Haynes, R B et al (1994) Developing optimal search strategies for detecting clinically sound studies in Medline, *Journal of the American Medical Informatics Association*, **1** (6), 447–58.

Hayward, J and Boore, J R P (1994) *Information a prescription against pain. Prescription for recovery*, Scutari Press.

Head, A (1996) *An examination of the implications for NHS information providers of staff transferring from functional to managerial roles*, MSc dissertation, University of Wales Aberystwyth.

Heald, R J and Morgan, B J (1997) General surgery at the crossroads, *Lancet*, **350** suppl 111, 26.

Health Education Board for Scotland (1997) *HEBS. The first six years*, Health Education Board for Scotland.

Heery, M (1999) Winning resources, *Bottom Line*, **12** (2), 57–67.

Heidenreich, F (1997) Know your search engine: a comparison of 6 popular Web search engines, *Health Care on the Internet*, **1** (2), 45–8.

Hemsley, R (1999) Adding to the confusion, *Library Association Record*, **101**(11), 642.

Henexson, F (1994/5) Planning and moving a library: don't panic – plan it, *Trends in Law Library Management and Technology,* **6** (5), 2–5.

Hepworth, J B (1991) Training staff and end users for automated retrieval systems in the health sciences, *Education for Information*, **9** (2), 97–106.

Hepworth, J B (1992) Developing information handling courses for end users. *Database 2000: Proceedings of the UKOLUG State of the Art Conference*, Learned Information.

Herala, M K, Ravi, A S and Rajashekar, T B (1995) Automated SDI using CD-ROM databases, *Online and CD ROM Review,* **19** (3), 137–41.

Hernandez-Borges, A A, Pareras, L G and Jimenez, A (1997) Comparative analysis of pediatric mailing lists on the internet, *Pediatrics*, **100**, E8

Hernando, S (1997) Promoting library services to qualified nurses: towards a market-led approach, *Health Libraries Review*, **14** (2), 105–19.

Hersh, W (1993) Relevance and retrieval evaluation: perspectives from medicine, *Journal of the American Society of Information Science*, **45** (3), 201–6.

Hersh, W R and Hickam, D H (1998) How well do physicians use electronic information retrieval systems? A framework for investigation and systematic review, *Journal of the American Medical Association*, **280** (15), 1347–52.

Heseltine, R (1995) The challenge of learning in cyberspace, *Library Association Record*, **97** (8), 432–3.

Hewlett, J (1988) Pre-registration training in health-care libraries, II. Progress assessment checklist, *Health Libraries Review*, **5** (4), 237–45.

Hewlett, J (1992) Who uses NHS libraries? Preliminary results from a survey of postgraduate medical libraries in North East Thames, *Health Libraries Review*, **9**, 66–76.

Heyes, K (1999) Sifting Sandwell, *Library Association Record*, **101**(6), June, 352–3.

Hicks, A (1998) Developing information skills training for National Health Service personnel: experiences at the Trent Institute for Health Services Research, *Program*, **32** (2), 123–36.

Hicks, A, Booth, A and Sawers, C (1998) Becoming ADEPT: delivering distance learning on evidence-based medicine for librarians, *Health Libraries Review*, **15** (3), 175–84.

Hicks, N R et al (1999) Evidence based case report: chlamydia infection in general practice, *British Medical Journal*, (20 March), **318** (7186), 790–2.

Higher Education Funding Council for England (1993) *Joint Funding Council's Libraries Review Group: a report for HEFCE, SHEFC, HEFCW and DENI* (Follett Report), Higher Education Funding Council for England.

Hill, D R and Stickell, H N (1999) Brandon/Hill selected list of books and journals for the small medical library, *Bulletin of the Medical Library Association*, **87** (2), 145–69.

Hilton, C and Gold, S (1998) A publicity working party at the Wellcome Institute, *Journal of the Society of Archivists*, **19** (1), 41–52.

Hiscock, J and Pearson, M (1999) Looking inwards, looking outwards: dismantling the 'Berlin Wall' between health and social services, *Social Policy and Administration*, **33** (2), 150–63.

Holdsworth, J (1991) *The provision of healthcare information in the UK: a summary report*, BL Research Paper 98, British Library.

Holmes, O W (1911) Medical essays 1842–1882. Quoted in Rees, A M (1993) Communication in the physician–patient relationship, *Bulletin of the Medical Library Association*, **81** (1), 1–10.

Holt, R (1989) *Planning library buildings and facilities from concept to completion*, Scarecrow Press.

Honigsbaum, F et al (1994) *Priority setting for healthcare*, Radcliffe Medical Press.

Hope, T (1996) *Evidence-based patient choice*, The King's Fund.

Horton, R and Smith, R (1999) Time to register randomised trials, *British Medical Journal*, **319**, 865–6.

Hukins, C (1995) A librarian's guide to DIY publishing on the Web, *Information World Review*, **105**, 24–5.

Hunt, D L and McKibbon, K A (1997) Locating and appraising systematic reviews, *Annals of Internal Medicine*, **126** (7), 532–8.

Hunter, D J (1995) Rationing health care: the political perspective, *British Medical Bulletin*, **51** (4), 876–84.

Hurych, J (1982) The professional and the client: the reference interview revisited, *Reference Librarian*, 5/6, 199–205.

Hyatt, P (1990) Automating a college library: a check list compiled after the event, *Library Micromation News*, **29**, 2–5.

Hyde, C (1996) Active research dissemination in the West Midlands, *Journal of Clinical Effectiveness*, **1** (1), 30.

HyLiFe project. The hybrid library of the future. Second Annual Report (1999) available at:
   http://www.unn.ac.uk/~xcu2/hylife/

IHS Library Filters (1998–), available at:
   http://www.ihs.ox.ac.uk/library/filters.html

Ikeda, N R and Schwartz, D G (1992) Impact of end-user search training on pharmacy students: a four-year follow-up study, *Bulletin of the Medical Library Association*, **80** (2), 124–30.

Impicciatore, P et al (1997) Reliability of health information for the public on the world wide web: systematic survey of advice on managing fever in children at home, *British Medical Journal*, **314** (7098), 1875–9.

Jadad, A R and Gagliardi, A (1998) Rating health information on the internet: navigating to knowledge or to Babel?, *Journal of the American Medical Association*, **279** (8), 611–4 .

Jaeschke, R et al (1999) Searching for information as you work, *Evidence Based Health Care Newsletter,* (November), 2–3.

Jaeschke, R, Guyatt, G and Sackett, D L (1994) Users' guides to the medical literature. III. How to use an article about a diagnostic test. A. Are the results of the study valid?, *Journal of the American Medical Association,* **271**, 389–91.

Jago, A (1996) Selecting your team: how to find the right people, *Librarian Career Development*, **4** (3), 1–7.

James, S M (1991) Costing library and information services: an overview, *Health Libraries Review*, **8** (3), 120–30.

Jenkins, R D, Grey-Lloyd, J and Hancock, C (1998) Medical resources on the Internet: searching and appraising, *Hospital Medicine*, **59** (5), 408–10.

Jensen, A and Sih, J (1995) Using email and the Internet to teach users at their desktops, *Online*, **19** (5), 82–6.

Jobber, D (1995) *Principles and Practices of Marketing*, McGraw Hill.

Johnson, E D, McKinin, E J and Sievert, M (1992) The application of quality filters in searching the clinical literature: some possible heuristics, *Medical Reference Services Quarterly,* **11** (4), 39–59.

Johnson, P (1997) Collection development policies and electronic information resources. In Gorman, G E and Miller, R H (eds) *Collection management for the 21st century: a handbook for librarians*, Greenwood Press.

Johnson, G and Scholes, K (1999) *Exploring corporate strategy*, 5th edn, Prentice-Hall.

Jones, D and Larkin, G (1993) Securing a good design: a library building consultant and an architect consider library security, *Australasian Public Libraries and Information Services,* **6** (4), 164–70.

Jones, L and Cahoon, J (1998) Overcoming network barriers: the implementation of the NISS BIOMED Service in the Trent NHS Region, *Health Libraries Review*, **15** (3), 200–4.

Jones, R G (1993) Personal computer software for handling references from CD-ROM and mainframe sources for scientific and medical reports, *British Medical Journal*, **307** (6897), 180–4.

Jordaan, M and Jones, R (1999) Adoption of Internet technology by UK postgraduate centres: a questionnaire survey, *Health Libraries Review*, **16** (4), 166–73.

Jowett, S, Walton, I and Payne, S (1994) *Challenges and change in nurse education – a study of the implementation of Project 2000,* National Foundation for Educational Research.

Kahin, B (1996) Scholarly communication in the networked environment: issues of principle, policy and practice. In Peek, R and Newby, G (eds) *Scholarly publishing: the electronic frontier,* MIT Press, 277–98.

Kaser, D (1995) The 'user-friendly' academic library building, *Journal of Information, Communication, and Library Science*, **1** (4), 9–16.

Kassirer, J P (1995) The next transformation in the delivery of health care, *New England Journal of Medicine*, **332**, 52–4.

Kelly, J (1994) Downloading information using bibliographic management software, *CD ROM Professional,* **7** (4), 123–6, 128.

Kempson, E (1984) Review article: consumer health information services, *Health Libraries Review*, **1**, 127–44.

Kempson, E and ACUMEN (1984) Consumer health information services, BLRD Report 5806, British Library Research and Development Department.

Kentucky University Medical Center Effective presentations, available at:
http://www.kumc.edu/SAH/OTEd/jradel/effective.html

Kenny, P (1983) *A handbook of public speaking for scientists and engineers*, Adam Hilger.

Kerr, M (1999) *How to promote your web site effectively,* Aslib.

Kesselman, M (1994) Ideas coming from everywhere, *Wilson Library Bulletin*, **68** (9), 42–4.

Kibbee, J (1994) A virtual library for librarians: JANET's Bulletin Board for Libraries, *Reference Librarian*, **41/42**, 99–107.

Kiley, R (1997a) Current awareness services on the Internet, *Journal of the Royal Society of Medicine,* **90** (10), 540–2.

Kiley, R (1997b) Medical databases on the Internet, part 1, *Journal of the Royal Society of Medicine*, **90** (11), 610–11.

Kiley, R (1997c) Medical databases on the Internet, part 2, *Journal of the Royal Society of Medicine*, **90** (12), 679–80.

Kim, P et al (1999) Published criteria for evaluating health related web sites: review, *British Medical Journal*, **318** (7184), 647–9.

King, H (1993) Walls around the electronic library, *Electronic Library,* **11** (3), 165–74.

King Edward's Hospital Fund for London (1985) *Providing a district library service: proposals arising from a series of workshops held in 1983 about the contribution library services can make to the provision and use of information in the NHS*, King's Fund Centre.

Kjaer, K, Tseng, S C and Lucas, B (1997) The integration of science serial collections into a consolidated science library, *Advances in serials management*, **6**, 147–67.

Klein M S et al (1994) Effect of online literature searching on length of stay and patient care costs, *Academic Medicine*, **69** (6), 489–95.

Klein, M S and Ross, F (1997) End-user searching: impetus for an expanding information management and technology role for the hospital librarian, *Bulletin of the Medical Library Association,* **85** (3), 260–8.

Klein R, Day, P and Redmayne, S (1996) *Managing scarcity: priority setting and rationing in the National Health Service,* Open University Press.

Korfhage, R R (1997) *Information storage and retrieval*, Wiley Computer Publishing.

Kotter, J P and Schlesinger, L A (1989) Choosing strategies for change. In Asch, D and Bowman, C (eds) *Readings in strategic management*, Macmillan, 294–307.

Lacey Bryant, S (1995) *Personal professional development and the solo librarian*, Library Association Publishing.

LaGuardia, C et al (1996) *Teaching the new library: a how-to-do-it manual for planning and designing instructional programs*, Neal-Schuman.

Lambert, J (1996) *Information resources selection*, Aslib Know How Series, Aslib.

Lancaster, F W (1997) Evaluating the digital library. In *Proceedings of the second Northumbria International Conference on Performance Measurement in Libraries and Information Services, 7–11 September,* Department of Information and Library Management, University of Northumbria at Newcastle, 47–57.

Langlands, A (1998) Introduction to the NHS 50 issue of *Health Libraries Review*, **15** (4).

Lapsley, A (1995) Writing winning grant proposals, *Bottom Line*, **8** (4), 38–41.

Lau, J et al (1992) Cumulative meta-analysis of therapeutic trials for myocardial infarction, *New England Journal of Medicine*, **327**, 248–54.

Laupacis, A et al (1994) Users' guides to the medical literature. V. How to use an article about prognosis, *Journal of the American Medical Association*, **272** (3), 234–7.

Laurence, J (1999) Preventable deaths grow as health gap widens, *Independent,* (2 December), 10.

Lawrence, S and Giles, C L (1998) Searching the World Wide Web, *Science* (3 April), 98–100.

Lawrence, S, and Giles, C L (1999) Accessibility of information on the Web, *Nature*, **400** (6740), 107–9.

Lee, K (1998) Shaping the future of global health cooperation: where can we go from here?, *Lancet,* **351** (9106), 899–902.

Lemkau, H L, Burrows, S and Stolz, F (1991) An entrepreneurial approach to integrating information production services into an academic medical center library, *Bulletin of the Medical Library Association,* **79** (3), 271–5.

Leonard, B G (1994) The metamorphosis of the information resources budget, *Library Trends*, **42** (3), 490–8.

Levine, M et al (1994) Users' guides to the medical literature. IV. How to use an article about harm, *Journal of the American Medical Association,* **272** (20), 1615–9.

Levy, P (1999) Professional development in a virtual learning community, *Health Libraries Review*, **16** (4), 270–3.

Ley, P (1988) *Communicating with patients. Improving communication, satisfaction and compliance*, Chapman & Hall.

Library Association (1965) *Hospital libraries: recommended standards for libraries in hospitals*, Library Association.

Library Association (1972) *Hospital libraries: recommended standards for libraries in hospitals*, Library Association.

Library Association (1980) *Guidelines for library provision in the health service: a consultative document*, revised edn, Library Association.

Library Association Health Libraries Group *Directory of medical and health care libraries in the United Kingdom and Republic of Ireland 1997–8*, 10th edn compiled by William H Forrester, Library Association Publishing (new edition due 2000).

Library Association Record (1998) Health Libraries checklist will boost quality, *Library Association Record*, **100** (12), 620.

Limits of evidence-based medicine (1997) focused issue of *Journal of Evaluation in Clinical Practice*, **3** (2).

LINC (Library and Information Co-operation Council). Health Panel (1997) *Library and information services for the nursing profession: methods of funding and delivery. Research commissioned by the LINC Health Panel and undertaken by the Department of Library and Information Management, University of Northumbria at Newcastle. Researcher: Sue Capel*, LINC Health Panel.

LINC (Library and Information Co-operation Council). Health Panel (1998a) *Accreditation of library and information services in the health sector: a checklist to support assessment*, LINC Health Panel.

LINC (Library and Information Co-operation Council). Health Panel (1998b) *Accreditation of library and information services in the health sector: implementation guide and toolkit for libraries in NHS Trusts. Author: Val Trinder*, LINC Health Panel.

Line, M B (1969) Information requirements in the social sciences: some considerations, *Journal of Librarianship*, **1** (1), 1–19.

Lingle, V A (1997) Journal searching in non-MEDLINE resources on Internet Web sites, *Medical Reference Service Quarterly*, **16** (3), 27–43.

Lingle, V and Delozier, E (1996) *World Wide Web and other Internet information services in the health sciences: a collection of policy and procedure statements,* MLA DocKit 7, Medical Library Association.

Lipman, T (2000) Netting the Evidence [review], *Evidence Based Medicine,* **5** (1), 7.

Littleton, D (1998) A review of strategies for finding health information on the World-Wide Web, *Medical Reference Services Quarterly,* **17** (2), 51–5.

Loop, F D (1998) Coronary artery surgery: the end of the beginning, *European Journal of Cardio-Thoracic Surgery,* **14** (6), 554–71.

Lopatin, W (1997) Knowledge is power, *Health Service Journal,* (16 October), 28–31.

Loughran, J J (1996) *Developing reflective practice: learning about teaching and learning through modelling,* Falmer Press.

Lowe, H J E and Barnett, G (1994) Understanding and using the Medical Subject Headings (MeSH) vocabulary to perform literature searches, *Journal of the American Medical Association,* **271**(14), 1103–8.

Lucier, R E (1995) Building a digital library for the health sciences: information space complementing information place, *Bulletin of the Medical Library Association,* **83** (3), 346–50.

Ludwig, L (1995) Tomorrow's library: will it be all infrastructure?, *Bulletin of the Medical Library Association,* **83** (3) 307–10.

Lynch, C (1999) Medical libraries, bioinformatics, and networked information: a coming convergence?, *Bulletin of the Medical Library Association,* **87** (4), 408–14.

Macadam, C (1996) Addressing the barriers of managing change, *Management Development Review,* **9** (3), 38–40.

MacCall, S L (1997) A metastrategy for World-Wide Web information retrieval in clinical medicine, *Medical Reference Services Quarterly,* **16** (4), 69–74.

MacDougall, J (1995) *Information for health: access to healthcare information services in Ireland. A research report on the information needs of healthcare professionals and the public,* Library Association of Ireland.

MacDougall, J (1998) *Well read: developing consumer health information in Ireland,* Library Association of Ireland.

MacDougall, J and Brittain, J M (1992) *Use of information in the NHS,* Library and Information Research Report 92, The British Library.

MacDougall, J and Brittain, J M (1998) *Health services information*. In Line, M B et al (ed) *Librarianship and information world workwide*, Bowker-Saur, 171–99.

MacDougall, J et al (1996) Health informatics: an overview, *Journal of Documentation*, **52** (4), 421–48.

Mackenbach, J et al (1997) Socioeconomic inequalities in morbidity and mortality in Western Europe, *Lancet,* **349** (9066), 1655–9.

Majaro, S (1988) *The creative gap*, Longman.

Makowski, G (1994) Clinical medical librarianship: a role for the future, *Bibliotheca medica canadiana*, **16** (1), 7–13.

Marshall, J (1998) The need for a national network of health libraries in Canada, *Bibliotheca Medica Canadiana*, **19** (4), 150–2.

Marshall, J G (1992) The impact of the hospital library on clinical decision making: the Rochester study, *Bulletin of the Medical Library Association*, **80** (2), 169–78.

Marshall, J G (1995) Using evaluation research methods to improve quality, *Health Libraries Review,* **12** (3), 159–72.

Marshall, J G et al (1993) A study of library use in problem-based and traditional medical curricula, *Bulletin of the Medical Library Association,* **81** (3), 299–305.

Martin, S (1998) Reflections on a user education session with nursing students, *Health Libraries Review*, **15** (2), 111–16.

Masterson, A and Maslin-Protheroe, S (eds) (1999) *Nursing and politics: power through practice*, Churchill Livingstone.

Matthews, J (1999) Reference Managers, *Nature*, 29 July.

Maxwell, R J (1995) Why rationing is on the agenda, *British Medical Bulletin*, **51** (4), 761–8.

Maxymuk, J (1997) *Using desktop publishing to create newsletters, handouts, and Web pages: a how-to-do-it manual*, How-To-Do-It Manuals for Librarians, 74, Neal-Schuman.

McCarthy, R (1995) *Designing better libraries: selecting and working with building professionals*, Highsmith Press.

McClure, C R (1999) Issues and strategies for developing national statistics and performance measures for library networked services and resources. In *Proceedings of the third Northumbria International Conference on Performance Measurement in Libraries and Information Services, 27–31 August,*

Department of Information and Library Management, University of Northumbria at Newcastle.

McClure, C R and Lopata, C (1996) *Assessing the academic networked environment: strategies and options,* School of Information Studies, Syracuse University.

McCray, A T and Nelson, S J (1995) The representation of meaning in the UMLS, *Methods of Information in Medicine*, **34** (1/2), 193.

McCray, J C and Maloney, K (1997) Improving access to knowledge-based health sciences information: early results from a statewide collaborative effort, *Bulletin of the Medical Library Association*, **85** (2), 136–40.

McCurry, P and White, C (1999) United, in sickness and in health?, *Community Care*, (27 January), 8–9.

McDonald, A (1994) *Moving your library,* Aslib.

McFadzean, E (1998) Enhancing creative thinking within organisations, *Management Decision*, **36** (5), 309–15.

McGowan, J (1997) Creating an institutional Web presence, *Information Outlook*, **1** (11), 18–21.

McGowan, J J (1995) The role of health sciences librarians in the teaching and retention of the knowledge, skills, and attitudes of lifelong learning, *Bulletin of the Medical Library Association*, **83** (2), 184–9.

McKibbon, K, Wilczynski, N, Hayward, R, Walker-Dilks, C and Haynes, R (1995) The medical literature as a resource for health care practice, *Journal of the American Society for Information Science*, December, **46**, 737–42.

McKibbon, K A (1998) Using *Best Evidence* in clinical practice, *Evidence-Based Medicine,* (March–April), 339.

McKibbon, K A (1999) *PDQ: evidence-based principles and practice,* Decker.

McKibbon, K A, Richardson, W S and Walker-Dilks, C (1999) Finding answers to well-built questions, *Evidence-based Medicine*, **4** (6), 164–7.

McKibbon, K A and Walker-Dilks, C J (1994a) Beyond *ACP Journal Club*: how to harness MEDLINE for therapy questions, *ACP Journal Club*, (July–August), 121, A-10.

McKibbon, K A and Walker-Dilks, C J, (1994b) Beyond *ACP Journal Club*: how to harness MEDLINE for diagnostic problems, *ACP Journal Club*, (September–October), 121, A-10.

McKibbon, K A and Walker-Dilks, C J (1995) The quality and impact of MEDLINE searches performed by end users, *Health Libraries Review*, **12** (3), 191–200.

McKibbon, K A et al (1995) Beyond *ACP Journal Club*: how to harness MED-LINE for prognosis problems, *ACP Journal Club*, (July–August), 123, A-12.

McMahon, K (1995) Using the BUBL information service as an Internet reference resource, *Managing Information, 2* (4), 33–5.

McMahon, K (2000) Journal information goes up in Bubl, *Library Association Record*, **102** (1), 36.

McMahon, T E (1998) Procite 4: a look at the latest release in bibliographic management software, *Library Software Review, 17* (1), 4–13.

McNab, A and Winship, I (1996) Internet: use in academic libraries, *Library Association Record, 98* (12), 636–8.

Merry, P (1997a) *Effective use of health care information, a review of recent research*, Bowker-Saur.

Merry P (1997b) Slow to learn, *Health Service Journal*, **107**, (24 July), 28–9.

Mikita, E G and Drusedum, L A (1993) Introducing health sciences librarians to the Internet, *Medical Reference Services Quarterly, 12* (3), 1–12.

Miles, M B and Huberman, A M (1995) *Qualitative data analysis: an expanded source book,* 2nd edn, Sage.

Mintzberg, H (1979) *The structuring of organizations,* Prentice-Hall.

Montague, M and Tomlin, A (1999) Primary Care Sharing the Evidence (PRISE) project website: bringing high-quality information to primary health care teams, *Health Libraries Review*, **16** (2), 121–4.

Montanelli-Dale, S (1987) What reference librarians should know about library finances, *Reference Librarian*, **19**, 15–25.

Montgomery, C H and Keenan, P (1995) Facilitating faculty communications using an electronic bulletin board to store and organize listserv messages, *Bulletin of the Medical Library Association*, **83** (2), 234–7.

Moore, C (1991) Personal reference management software – how to evaluate it?, *Health Libraries Review*, **8** (1), 4–10.

Moore, J (1998) *Core list for nurses, midwives and health visitors*, Medical Information Working Party.

Morgan, P (1992) Formula funding: a prescription for improvement (editorial), *Health Libraries Review*, **9** (2), 49–51.

Morgan, P (1995) Issues in funding of health science libraries. In Carmel, M (ed) *Health care librarianship and information work,* 2nd edn, Library Association Publishing, 232–45.

Morris, R T, Holman, E A and Curry, D S (1982) Being there: the effect of the user's presence on MEDLINE search results, *Bulletin of the Medical Library Association*, **70** (3), 298–304.

Moulton, B (1975) Components for consideration by emerging consortia, *Bulletin of the Medical Library Association,* **63** (1), 23–8.

Muir, A and Oppenheim, C (1995) The legal responsibilities of the health-care librarian, *Health Libraries Review,* **12** (2), 91–9.

Muir Gray, J A (1998) Where's the chief knowledge officer?, *British Medical Journal,* **317**, 832–40.

Muir Gray, J A and de Lusignan, S (1999) National electronic Library for Health (NeLH), *British Medical Journal*, **319** (7223), 1476–9.

Mullaly-Quijas, P, Ward, D H and Woelfl, N (1994) Using focus groups to discover health professionals' information needs: a regional marketing study, *Bulletin of the Medical Library Association*, **82** (3), 305–11.

Mulrow, C D (1987) The medical review article: state of the science, *Annals of Internal Medicine*, **106**, 485–8.

Mulrow, C D (1998) Helping an obese patient make informed choices, *British Medical Journal*, (25 July), **317** (7153), 266–7.

Mulrow, C D and Cook, D J (eds) (1998) *Systematic reviews: synthesis of best evidence for health care decisions*, ACP.

Mulrow, C D and Oxman, A D (eds) (1997) Optimal search strategy for RCTs. Cochrane Collaboration Handbook [updated September 1997]; Appendix 5c. In: *The Cochrane Library* [database on disk and CDROM], The Cochrane Collaboration.

Murphy, A (1998) *Statistics from the NHS Regional Librarians Group 1996–7*, Library and Information Statistics Unit, Department of Information Science, Loughborough University.

Murphy, A (1999) *A survey of NHS libraries: statistics from the NHS Regional Librarians Group 1997–8*, Library and Information Statistics Unit, Department of Information Science, Loughborough University.

Murray, B (1997) Success factors in obtaining funding, *New Zealand Libraries*, **48** (12), 218–31.

Murray, J, Carey, E and Walker, S (1999) The information needs and information seeking behaviour of medical research staff, *Health Libraries Review*, **16** (1), 46–9.

Naidoo, N (1998) Information 'Nuggets' are not easy to find quickly, *British Medical Journal*, **316** (7145), 1676.

National Consumer Council (1998) *Consumer concerns 1998: a consumer view of health services,* National Consumer Council.

National Library of Medicine, available at:
http://www.nlm.nih.gov/oubs/factsheets/umls.html

Naylor, C D (1995) Grey zones of clinical practice – some limits to evidence based medicine, *Lancet*, **345** (8953), 840–2.

NCCHTA (National Co-ordinating Centre for Health Technology Assessment), available at:
http://www.hta.nhsweb.nhs.uk/index.htm

Nelson, J L (1992) An analysis of transaction logs to evaluate the educational needs of end users, *Medical Reference Services Quarterly*, **11** (4), 11–21.

Newman, M et al (1998) Barriers to evidence based practice, *Intensive and Critical Care Nursing,* **14** (5), 231–8.

NHS Centre for Reviews and Dissemination (1996) *Undertaking systematic reviews of research on effectiveness: CRD guidelines for those carrying out or commissioning reviews*, CRD Report 4, University of York, NHS CRD.

NHS CRD databases, available at:
http://nhscrd.york.ac.uk/welcome.html

NHS Executive (1996) *Patient partnership: building a collaborative strategy,* 96HR0016, NHS Executive.

NHS Executive (1997) *Executive Letter: education and training planning guidance*, EL (97)58, NHS Executive.

NHS Executive (1998) *Information for health. An information strategy for the modern NHS 1998–2005,* NHS Executive.

NHS Executive (1999a) *Health Service Circular:* a *first class service: quality in the new NHS*, HSC 1999/033, NHS Executive.

NHS Executive (1999b) *Information for health: full local implementation strategies,* HSC 1999/200 and Annexes, NHS Executive.

NHS Executive (1999c) *Working together with health information,* NHS Executive, available at:
http://www.doh.gov.uk/nhsexipu/develop/nip/etdsumm.htm [accessed 24/12/99]

NHS Executive North Thames, Education and Training Directorate (1997*) The strategic framework for the provision of library services in North Thames*, NHS Executive.

NHS Executive North West (1998) *North west health library and information services review. Version 1.0*, NHS Executive North West Regional Office.

NHS Executive Northern and Yorkshire Library and Information Services Standing Group (1997) *Improving NHS library and information services: plans for a regional library advisory service,* NHS Northern and Yorkshire.

NHS Executive Northern and Yorkshire Regional Library Advisory Service (1998) *Supporting better health: a strategy for library information services,* NHSE Northern and Yorkshire.

NHS Executive Northern and Yorkshire Regional Library Advisory Service (1999) *Supporting better health: stage II: local library information service strategies: a report on local library information service strategies and their development*, NHS Executive Northern and Yorkshire Regional Library Advisory Service.

NHS Executive Northern and Yorkshire Regional Library Advisory Service (2000) *Supporting better health, stage III: continuing professional development for library information staff, strategy and training programme, 1999/2000*, Regional Library Advisory Service.

NHS Executive Northern and Yorkshire Research and Development Directorate (1997) *Information needs assessment: revised report*, NHS Northern and Yorkshire.

NHS Executive South and West. Public Health Department (1997) *Access to the knowledge base: a review of libraries: Steering Group report*, NHS Executive South and West.

NHS Executive Trent (1998) *A regional framework for library and information services*, NHS Executive Trent Regional Office.

NHS Information Authority (1996) *Standards Enforcement in Procurement (STEP)*, NHS Information Authority.

NHS Information Authority (1999a) National electronic library for health (NeLH) prototype. Bias, available at:
http://www.nelh.nhs.uk/bias.htm [accessed 25/1/00]

NHS Information Authority (1999b) National electronic library for health (NeLH) prototype. Results may be impossible to appraise, available at:
http://www.nelh.nhs.uk/imposs.htm [accessed 25/1/00]

NHS Regional Librarians Group (1979) *Census of staff providing library services to NHS personnel, April 1978*, NHS RLG.

NHS Regional Librarians Group (1987) *Census of staff providing library services to NHS personnel, December 1985*, NHS RLG.

NHS/DHSS Health Services Information Steering Group (1985) *Providing a district library service*, The King's Fund.

Nicholas, D (1996) *Assessing information needs: tools and techniques*, Aslib.

Nicholas, D and Marden, M (1998) Parents and their information needs. A case study, *Journal of Librarianship and Information Science*, **30** (1), 35–47.

Nicoll, L H et al (1996) Bibliography database managers – a comparative review, *Computers in Nursing,* **14** (1), 45–56.

Noble, D (1996) Medical books in an age of technology: selection and purchase, *Health Libraries Review*, **13**, 149–56.

Nolan, M et al (1998) Evidence based care: can we overcome the barriers?, *British Journal of Nursing*, **7** (20), 1273–8.

Norman, F and Hibbott, Y (1999) The Superjournal project: the value of electronic journals to biomedical users, *Health Libraries Review*, **16** (4), 263–7.

Northern Ireland. Department of Health and Social Sciences. Queen's University of Belfast. Joint working party on Library Services (1990) *Library support for medicine, health and social services in Northern Ireland*, DHSS.

Notess, G R (1998) DejaNews and other Usenet search tools, *Online* **22** (4) 74–6, 78.

Nowlen, P M (1988) *A new approach to continuing education for business and the professions: the performance model,* Macmillan.

Obst, O (1998) Use of Internet resources by German medical professionals, *Bulletin of the Medical Library Association*, **86** (4), 528–33.

Odlyzko, A (1994) *Tragic loss or good riddance?*, available at: **http://www.math.upenn.edu/lib/tragic-loss.html**

Office of Health Economics (1997) *Compendium of health statistics*, 10th edn, Office of Health Economics.

Olson, C A (1993) Test your library's marketing IQ, *Medical Reference Services Quarterly*, **12** (3), 75–83.

Olszewski, D and Jones, L (1998) *Putting people in the picture. Information for patients and the public about illness and treatment,* Scottish Association of Health Councils, Scottish Health Feedback.

Organisation for Economic Cooperation and Development (1999) *Labour force statistics 1977–1997,* OECD.

O'Rourke, A et al (1999) The Wisdom Project: virtual education in primary care, *Health Libraries Review*, **16** (2), 73–81.

Osheroff, J A and Bankowitz, R A (1993) Physicians' use of computer software in answering clinical questions, *Bulletin of the Medical Library Association*, **81** (1), 11–19.

Owen, D J (1997) Using personal reprint management software to teach information management skills for the electronic library, *Medical Reference Services Quarterly,* **16** (4), 29–41.

Oxman, A D et al (1994) Users' guides to the medical literature. VI. How to use an overview, *Journal of the American Medical Association*, **272** (17), 1367–71.

Palmer, J (1994) Professional associations in health information, *Newsletter, Library Association, Medical Health and Welfare Libraries Group*, **11** (1), viii–xiii.

Palmer, J (1996) Effectiveness and efficiency: new roles and new skills for health librarians. In *The future information professional: proceedings from the Aslib conference, 28–29 May 1996,* Aslib, 1–9.

Palmer, J (2000) Schooling and skilling librarians for an evidence-based culture, *Advances in Librarianship*, **23**, 145–67.

Palmer, J et al (1997) The twenty-first century is here, *Library Association Record*, **99** (6), 315–7.

Parker, M J (2000) Evidence based case report: managing an elderly patient with a fractured femur, *British Medical Journal*, (8 January), **320** (7227), 102–3.

Patel, V L, Evans, D A and Groen, G J (1989) Biomedical knowledge and clinical reasoning. In Evans, D A and Patel, V L (eds) *Cognitive science in medicine,* MIT Press.

Pavlenko, R L and Weinberg, M A (1990) Some psychological aspects of the professional reading of medical specialists, *Health Information and Libraries*, **1** (4), 32–6.

Pettigrew, K (1996) Nurses' perceptions of their needs for community information. Results of an exploratory study in Southwestern Ontario, *Journal of Education for Library and Information Science*, **37** (4), 351–60.

Pfeiffer, S and Algermissen, V (1992) A unique heavy users forum: a program to involve a library's most frequent users, *Medical References Services Quarterly*, **11** (3), 17–27.

Pifalo, V (1994), Outreach to health professionals in a rural area, *Medical Reference Services Quarterly*, **13** (3), 19–26.

Pinder, C and Melling, M (1996) *Providing customer-oriented services in academic libraries,* Library Association Publishing in association with SCONUL.

Porter, M E (1980) *Competitive strategy*, Free Press.

Potter, L A (1995) A systematic approach to finding answers over the Internet, *Bulletin of the Medical Library Association*, **83** (3), 280–5.

Powell, R R (1997) *Basic research methods for librarians*, 3rd edn, Ablex Publishing Corporation.

Preston, H and Hayward, T (1998) An evaluation of case study methodology within information system research. In *Exploring the contexts of information behaviour: proceedings of the second international conference on research in information needs seeking and use in different contexts*, 13–15 August, University of Sheffield, 597–608.

Pritchard-Schoch, T (1993) Natural language comes of age, *Online*, (May), 33–43.

Proud, V K, Johnson, E D and Mitchell, J A (1993) Students online: learning medical genetics, *American Journal of Human Genetics*, **52**, 637–42.

PubMed, available at:
http://www.ncbi.nlm.nih.gov/entrez/

Pye, J and Ball, D (1999) Purchasing consortia: trends and activity in the UK, *Bottom Line,* **12** (1), 12–18.

Pyne, T et al (1999) Meeting the information needs of clinicians for the practice of evidence-based healthcare, *Health Libraries Review*, **16** (1), 3–14.

Quint, B (1994) Connect time: the artifices of natural language searching, *Wilson Library Bulletin*, **69** (December), 61.

Quintana, Y and Bardyn, T (1996) Evaluating health libraries on the World Wide Web: design guidelines and future development, *Bibliotheca Medica Canadiana,* **18** (2), 61–4.

Raitt, D (1998) Factors and issues in creating an Internet strategy, *Electronic Library,* **16** (3), 155–9.

Ramsden, P (1992) *Learning to teach in higher education*, Routledge.

Rankin, J A (1996) Problem-based learning and libraries: a survey of the literature, *Health Libraries Review*, **13** (1), 33–42.

Rashid, S and Burns, T (1998) Innovation and survival: a case study in planning medical library services, *Bulletin of the Medical Library Association*, **86** (4), 508–17.

Ray, K and Day, J (1998) Student attitudes towards electronic information resources, *Information Research*, **4** (2), available at:
http://www.shef.ac.uk/~is/publications/infres/paper54.html

Rees, A (ed) (1991) *Managing consumer health information*, Phoenix.

Rees, A (1998) Project connect: information for health care networked across North Thames, *Health Libraries Review*, **15** (1), 59–63.

Richards, T (1998) Partnership with patients, Editorial, *British Medical Journal*, **316** (7125), 85–6.

Richardson, R (1999) Clinical governance: PA for the course?, *Health Service Journal,* **109** (5645), 26.

Richardson, W S (1995) Ask and ye shall retrieve, *Evidence Based Medicine*, **3**, 100–1.

Richardson, W S et al (1995) The well-built clinical question: a key to evidence based decisions, *ACP Journal Club*, **123** (3), A12–3.

Richardson, W S and Wilson, M C (1997) On questions, background and foreground, *Evidence Based Healthcare Newsletter*, **17**, 8–9.

Robbins, K and Holst, R (1990) Hospital library evaluation using focus group interviews, *Bulletin of the Medical Library Association,* **78** (3), 311–13.

Roberts, S A (1998) *Financial and cost management for libraries and information services*, 2nd edn, Bowker-Saur.

Robinson, B M and Robinson, S (1994) Strategic planning and program budgeting for libraries, *Library Trends,* **42** (3), 420–47.

Rooney, J (1994) Ergonomics in academic libraries, *Library Management*, **15** (1), 26–35.

Rose, S (1998) Challenges and strategies in getting evidence-based practice into primary health care – what role the information professional?, *Health Libraries Review*, **15** (3), 165–74.

Rosenberg, W M C et al (1998) Improving searching skills and evidence retrieval, *Journal of the Royal College of Physicians of London*, **32** (6), 557–63.

Rosenberg, W and Donald, A (1995) Evidence based medicine: an approach to clinical problem solving, *British Medical Journal*, **310** (6987), 1122–6.

Rosenfeld, R and Servo, J C (1991) Facilitating innovation in large organizations. In Henry, J and Walker, D (eds) *Managing innovation*, Sage, 28–38.

Rowley, J (1998a) The changing face of current awareness services, *Journal of Librarianship and Information Science,* **30** (3), 177–83.

Rowley, J (1998b) Current awareness in an electronic age, *Online and CD ROM Review*, **22** (4), 277–9.

Rowley, J (1998c) *The electronic library,* Library Association Publishing, 4.

Rowley, J and Slack, F (1997) The evaluation of interface design on CDROMs, *Online and CD ROM Review,* **21** (1), 3–11.

Royle, J A et al (1997) Do nurses have the information resources and skills for research utilization?, *Canadian Journal of Nursing Administration*, **10** (3), 9–30.

Rusbridge, C (1998) Towards the hybrid library, *D-Lib Magazine*, (July/August), available at:
http://www.dlib.org/dlib/july98/rusbridge/07rusbridge.html

Sackett, D et al (1996) Evidence-based medicine: what it is and what it isn't, *British Medical Journal*, **312** (7023), 71–2.

Sackett, D et al (1997) *Evidence-based medicine: how to practise and teach EBM,* Churchill Livingstone.

Sackett, D L and Rosenberg, W M C (1995) On the need for evidence based medicine, *Journal of Public Health Medicine*, **17** (3), 330–4.

Sackett, D L and Straus, S E (1998) Finding and applying evidence during clinical rounds: the 'evidence cart', *Journal of the American Medical Association*, **280** (15), 1336–8.

Samanta, A and Beardsley, J (1999) Sciatica: which intervention?, *British Medical Journal*, (31 July), **319** (7205), 302–3.

Sandall, J (1998) Bridging the gap between evidence and practice, *British Journal of Midwifery*, **6** (10), 624–5.

Sandvik, H (1999) Health information and interactions on the Internet: a survey of female urinary incontinence, *British Medical Journal*, **319** (7201), 29–32.

Sargent, C W (1978) Zero-base budgeting and the library, *Bulletin of the Medical Library Association*, **66** (1), 31–5.

Sauve, S et al (1995) The critically appraised topic: a practical approach to learning critical appraisal, *Annals of the Royal Society of Physicians and Surgeons of Canada*, **28**, 396–8.

Savard, R (1998) Hiring a Web site manager: what skills are important?, *Medicine on the Net,* **4** (8), 17–19.

Sawers, C (1997) *Getting clinical effectiveness into practice and the role of the library service*, South Thames Library and Information Service.

Scally, G and Donaldson, L J (1998) Looking forward: Clinical governance and the drive for quality improvement in the new NHS in England, *British Medical Journal*, **317** (7150), 61–5.

Schauer, B P (1986) *Economics of managing library service*, American Library Association.

Scherrer, C S, and Dorsch, J L (1999) The evolving role of the librarian in evidence-based medicine, *Bulletin of the Medical Library Association*, **87** (3), 322–8.

Schilling, K et al (1995) Integration of information-seeking skills and activities into a problem-based curriculum, *Bulletin of the Medical Library Association*, **83** (2), 176–83.

Schmidt, H G, Norman, G R and Boshuizen, H P A (1990) A cognitive perspective on medical expertise: theory and implications, *Academic Medicine* **65** (10), 611–21.

Schnell, E H (1997) Principles of web document structure and design, *Medical Reference Services Quarterly*, **16** (1), 47–52.

Schon, D A (1987) *Educating the reflective practitioner,* Jossey-Bass.

SCONUL (1999) Annual library statistics 1997–98, SCONUL.

Scottish Library and Information Council (1998) *Enabling access to the knowledge base of healthcare: library and information provision for the NHS in Scotland: report of a working group of the Scottish Library and Information Council,* SLIC.

Scottish Office (1991) *The patient's Charter – a charter for health,* The Scottish Office.

Scottish Office (1992) *Scotland's health: a challenge to us all: a policy statement,* HMSO.

Scottish Office (1997) *Designed to care. Renewing the National Health Service in Scotland,* The Scottish Office.

Secker, J, Stoker, D and Tedd, L (1997) Attitudes of library and information professionals to current awareness services: results from a user needs survey, using focus groups, for the NewsAgent project. In *Proceedings of the 2nd British Nordic Conference on Library and Information Studies, Edinburgh, 1997. Organized by the British Association for Information and Library Education (BAILER). Edited by Micheline Beaulieu, Elisabeth Davenport and Niels Ole Pors,* Taylor-Graham.

Sewell, W and Bevan, A (1976) A nonmediated use of MEDLINE and TOXLINE by pathologists and pharmacists, *Bulletin of the Medical Library Association*, **64** (4), 382–91.

Shackley, P and Ryan, M (1993) *The role of the consumer in healthcare,* HERU Discussion Paper 03/93, Health Economics Research Unit, University of Aberdeen.

Shahar, E (1997) A Popperian perspective of the term 'evidence-based medicine', *Journal of Evaluation in Clinical Practice*, **3** (2), 109–16.

Shapland, M (1999) Evaluation of Reference Management, Software on NT (comparing Papyrus with ProCite, Reference Manager, Endnote, Citation, GetARef, Biblioscope, Library Master, Bibliographica, Scribe, Refs), 28 July 1999, available at:
http://www.cse.bris.ac.uk/nccmjs/rmeval99.htm [accessed 19/3/00]

Sharp, S (1999) Evidence based accreditation: the experience of preparing for and undergoing LINC accreditation, *Library Association Health Libraries Group Newsletter*, **16** (4), 6–9.

Shaw, M, Dorling, D and Brimblecombe, N (1998) Changing the map: health in Britain: 1951–1991, *Sociology of Health and Illness*, **20** (5), 694–709.

Shaw, S and Payne, P (1998) e-Lib: an evaluation, *Library and Information Research News*, **21** (69), 3–4.

Shedlock, J and Ross, F (1997) A library for the twenty-first century: the Galter Health Sciences Library's renovation and expansion project, *Bulletin of the Medical Library Association*, **85** (2), 176–86.

Shedlock, J, Barkey, D C and Ross, F (1996) Building the electronic health sciences library for the twenty-first century: the Galter Library experience, *Medical Reference Services Quarterly*, **15** (4), 1–12.

Sheldon, T (1996) Research intelligence for policy and practice: the role of the National Health Service Centre for Reviews and Dissemination, *Evidence-Based Medicine*, (September–October), 167–8.

Sherwill-Navarro, P (1998) Internet in the workplace: censorship, liability, and freedom of speech, *Medical Reference Services Quarterly*, **17** (4), 77–84.

Shewan, J A and Read, S M (1999) Changing roles in nursing: a literature review of influences and innovations, *Clinical Effectiveness in Nursing*, **3** (1), 75–82.

Shipman, B L (1994) Implementing a campuswide electronic current awareness service, *Bulletin of the Medical Library Association*, **82** (3), 315–7.

Shipman, J P et al (1998) Desktop document delivery using portable document format (PDF) files and the Web, *Bulletin of the Medical Library Association*, **86** (3), 307–15.

Short, M W (1999) CD-ROM use by rural physicians, *Bulletin of the Medical Library Association*, **87** (21), 206–10.

Shultz, S M (1996) Medical jargon: ethnography of language in a hospital library, *Medical Reference Services Quarterly*, **15** (3), 41–7.

Shuman, B (1996) Designing personal safety into library buildings, *American Libraries*, **27** (7), 37–9.

Sievert, M et al (1996) Beyond relevance: characteristics of key papers for clinicians : an exploratory study in an academic setting, *Bulletin of the Medical Library Association,* **84** (3), 351–8.

Silberg, M, Lundberg, G D and Musacchio, R A (1997) Assessing, controlling, and assuring the quality of medical information on the internet. Caveat lector et viewor: let the reader and viewer beware, *Journal of the American Medical Association*, **277**, 1244–5.

Silverstein, J L (1995) Strengthening the links between health sciences information users and providers, *Bulletin of the Medical Library Association*, **83** (4), 407–17.

Simmons, S (1997) The Internet for NHS managers: endless potential or information overload?, *Managing Information*, **4** (3), 40–1, 43–4.

Simon, M and Yourke, G (1987) Building a Solid Architect–Client Relationship, *Library Administration & Management*, **1** (3), 100–4.

Simon, M J (1990) The Sick (Library) Building Syndrome, *Library Administrator & Management*, **4**, 87–91.

Singer, H (1997) *The spiralling costs of journal subscriptions: some alternatives and their implications*, SLS UK User Group, Yvonne Fullerton Memorial Bursary 1997: winning paper, available at: **http://www.lib.ic.ac.uk:8081/helen.htm**

Skelton, A M (1997) Patient education for the millennium: beyond control and emancipation, *Patient Education and Counselling*, **31** (2), 151–8.

Smith, R (1996) What clinical information do doctors need? *British Medical Journal*, **313** (7064), 1062–8.

Smith, R (1997) Peer review: reform or revolution? *British Medical Journal*, **315**, 759–60.

Smith, R (1998) The internet and the developing world, *British Medical Journal*, **316**, 1116.

Snowball, R (1997) Using the clinical question to teach search strategy: fostering transferable conceptual skills in user education by active learning, *Health Libraries Review*, **14** (3), 169–72.

Snyder, H (1997) *Costing and pricing in the digital age*, Library Association Publishing.

Somerville, A N (1977) The place of the reference interview in computer searching: the academic setting, *Online*, **1** (4), 14–23.

Somerville, A N (1982) The pre-search reference interview – a step by step guide, *Database*, **5** (1), 32–8.

Special Libraries Association (1996) *The information audit: an SLA information kit*, Special Library Association.

Spitzer, A (1998) Nursing in the health care system of the modern world: cross-roads, paradoxes and complexities, *Journal of Advanced Nursing*, **28** (1), 164–71.

St Clair, G (1995) Ask the customers, 2. Information audit, *One-Person Library,* **11** (10), 6–8.

Starr, S S and Renford, B L (1987) Evaluation of a program to teach health professionals to search MEDLINE, *Bulletin of the Medical Library Association*, **75** (3), 193–201.

Stavri, P Z (1996) Medical problem attributes and information-seeking questions, *Bulletin of the Medical Library Association*, **84** (3), 367–74.

Stenson, A, Raddon, R and Abell, A (1999) *Skills and competencies in the corporate sector,* British Library Research and Innovation Report 162, BL Research and Innovation Centre.

Stephen, P and Hornby, S (1997) *Simple statistics for library and information professionals*, 2nd edn, Library Association Publishing.

Stephenson, J and Fowler, C (1997) South and West Health Care Libraries Home Page: providing a local interface to health-related information resources, *Health Libraries Review*, **14**, 247–50.

Stevens, J (1998) Dental books: recommended purchase by postgraduate libraries. In Donnugh, A et al, *Books for primary health care: a core guide to collection development*, Tomlinsons.

Stewart, D (1992) Responsibility for funding NHS library services, *Health Libraries Review,* **9**, 62–5.

Stewart, D (1995) Staff training and development in the [Oxford] Health Libraries and Information Network, *Health Libraries Review*, **12** (1), 53–5.

Stoker, D and Secker, J (1997) The design and content of an electronic current awareness service for information professionals: the NewsAgent project. In *Proceedings of the 4th Electronic Library and Visual Information Research Conference, ELVIRA4, De Montfort University, Milton Keynes, UK, May 1997*, Aslib, 57–64.

Strube, K et al (1989) The librarian as consultant and educator for personal file management software, *Medical Reference Services Quarterly,* **8** (1), 33–43.

Suarez, H H, Hao, X and Chang, I F (1997) Searching for information on the Internet using the UMLS and Medical World Search. In *Proceedings AMIA Annual Fall Symposium*, 824–8.

Suh, H (1998) Recent advances in biomaterials, *Yonsei Medical Journal,* **39** (2), 87–96.

SUMSearch available at:
   http://SUMSearch.UTHSCSA.edu/cgi-bin/SUMSearch.exe

Swaffield, L (1999) Competition wasn't healthy, *Library Association Record*, **101** (5), 290–1.

Swerissen, H (1998) Health policy – the process and the politics, *Medical Journal of Australia,* **168** (5), 205–6.

Tannery, N H and Wessel, C B (1998) Academic medical center libraries on the Web, *Bulletin of the Medical Library Association*, **86** (4), 541–4.

Tavistock Institute (1996) *Guidelines for eLib project evaluation*, Tavistock Institute.

Taylor, D (1999) NHS quality – how will better care be achieved? In *Wellard's NHS Handbook 1999/2000,* JMH Publishing.

Taylor, G (1998) Surviving the information explosion – Reference Manager version 8.01, *Trends in Genetics,* **14** (1), 41.

Taylor-Gooby, P (1996) The future of health care in six European countries: the views of the elite, *International Journal of Health Services*, **26** (2), 203–19.

Tedd, L A and Yeates, R (1998) A personalised current awareness service for library and information services staff: an overview of the NewsAgent for Libraries project, *Program,* **32** (4), 373–90.

Theis, L M (1998) Cost containment and quality: coexisting in total joint care, *Orthopedic Nursing*, **6**, 70–7.

Thibodeau, P and Melamut, S (1995) Ergonomics in the Electronic Library, *Bulletin of the Medical Library Association,* **83** (3), 322–9.

Thompson, M L (1997) Characteristics of information resources preferred by primary care physicians, *Bulletin of the Medical Library Association*, **85** (2), 187–192.

Tiefel, V M (1995) Library user education: examining its past, projecting its future, *Library Trends*, **44** (2), 318–38.

Tomaiuolo, N and Packer, J (1998) Maximizing relevant retrieval: keyword and natural language searching, *Online* (November/December), 57–60.

Tomlin, A C (1992) One-person library budgeting, *One-Person Library*, **9** (3), 1–3.

Toth, B and Fraser, V (1999) The NeLH and health libraries: working together for better services, *Library Association Health Libraries Group Newsletter*, **16** (3), 4–6.

Trench, S (1997). Dissemination of information. In Scammell, A (ed) *Handbook of Special Librarianship and Information Work*, 7th edn, Aslib.

Urquhart, C (1998) Personal knowledge: a clinical perspective from the Value and EVINCE projects in health library and information services, *Journal of Documentation*, **54** (4), 420–42.

Urquhart, C and Davies, R (1997) EVINCE: the value of information in developing nursing knowledge and competence, *Health Libraries Review*, **14** (2), 61–72.

Urquhart, C J (1995) *The value of information services to clinicians: a toolkit for measurement*, Department of Information and Library Studies, University of Wales.

Urquhart, C J (1999) *Models of information value based on reliability and risk for clinical decision making,* PhD thesis, University of Wales Aberystwyth.

Urquhart, C J and Crane, S (1995) Preparing for PREP: the support role of the library, *Nurse Education Today*, **15** (6), 459–64.

Urquhart, C J and Hepworth, J B (1995a) *The value to clinical decision making of information supplied by NHS library and information services,* British Library R&D Report 6205, British Library.

Urquhart, C J and Hepworth, J B (1995b) *The value of information services to clinicians; a toolkit for measurement*, British Library R&D Report 6206, British Library.

Urquhart, C and Hepworth, J (1995c) The value of information supplied to clinicians by health libraries: devising an outcomes-based assessment of the contribution of libraries to clinical decision-making, *Health Libraries Review*, **12** (3), 201–13.

Urquhart, C J and Hepworth, J B (1996) Comparing and using assessments of the value of information to clinical decision making, *Bulletin of the Medical Library Association*, **84** (4), 482–9.

Urquhart, C J et al (1999) *Getting information to vocational trainees,* LIC Research Report 26, Library and Information Commission.

Van Eijsk, J Th M and Haan, M de (1998) Care for the chronically ill: the future role of health care professionals and their patients, *Patient Education and Counselling*, **35** (3), 232–40.

van Loo, J (1984) Marketing the library service: lessons from the commercial sector, *Health Libraries Review*, **1** (1), 36–47.

van Loo, J (1991) Costing, contracts and standards for libraries: introduction to workshop sessions, *Health Libraries Review*, **8** (3), 135–41.

VanGundy, A M (1998) *Techniques of structure problem solving*, 2nd edn, Van Nostrand Reinhold.

Vause, S and Macintosh, M (1999) Evidence based case report: use of prostaglandins to induce labour in women with a caesarean section scar, *British Medical Journal*, (17 April), **318** (7190), 1056–8.

Veenstra, R J (1992) Clinical medical librarian impact on patient care: a one-year analysis, *Bulletin of the Medical Library Association*, **80** (1), 19–22.

Vincent, C and Furnham, A (1999) Complementary medicine: state of the evidence, *Journal of the Royal Society of Medicine*, **92** (4), 170–7.

Vine, R (1997) Free MEDLINE on the Web: a practical view, *Bibliotheca Medica Canadiana*, **18** (3), 100–1.

Vine, R (1998) Entrepreneur, ME?, *Bibliotheca Medica Canadiana*, **20** (2), 68–9.

Wakeham, M (1993) Nurses – their information needs and use of libraries: the views of some librarians, *Health Libraries Review*, **10** (2), 85–94.

Wakeham, M, Houghton, J and Beard, S (1992) *The information needs and seeking behaviour of nurses*, British Library R&D Report 6078, British Library.

Wakeley, P J, Poole, C and Foster, E C (1988) The marketing audit: a new perspective on library services and products, *Bulletin of the Medical Library Association*, **76** (4), 323–7.

Wakiji, E M (1997) Mapping the literature of physical therapy, *Bulletin of the Medical Library Association*, **85** (3), 284–8.

Walcott, B M (1999) Mapping the literature of diagnostic medical sonography, *Bulletin of the Medical Library Association*, **87** (3), 287–91.

Walker, C J et al (1991) Problems encountered by clinical end users of MEDLINE and GRATEFUL MED, *Bulletin of the Medical Library Association*, **79** (1), 68–9.

Walker, M E (1995) A new hospital library: a marketing opportunity, *Bulletin of the Medical Library Association*, **83** (3), 330–2.

Walker-Dilks, C J, McKibbon, K A and Haynes, R B (1994) Beyond *ACP Journal Club*: how to harness MEDLINE for etiology problems, *ACP Journal Club,* (November–December), 121, A–10.

Wallace, S (1998) Telemedicine in the NHS for the millennium and beyond. In Lenaghan, J (ed) *Rethinking IT and health*, Institute for Public Policy.

Wallingford, K T et al (1990) Bibliographic retrieval: a survey of individual users of MEDLINE, *MD Computing*, **7**, 166–71.

Walton, G and Edwards, C (1997) Strategic management of the electronic library service in the UK higher education sector: implications of eLib's IMPEL2 project at the University of Northumbria at Newcastle. In Raitt, D (ed) *Libraries for the new millennium*, Library Association Publishing.

Walton, G and Edwards, C (1999) Staff development in the electronic library: lessons for the health sector from the IMPEL2 eLib project, *Health Libraries Review*, **16** (4), 226–33.

Walton, G, Day, J M and Edwards, C (1995) Training needs for staff competencies in a quality library service: relevance of the IMPEL project, *Liber Quarterly*, **5** (4), 389–400.

Warling, B N and Stave, C D (1995) The health sciences librarian as Internet navigator and interpreter, *Bulletin of the Medical Library Association*, **83** (4), 395–401.

Wasunna, A E and Wyper, D Y (1998) Technology for health in the future, *World Health Statistics Quarterly*, **51** (1), 33–43.

Watson, M, Christopher, K A and Wood, R T (1997) Internet access to National Library of Medicine SDI search results: the benefits of locally written software for automated postprocessing, *Internet Reference Services Quarterly,* **2** (1), 81–92.

Webber, G C (1990) Patient education. A review of the issues, *Medical Care*, **28** (11), 1089–1103.

Weinberg, A D et al (1981) Informal advice- and information-seeking between physicians, *Journal of Medical Education*, **56**, 174–80.

Weisbord, S D, Soule, J B and Kimmel, P L (1997) Brief report: poison online: acute renal failure caused by oil of wormwood purchased through the internet, *New England Journal of Medicine*, **337**, 825–7.

Weise, F O and Tooey, M J (1995) The building-planning process: tips from the UMAB experience, *Bulletin of the Medical Library Association,* **83** (3), 315–21.

Weist, A (1995) Maintaining quality: the accreditation experience. In McSéan, T, van Loo, J and Coutinho, E (eds) *Health information – new possibilities. Proceedings of the fourth European Conference of Medical and Health Libraries, Oslo, Norway, 28 June to 2 July, 1994*, Kluwer Academic, 60–2.

Wellard's NHS handbook 1999/2000 (1999), JMH Publishing.

Welsh, S (1997) OMNI: Organising Medical Networked Information, *Health Libraries Review,* **14** (3), 182–4.

Wennberg, J E and Sackett, D L (1997) Choosing the best research design for each question – it's time to stop squabbling over the 'best' methods, *British Medical Journal*, **315** (7123), 1636.

West, M and Poulton, B (1997) Primary health care teams: in a league of their own. In Pearson, P and Spencer, J (eds) *Promoting teamwork in primary care: a research based approach,* Arnold.

White, M D (1998) Questions in reference interviews, *Journal of Documentation*, **54** (4), 443–65.

Whitehead, M, Scott-Samuel, A and Dahlgren, G (1998) Setting targets to address inequalities in health, *Lancet*, **351** (9111), 1279–82.

Whittlestone, R (1998) *What is Project APPLE? A programme guide,* Regional Library Unit of the West Midlands.

Whittlestone, R, Low, B Y M and Pope, A (1999) Partnerships for the new NHS, *Library Association Record*, **101** (12), 704–5.

Wildemuth, B M, de Bliek, R, Friedman, C P and Miya, T S (1994) Information-seeking behaviors of medical students: a classification of questions asked of librarians and physicians, *Bulletin of the Medical Library Association*, **82** (3), 295–304.

Wildemuth, B M and Moore, M E (1995) End-user search behaviors and their relationship to search effectiveness, *Bulletin of the Medical Library Association*, **83** (3), 294–304.

Wilson, J W (1997) PubMed: a winner on the Web for the National Library of Medicine, *Online*, **18** (3), 100–1.

Wolfe, L (1997) *Library public relations, promotions, and communications: a how-to-do-it manual*, How-To-Do-It Manuals for Librarians 75, Neal-Schuman.

Wood, D J (1998) Peer review and the Web: the implications of electronic peer review for biomedical authors, referees and learned society publishers, *Journal of Documentation*, **54** (2), 173–97.

Wood, K (1999) CPD: what the Library Association offers, *Health Libraries Review*, **16** (4), 234–42.

Woodward, C (1997) What can we learn from programme evaluation studies in medical education? In Boud, D and Feletti, G (eds) *The challenge of problem-based learning,* 2nd edn, Kogan Page.

Woolf, S H and Benson, D A (1989) The medical information needs of internists and pediatricians at an academic medical center, *Bulletin of the Medical Library Association*, **77** (4), 372–80.

World Health Organisation (1978) *Declaration of Alma Ata,* World Health Organisation.

World Health Organisation (1986) *Ottawa charter for health promotion,* World Health Organisation.

Wright, L W et al (1999) Hierarchical concept indexing of full-text documents in the Unified Medical Lanaguage System Information Sources Map, *Journal of the American Society for Information Science*, **50** (6), 514–23.

Wu, G and Li, J (1999) Comparing Web search engine performance in searching consumer health information: evaluation and recommendations, *Bulletin of the Medical Library Association*, **87** (4), 456–61.

Wyer, P C (1997) The critically appraised topic: closing the evidence-transfer gap, *Annals of Emergency Medicine*, **30** (5), 639–40.

Zanna, M P (1987) *The Compleat Academic: a practical guide for the beginning social scientist*, Random House.

Zick, L (1999) *The work of information mediators: a comparison of librarians and intelligent software agents*, available at:
http://php.iupui.edu/~lzick/ai/index.html

Index